D0411952

The Cokesbury Game Book

The Cokesbury Game Book

Revised Edition

arthur m. depew

ABINGDON PRESS
new york nashville

THE COKESBURY GAME BOOK

Library of Congress Catalog Card Number: 60-14771

SET UP, PRINTED, AND BOUND BY THE PARTHENON PRESS, AT NASHVILLE, TENNESSEE, UNITED STATES OF AMERICA

To My Wife

LOUISE KELLER DEPEW

A helper with every task,
a counselor in every problem,
and a devoted companion always

preface

The *Cokesbury Party Book* and the *Cokesbury Stunt Book* were so graciously received both by recreational leaders and local groups of all kinds that, when the call came from the publishers for me to meet the demand for a book of games, I was constrained to put together materials I had been collecting for the past several years into the third of the series, *The Cokesbury Game Book,* which is being brought up to date with this revision.

At the time of starting the compilation of this volume, I found myself with many thousand suggestions in hand. The task was to select several hundred that would be the most helpful. Almost all of these have been tried, and many of them have been tried time and again by me during many years of work with young people and older groups.

I have tried to produce a volume that will be helpful for many groups of people. The first thought has been to provide a ready reference book for recreational leaders and workers with church, school, and playground groups. A selection of Active, Quiet, and Writing Games is given. With great care I have assembled a representative selection of outdoor games. There are games in this group to fit all ages who will desire to participate in this type of recreation.

A great deal of stress is being placed today on creative recreation.

I am therefore giving in this volume a group of games which may be made or improvised and played. Many of these games when made will constitute permanent equipment for the recreation room and be a constant source of recreation and amusement.

But I have had in mind much more than this. I have considered the individual and have sought to suggest ways and means by which individuals may improve their leisure time. Hobbies are suggested as a means of affording leisure time activities for the individual and of making any individual more interesting to himself and others. Many people like puzzles. This is evidenced by the large number of puzzle books that are sold every year. From many sources I have brought together one hundred puzzles. These are designed to help small groups pass an interesting evening together. Many times when a small group drops in without any planned entertainment, some person will think of a puzzle, a riddle, or a brain twister, and this will suggest one to someone else and, presto! a pleasant evening has been enjoyed by all.

A number of other suggestions are given for full evening entertainments to be spent in a different way than the usual party. Among these are such suggestions as a Story Tellers' Convention, Book Lovers' Convention, and Handicrafts.

The special day idea has almost monopolized the party spotlight, and most parties are planned around the special events of the year, such as New Year's Eve, Valentine's Day, Halloween, etc. For this reason I have included a large number of ideas for the special occasions. The user will find, in addition to all the other material in the volume, at least ten ideas for each one of the special days of the year.

This volume is sent forth with the hope that it will prove helpful to anyone who uses it, young or old. May it be the means of making new friendships and strengthening many more.

ARTHUR M. DEPEW

acknowledgments

I WISH TO make the following acknowledgments for the help received in the preparation of this volume: I purchased the copyright on more than two hundred pages of material written by the late Miss Goldie Green, entertainment editor of *Holland's Magazine,* published at Dallas, Texas, and have used much material from this source. Mrs. Roy L. Brown of Bellefontaine, Ohio, who spent more than thirty years in the leadership of social life, collected materials during these years, including thousands of games, which were presented to me for use in this volume. I have secured the permission of H. D. Edgren and J. T. Eiswald to use in this volume a small book published by them under the name, *Game Craft.* In this little volume is found the description of more than sixty games that may be improvised and played, together with complete instructions for making them. These games originally appeared in a mimeographed booklet published by Mr. Edgren and Mr. Eiswald. They are used in this volume with the consent of the authors.

contents

Section I

active games

Numbered Chairs

NUMBERED CHAIRS is a game that a group will not soon tire of playing. It can be used also with a large group, by dividing the large group into small groups of fifteen or sixteen each. It is best played by about sixteen players. The chairs are placed in a circle. Beginning from the leader, who takes the number one, the chairs are numbered to the leader's left from one to sixteen. All chairs must be occupied. It is necessary for all players to be constantly on the alert. After the first move or so, each will have a different number and must always be able to speak his number promptly. The game proceeds in the following manner. The leader calls a number, for example, five. Number five must thereupon immediately call a number, for example, seven. The game proceeds in this way until someone's number is called who does not respond or who hesitates. In this case, suppose, for example, number seven does not respond; number seven must then take the last chair to the right of the leader which in this case would be number sixteen. Everyone from eight to sixteen must then move one chair to the right, in other words, number eight would now become number seven, number thirteen would become number twelve, and so on. Each player takes the number of the chair into which he moves.

It is always permissible to call number one, the leader's number, and unless number one immediately responds by calling another number, he must move, and in this case number two will become number one and lead the game. The important thing to remember is that the chairs are numbered and the player always takes the number of the chair. However interesting this game, it should not be played more than thirty or forty-five minutes.

College Bingo

THE LEADER should prepare papers for this game by taking an 8½" by 11" sheet of paper and dividing it into sixteen squares. The leader should also prepare slips of paper on which are written the names of the more familiar colleges, such as Harvard, Yale, Princeton, Notre Dame. This game might be used in a "go-away-to-college party," in which case the leader should learn in advance the names of the colleges to which the guests go and use these to pin on the guests. In playing with sixteen squares, there should be at least twenty-four colleges used. After the names of these colleges have been pinned on the guests, each guest is given a sheet of paper, with the sixteen squares blocked off, and a pencil. The guests are then told to go around among the group and copy the names of colleges until they have filled their card. When every guest has his card filled, the guests are seated at tables. On each table the leader has placed grains of corn or beans to be laid on the spaces as the names of the colleges are called. The leader then having in his possession a list of all the colleges that have been pinned on the guests starts calling the names, and if a guest has the name of that college on his paper, he places a grain of corn on that square. The leader continues to call the names of these colleges until one of the guests chances to have four grains of corn in a row either horizontally or vertically. In this case the guest calls out Bingo, everyone removes the grains of corn from his paper, and the leader starts again calling names of the colleges. It would create a little interest if some small prize, such as a piece of candy or a lollipop, were given to each one who had a Bingo.

Housewarming Bingo

THE GAME described above might be used as well at a housewarming party. Instead of using the names of colleges, the parts of the house or articles of furniture might be used, for example, living room, dining room, back porch, front yard, etc.

Fish Swim

GET from the five- and ten-cent store a plastic fish. Use a large pan for a pool and let guests try to blow the fish across the pan, counting the number of "blows" it takes. The one finishing in the smallest number of blows should win a prize.

This may also be worked as a contest, a boy and girl starting at opposite sides of the pan, each having a fish, the object being to see which one can blow the fish across first. This may be carried on in an adjoining room and the guests taken in a few at a time.

Zip

FORM the crowd in two circles of players, if necessary, to get all of the crowd in the fun of the game. One player stands in the center of each circle. Each player in the circle acquaints himself with the name of the person to the left. The person in the center points his finger at anyone in the circle and shouts: "One, two, three, four, five, zip!" While he is thus shouting, the person to whom he points must say the name of the person to his left before "Zip" is said. Failing to do this, he must exchange places with the player in the center.

What's My Line?

THE GUESTS are seated around the room. Each one in turn is asked to stand and act out in pantomime the type of work which he does. In the case of students, they may act out what they plan to do in life. For example, a law student might pantomime a lawyer speaking before a jury. A secretary might pretend to be taking dictation. A medical student could portray a physician making a diagnosis. When a player completes his demonstration, all other players may guess his line. Then the next player in line begins his pantomime.

If some of the players are well known, they should not participate, but leave the action to those who are not so well known. If the group is small and well acquainted with each other, the game may be played by having each player act out his secret ambition—a lion tamer, a movie star, and so on.

Hat in the Ring

PLAYERS are divided into groups of not over six. Each group joins hands, forming a circle. Two cans are placed in each circle, one on top of the other, and at the given signal each player tries to make some other player upset the cans. Any person doing so must drop out of the game. After all players have been eliminated except one, that winner is allowed to compete with winners of the other circles. Should two persons unclasp hands while playing, both are eliminated. This game is as much fun to watch as to play, which makes it possible for those eliminated to still enjoy the game.

International Yacht Race

INTERNATIONAL YACHT RACES are frequently held, usually the most important contenders being England and America. Before the guests arrive, the hostess gets ready for a yacht race by stretching two strings across the room in the longest room available. These strings should be exactly the same length and about as high as the chin and about one yard apart. On each of the strings is placed a piece of funnel-shaped paper. These may be put together with pins, or if preferred, in advance with library paste. Print on one of these the name of an English yacht and on the other the name of an American yacht. Or, the English and American flags may be painted on the funnels.

The guests are divided into two groups, which may be done by two parties choosing sides, one group representing the English and the other group representing America. When the game actually starts, player number one from one group and player number one from the other group take their places at the string and must blow the funnel-shaped paper all the way to the other side of the room. The one who reaches there first is declared the winner. The hostess should prepare in advance small flags to represent each country.

Each player who wins in the contest receives a flag. He must plant this in his "fort" which has been provided by the hostess in the shape of two boxes full of dirt. The funnels are then moved back to the starting point, and players number two from each group compete. Thus the game continues, until everyone has had a chance. The winners are determined by the side that has the largest number of flags or tokens after all have competed. The game will be made very much more interesting if, while one player is blowing the funnel, the others should root for him.

The War of Roses

DISTRIBUTE sheets of red and white tissue paper and some wire to enable each guest to make one rose, tying the petals together and placing in each rose a bit of shot for weight. The company then chooses sides, and each player is armed with a fan, one side using the fans as shields for defense, the other side using them as bats. Those on the aggressive side try to pelt with red roses those on the defensive side, who ward off the roses with the fans. If, however, a player is touched with a rose he joins the conquering side and fights for that side until all the other players are won over. Then the company divides as before, the white roses are used and the defensive side becomes the aggressive side.

Ball Catch

THE PLAYERS are arranged in a circle with the leader in the center. One of the players is holding a large ball, and when the leader says "go" the player must throw the ball to some other player, and then that player will throw it to another and so on. In the meantime the leader tries to catch it as it passes back and forth. When the leader succeeds in catching it, the player who threw it must take the center of the circle, the leader taking that person's place in the circle. The game then goes on as before. Each time the player in the middle catches the ball, he takes his place in the ring or circle, and the last thrower takes the center of the circle.

Balloon Blow

ANOTHER GROUP game is that of "balloon blow." Fasten a sheet in a vertical position across the room, or two players might hold the sheet at either side. The rest of the company is divided into two sides, stationed in a kneeling position on either side of the sheet. The leader then tosses a balloon into the air, and the players on either side of the sheet must keep the balloon from descending on their side by blowing it back toward the opponents' side. If the balloon falls on a player, that player must drop out of the game.

Defend the Fort

THIS GAME might be used on any patriotic occasion by using the names of forts which are connected with the occasion. Arrange four tables, marking them A, B, C, and D and use the name of a fort for each one, as suggested above. In the center of each table arrange a cardboard fort, placing a flag on top of the fort, bearing the name of the fort if possible. A company of six is arranged for each table, the hostess or leader selecting the players so that there will be players of different caliber in each company, in order to make the games even. Arrange a different game for each table using the following as suggestions: Jack Straws, Old Maid, Rook, Parcheesi, Dominoes, etc. In order to begin the battle, the captain of company A selects three from his company and sends them to fight company B; B sends three to fight company C: C sends three to fight company D; and D sends three to fight company A. Of course, the battle which is fought is the playing of the game located at that table.

When each game is finished, the players return and report to their captains, placing a flag on their fort if they have won a game. The playing then progresses in regular order, with three of the company always remaining to defend the fort. When the fighting is over, that is, when each company has attacked all of the other forts and returns to his own fort, the signal is given to stop. The fort on which the greatest number of flags has been placed wins the entire engagement.

Weathercocks

NAME the four corners of the room after the four points of the compass, North being diagonal to South, and East being diagonal to

West. The leader of the game is called the "Wind" and the players are called "Weathercocks." The Weathercocks stand in a line in the center of the room. The Wind takes his position in front of the players and points to one corner calling out the name of that point of the compass. The Weathercocks must immediately face in the opposite direction. For example, if the Wind calls East, the players face West. If, however, the Wind should name the point of the compass which the players are already facing, they must remain perfectly still. Sometimes the Wind may call "variable"; this is a signal for the Weathercocks to raise themselves on their toes and sway back and forth until the name of one of the points is called again, when, as before, they turn to the opposite point. To add interest to the game, the Wind may shout "Storm" or "Tempest" and each player must whirl around three times. Any player who fails to obey any one of these directions must pay a forfeit which is to be "redeemed" when the game is over.

Shoe Race

SHOE RACE may be either an inidvidual contest or a relay race. For the individual contest, have the boys at one end of the room with their partners seated at the other end of the room. When the signal is given to go, each one runs to his partner, takes off her shoe, runs back to the starting point, and then races back, and puts on the shoe. The one who first completely replaces the shoe is declared the winner.

For a shoe relay race, select two groups with an equal number of couples in each group. In this case, the first boy in group number one would have to replace his partner's shoe and run back to the starting point, touching off number two. The group that finishes first is declared the winner.

A shoe relay race may be used with the boys only participating. In this case, two groups of equal number would line up at a starting point and each in turn would have to run to the other end of the room, take off one shoe (or both shoes) and replace it, return to the starting point, and touch off number two.

Shoe relay race may be used as well with the girls or with a mixed group.

Basket Relay

TWO WASTEBASKETS for each side are needed for this relay. One player from each of two or more groups, equal in number, takes his place on the starting line with his foot in one basket and with another basket in his hand. A goal line has been marked on the floor as far from the starting line as possible. When the signal is given by the leader, the player sets the empty basket one step ahead and steps into it. He must then move the first basket with his hand and take the next step into it. Shuffling the baskets along the floor is not allowed. When the first player reaches the goal and returns to the starting line, he gives the baskets to the next player in his group, and the game continues. The group that finishes first wins.

Fruit to Market

PLAYERS are seated in two rows of chairs facing each other. The two rows should have an equal number of players. A basket is placed at the head of each line full of wrapped objects of different sizes and shapes. Each basket should contain articles that are a duplicate of those in the other basket in order to make the game fair. When the starting signal is given the player at the head of each line picks up an article from the basket, unwraps it, and passes the article down the line, followed by the wrapper. The players at the foot of the line must re-wrap each article when it reaches them and place it in the basket at the foot of the line. The line that first passes down all articles and gets them wrapped and into its basket first is the winner. Some suggestions for articles are a baby rattle, a diaper, a house slipper, a book end, a potato, an onion, an egg, a necktie, and so on.

Hooray

THIS GAME may be used for almost any occasion by changing the character. If it is for Valentine, use the name "Cupid," if for Washington's Birthday use the name of "George Washington," and if for St. Patrick's Day use the name of "St. Patrick." If the last occasion is being celebrated, the leader stands in the center of the circle of guests and starts telling a story about St. Patrick. It may be any kind of fanciful story, fabricated extemporaneously. The point is, that whenever the leader says, "St. Patrick," he is to raise either his left hand, his right hand, or both hands. If the leader raises his right hand, the players must cry "Hooray," until he lowers his hand. If he raises his left hand the players must clap their hands until he lowers his left hand, and if the leader raises both hands, the members of the group must both shout and clap their hands until the hands are lowered. Anyone failing to do so must take his place beside the leader. It will not be very long until a large group will be standing beside the leader.

Clothespin Relay

STRING A CLOTHESLINE at one end of the room, about shoulder high to the average guest. Snap on this line a number of spring clothespins to equal or exceed the number of players.

Divide the guests into two teams of equal number and line up each team facing the clothesline. When the signal is given, the first player in each line must run to the clothesline and remove a clothespin with his teeth, without using his hands. This may be difficult, as players from both teams will be shaking the line trying to dislodge a clothespin.

When a player has removed a pin, he runs with the pin still in his teeth, tags the player in the front of his line, and takes his position at the rear of the line. Each member of the team must remove a clothespin in this fashion, and the group whose members first accomplish this feat is declared the winner.

Five Pins

FIVE PINS is a game with plenty of action and interest. Five Indian Clubs or five soft drink bottles will serve as the five pins. All players except one form a circle around the room. The five pins, or bottles, are set in the middle of the circle on points marked on the floor with chalk. One of the players in the ring is given a large ball, preferably a large rubber ball, which he rolls along the floor in an effort to hit the pins and knock them down. If he misses them, the ball will roll across the floor to the one on the opposite side of the circle. That one then takes it and rolls the ball. If this player hits the pins, the ball will roll, likewise, to another player who now becomes the thrower. The player in the center of the circle, when the pins are knocked down, must try to replace all five of them or all that have been knocked down before another player throws. If the center player succeeds in replacing the pins before they are knocked down again, the player who last had the ball becomes the center man, and the game starts again.

Turkey Hunt

HERE is another game that may be adapted to almost any season of the year. The Thanksgiving turkey hunt might just as well be a valentine hunt, a shamrock hunt, or a flag hunt. A large number of paper turkeys are hidden about the room. This will have to be done by the leader in advance. These may be purchased from the five- and ten-cent store. The guests are divided into couples and march, skating fashion, to music. When the whistle is blown or the music stops all fall out of the circle and start hunting for turkeys. When a player finds a turkey he must shout "Hooray," run to the leader and drop his turkey in the basket. He may go hunting for another turkey. As soon as the whistle blows or the music starts, all players must immediately stop hunting, get a partner, and get into line of march. When the music stops again the hunt continues. It will be found that at each succeeding time the turkeys are getting scarcer. All players who are unsuccessful in their hunt for turkeys must drop out of the line of march and take their places in the center of the circle while the others march around them. The number in the circle will get smaller, and the number within the circle will get larger. When the time comes that a boy cannot find a girl for a partner he may take another boy, or vice versa with the girls. Finally the number of marchers will be reduced to one or two. The one to receive the prize should be the last one to find a turkey.

Fire in the Mountain

THE PLAYERS are formed into two concentric circles. The girls form the inner circle and the boys the outer. "It" remains in the center and calls "Fire in the Mountain." Everyone must then hold up his hands and move in opposite directions, the girls clockwise and the boys counter-clockwise. This must continue until the leader calls,

"Fire's out." All stop, and each boy tries to get behind a girl. "It," however, takes his place behind one of the girls and the player who is left without a girl becomes "It," and so the game continues.

Lion's Den

One person is the "lion," while the other players form a circle around him with a space between the players large enough for a player to pass through. One of the players is chosen to be the hunter and he too stands in the circle. When the game starts, all the players in the circle close their eyes and the lion starts counting ten. Meanwhile the hunter tries to slip out between two players. Anyone who hears the hunter make a sound may point to where he thinks the hunter is. If the lion says the direction is correct, the hunter must take a place in the circle and the one who pointed him out becomes the hunter. If the hunter succeeds in getting out without getting caught, he comes back into the circle and continues to act as the hunter until someone points him out.

S O S

One player acts as radio dispatcher, while the other players are arranged in a circle. Leave an opening on opposite sides of the circle so that players may pass through without having to break the circle. Behind each open space is located an imaginary hospital. These might be named after local hospitals. Before the play starts, the leader gives to each player a name of a trade or profession, such as doctor, nurse, dentist, preacher, undertaker, carpenter, painter.

When the game is ready to start, the dispatcher calls out, "A nurse and a doctor are wanted at City Hospital." The ones who have the names of the professions indicated break from the line and rush toward the hospital. The one to arrive first is admitted but the other must take his place in the center of the circle and act as catcher. The dispatcher may now call out, "A carpenter and a preacher are wanted at County Hospital." Both of these run for the hospital. The one in the center of the circle tries to tag one of them, and if he succeeds, this one must also take his place in the center of the circle and help catch others. The number in the center of the circle will constantly increase.

Another interesting feature of the game is that not more than one workman or profession may be in the hospital at the same time. If a doctor is in the hospital and the dispatcher says that a carpenter and nurse are wanted there, whenever either of them safely arrives, the doctor must then leave and take his place in the circle. He is subject to being tagged on his return as well, and if tagged must take his place in the center of the circle as a catcher.

Bird Market

THE "SHOPKEEPER" keeps a bird market to which the "Buyer" comes to buy birds. Each player must be given the name of a bird by the leader before the game starts. One corner of the room or another room is designated as the "bird sanctuary." When a player gets to the sanctuary he is safe from being sold.

The game proceeds as follows: The "Buyer" comes to the "Shopkeeper" and says, "I want to buy a bird." The "Shopkeeper" says, "What kind of a bird?" The buyer says, "A green bird." To which the shopkeeper replies, "Oh, then you want a parrot." When the parrot gets his cue, he gets ready to run, and when the shopkeeper says, "Parrot," he runs for the sanctuary. The shopkeeper tries to catch the bird before he gets to the sanctuary. If he is caught he then becomes the "Buyer," and if he gets to the sanctuary, the buyer must try to get another bird.

Noah's Ark

AT THE BEGINNING of the game each girl is asked to select a partner. This may be done in any number of ways. After the group has been divided into couples, the leader names each couple, the idea being that they represent two of the animals that went into Noah's Ark. Animals should be selected which make a noise that can be imitated. There might be two horses, two hogs, two sheep, two cows, two chickens, two ducks, two turkeys, two frogs, and so on.

The boys now retire from the room and the girls change seats so as to confuse them upon their return. The boys are all blindfolded and led back into the room. Each girl immediately tries to attract her partner by making a noise which is made by the animal which she represents. The girls stand behind chairs and the boys are supposed to find the chair of their partner. This will be no easy matter because of the babble of sound. A prize might be given to the first one to find the proper chair and a booby prize to the last one.

The game might be continued by having the girls retire and letting the boys imitate the animals.

Hidden Object

A GOOD game to break the ice and get everyone moving around is Hidden Object. The leader tells the group that he is going to mention the name of an object which will be found in plain view somewhere in the room. He tells the guests that they are not to point out the object or speak of its location to anyone else, but as soon as they find it, they are to come to the center of the room and start singing or whistling their favorite tune as loudly as possible. The leader then names some object which is somewhere in the room, and the fun starts. A prize might be given to the one first to find the object, and the last to find it might be penalized by being required to be "It" in another game.

Lemon Relay

THE GUESTS are divided into two groups for the lemon relay. The first player in each group is given a pencil and a lemon. A starting point and goal are marked off on the floor and each player must roll the lemon, by using the pencil, to the goal and return to the starting point. The next player in his group then has a turn, and so on until all have competed. The side that finishes first wins.

Feather Relay

THE GUESTS are divided into two groups and the first player in each group is given a feather. A small fluffy piece of cotton will do instead. The player must blow the feather or cotton to the goal, keeping it in the air. He then runs back and hands it to the next player on his side. The side that finishes first wins. This game may be made more difficult by requiring the players to take a position on their hands and knees instead of standing erect.

Drivers

Two or more teams are selected, each with two boys and a girl. The boys are blindfolded, and then they make a seat for the girl by each boy taking hold of his right wrist with his left hand and taking hold of the left wrist of the other boy with his right hand. The girl is then seated and all three are turned around two or three times so that the boys will lose the sense of direction. The signal to start is given and they must race to a goal and back, the blindfolded boys being guided by the girl who directs them. This will make many funny situations. It will probably create enough interest to have a second race with new teams after the first has been completed.

Each One Take One

Two active captains, boys preferably, are chosen to lead the game. The guests are seated in a circle of chairs around the room. If the room is very large, this will enhance the effectiveness of the game.

When the director of the game gives the signal, each of the captains grasps a girl by the wrist and pulls her to a standing position. The girl must then grasp the wrist of a boy and thus add another to their side. The object of the game is for each captain to assemble a chain of players, alternating boys and girls. The players must not break their holds at any time and if the chain is broken the team is disqualified. When all guests have been chosen as a part of one of the chains, a count is made to determine which captain has assembled the largest number of persons or "links" in his chain, and this group is declared the winner.

Touch It

A circle is formed for marching with couples in skating position, which means that they are firmly clasping hands. If during the game they break this clasp, they must rejoin hands to touch the articles indicated by the leader. The game proceeds as follows: The couples march around the room to music. As soon as the music stops, the leader calls out an object to be touched. The couples must go together and touch this object. It would be well to start with objects which are easily accessible such as the piano, or the front door.

All must touch this object before the music starts again. Any couple who fails must drop out of the line of march. This game could be made very humorous by the leader choosing some of the following objects to be touched: the fattest or thinnest person, a mustache, a red necktie, curly hair, bald spot, and others. A prize should be given to the couple that stays in the longest.

Bird in the Cage

THE GUESTS are divided into groups of three, two girls and one boy, or two boys and one girl. The couple in each case joins hands, with the third one in the center. In some cases there would be a boy in the center and sometimes a girl. In a group where there are more girls than boys, there might be a girl in each "cage"; that is, between the arms of the couple. In any case there must be two or three extra players. When the couples have all joined hands and each cage has a bird in it, the music starts, and all move about over the floor until the music stops. Then each bird must fly out of his own cage and into another. Of course, the extra players try to get into a cage, and the ones who can find no cage form the extra group, and the game continues.

Necktie Relay

THE GROUP is divided into two sides of equal number and these line up facing each other. The player at the head of each line is given a necktie. When the starting signal is given he must tie the tie around his neck, shake hands with the player on his right, untie the tie and hand it to the next player, who does likewise. Thus the tie passes down the line. There should be approximately an equal number of girls on each side, as it will be more difficult for them to manage the tie than it will be for the boys. The side whose last player is able first to tie and untie the necktie, wave it in the air and shout, is declared the winner.

Ring and Toothpick Relay

THE GUESTS are divided into two groups of equal number, and these groups line up facing each other. Each player on both sides is given a toothpick. The leader starts a ring down the line on each side, and it must be passed down by the contestants by slipping it onto the toothpick in the mouth of the next player without using the hands. If the ring falls, it must be handed to the player at the head of the line on its way down, or, if it falls on its way back, it must be handed to the player at the foot of the line. The team that can get the ring up and down the line first is declared the winner.

Rug Scramble

As music is played, couples march around over the room. A number of small rugs have been placed on the floor, and when the whistle blows or the music stops, all players must jump for a rug. The rule is that both feet of both players of the couple must be on the rug, or if they cannot get both feet on the rug the other foot must be held off the floor. If either member of the couple cannot get on the rug, the couple is counted out. All couples who fail to get on the rug must drop out of the line of march when the music starts again. The leader takes away one rug each time the music starts until finally only one small rug is left. The couple or couples who succeed in holding their position on this rug are declared the winners.

Word-spelling Race

There are so many things that may be done with letters that the recreation leader's equipment should always include them. They may be made at small expense by printing the letters on cards about five inches square with colored crayons.

For the word-spelling race, each of two or more groups should have lettered cards with all the letters of the alphabet on them that are needed to spell the words to be pronounced by the leader. The leader should first make out a list of about thirty or forty words and make sure that duplicate letters are provided if needed. It will not be necessary to use all letters of the alphabet—only those needed to spell the words to be pronounced.

When the leader pronounces a word, each group tries to line up in order so that the players who hold the proper letters will spell the word. The judges decide which group was able to do this first. Give one point to the group which first completes a word.

Sliding Square Relay

IN THIS GAME, a number of players divisible by four—such as thirty-two or forty—should participate. The players are seated with an equal number along all four sides of the room. If there were forty players, for example, they should be seated with ten on each side. Use chairs which do not have arms. Place four chairs near the center of the room, one in front of each team.

When all four teams are seated, the game is ready to start. The player on the right end of each team must run around the chair that has been placed in front of his group and take his place in the chair on the opposite end. The players in all chairs must slide over while the first player is making the run, placing player number two in the chair formerly occupied by player number one. After player number one has been seated, player number two makes the run, and so on down the line. The team that first gets its number one player back in his original chair is the winner.

U Turns

FOR THE GAME U Turns the players are formed into a circle and from this formation the line is broken so that all have their hands joined except the two players on the two ends of the figure U. While all the players keep their hands joined, the leader, who is on one end of the U, starts weaving in and out among the players in the line, in front of one and back of the next and at the same time pulling the other in the line behind her. The players in the line hold up their hands so that the leader and the line that follows her may march under the arch. Continue the game until all are back in their original places.

Passing

THE PLAYERS stand in a circle, and the leader passes out to them objects of various sizes, about one article for every five or six persons. These objects should be of different sizes and shapes. Objects which are valuable should not be used, as they may easily get broken. Such objects as a large dictionary, a doll, a stool, a suitcase, an old vase, a flower pot, or a waste basket may be used. The leader blows the whistle, and all start passing the articles. When the whistle is blown the second time, everyone who has hold of an object or who drops it when the whistle is blown must drop out of the circle. The rule of the game is that everyone must take the object when offered to him and must not hesitate. If he hesitates the leader, who stands in the center of the circle and acts as judge, may call him out and put him out of the circle. As the circle gets smaller, take away some of the objects. Finally there will only be two or three. The last one to be counted out should be given a prize.

Object Snatch

THE LEADER has placed objects around the room, or in some cases in an adjoining room. The guests are formed into couples and march around the room to music. Before the music starts, the leader tells the guests the object which they are to snatch as soon as the music stops. When the music stops, all make a run for it, going by couples, the rule being that one player alone cannot get it, but he must have hold of his partner's hand at the time he captures it. Leave time before the music starts each time for the leader to tell the location of the next object to be snatched. Give a prize at the conclusion of the game to the couple which has snatched the largest number of objects.

The Accused

THE GUESTS stand in a semicircle. The accused is seated on a stool in the opening of the semicircle, while the judge is in the circle and directly in front of the accused. Guests are given blank pieces of paper on which to write, and each one is asked to write some accusation against the accused, to which he must sign his name. This should not be anything serious or offensive but something humorous. When all have written their accusations, they pass them up to the judge. The judge addresses the accused and says to him, "You are accused by one of the guests of being a lady's man. Who do you think made this accusation against you?" The accused then makes a guess as to identity of the one who so accused him. Each accusation is read, and each time the accused makes a guess as to his accuser. When all have been read, if he has guessed one or more correctly, he takes his place in the semicircle; the first one whose accusation he guessed correctly takes his place, and the game continues.

Animated Numbers

PREPARE two sets of numbers from zero through nine. These may be printed on cardboard about five inches square. The printing may be done with colored crayons. The players are divided into two teams of ten each, and a judge is appointed. The players stand at one end of the room, one team in each corner, while those who are not playing stand at the opposite end of the room. The leader and the judge take their place in front of the spectators. Each player is given a number, and when the leader calls for the number, "789," the players having those numbers run to the end of the room and take their position in front of the judge. The team first completing the number wins a point. If there are more than ten players on a team, duplicate numbers should be given to the players, and the leader in calling the numbers should include large numbers which call for duplicates such as "25,752." The side that first makes twelve points is the winner.

Uncle Ben

PLAYERS are seated in a circle. The leader opens the game by turning to the one on his left and saying, "Did you know Uncle Ben?" The person addressed replies, "Which one of your uncles was that?" The leader replies, "The one that went like this." The leader than starts pounding on his right knee. The player on the leader's left then turns to the one on his left and says, "Did you know Uncle Ben?" The same dialogue takes place until all are imitating the leader's action. When the question has gone around the circle and has come back to the leader, he adds an action, as for example, striking the left knee with the fist. Each time the game goes around the circle an action is added, such as patting the right foot, the left foot, nodding the head. Do not play this game too long as it soon ceases to be amusing.

Under Cover

TWO GUESTS choose sides and thus divide the group into two teams of equal number. One team retires from the room of play into an adjoining room. This group then sends in one of its players who is covered with a sheet, blanket, or quilt. This one crawls on the floor and occasionally grunts, groans, whimpers, or makes some similar sound. The members of the opposing group try to guess who is under the cover, but must agree as a group, or at least a majority must agree on the selection, and they are allowed one guess as a group. If they guess correctly the opposing group must send in another player. If they guess incorrectly, they must go out and let the other group return to the large room, while they send in one of their players as the other side has done.

Rope Jumping

A WEIGHT is attached to the end of a small rope, such as a sash cord or a clothes line. A rubber ball would serve the purpose for the weight very well. The players stand in a circle. The leader swings the ball around, keeping it a few inches from the floor. The players must jump the rope as it comes to them. If the rope or the ball hits a player, he must drop out of the circle. As the players in the circle become fewer in number, the leader may swing the ball faster and higher.

Grandma

ONE PLAYER is grandma and stands with his face to the wall. The other players stand in a line on the other side of the room. The idea of the game is for the players to creep up on Grandma without being seen. Grandma may turn at any time and look over her left shoulder or her right shoulder. Unless players are perfectly still when grandma sees them, they may be sent back to the starting point. If they cease moving when Grandma happens to look, they retain their position. Grandma is not allowed to turn all the way around but must look over one shoulder at a time. This gives the players on the other side of the room an opportunity to advance while Grandma is looking over her other shoulder. The player who first is able to creep up on Grandma and touch her may take her place and continue the game.

Living Statues

THIS GAME may be played by any number of players. The only equipment needed is a tennis ball or other rubber ball. The players stand in a circle with one player having the ball. When the leader gives the signal for the game to start, the player who has the ball throws it to another player, who, if he catches it, throws it to another, and so the game continues. When a player fails to catch the ball when it has been thrown to him, he must retain the position in which he found himself when the ball was missed. His hands, feet, and body must remain as motionless as possible until the leader blows the whistle. If this is delayed too long, there will probably be a lot of grunts and groans.

Center Ball

A GAME which is a variation of the one described above is Center Ball. The players stand in a circle with "It" in the center. "It" has a tennis ball or other soft ball. He starts the game by tossing the ball to a player in the circle. "It" then darts out of the circle. The player who caught the ball must run to the center of the circle of players, place the ball on the floor and chase the one who threw him the ball. If he succeeds in tagging "It" before "It" can get back to the center of the circle and touch the ball, he may take his place in the circle again. If, on the other hand, the player who is being chased can get back to center and touch the ball before he is tagged, the chaser then takes his place in the center and tosses the ball, and the game continues.

Catch the Potato

EQUIPMENT for this game consists of a sheet and a small round potato. Players stand in a hollow square holding the sheet. Two players are designated as "Catchers" to start off the game. They stand behind the square of players. The leader tosses a potato into the middle of the sheet and the game is on. The "Catchers" try to get the potato. Of course, they may try to get it for themselves or help the other player get it. At the same time the players holding the sheet will try to prevent either of them from getting it. It is against the rules for any player who is holding the sheet to touch the potato with his hands. If he does, he must take the place of the catcher nearest him. When a catcher is able to catch the potato in his hand, the player on the right of him at the time he caught the potato must take his place.

There may be more than two catchers. One on each side would make the game much faster.

Orchestra

THE GUESTS sit in a circle and each one chooses the name of a musical instrument. It is better to choose the names of instruments which require distinctive motions to play, such as: Bass drum, trap drum, violin, bass viol, piano, cornet, among others. The leader starts the game by imitating the motion of one playing his instrument. For example, if the leader's instrument is the bass drum, he imitates one beating a bass drum. Each other player must then imitate the motions that go with the playing of his instrument. Whenever the leader desires, he may change his motions and start imitating the motions of any other player. While he is doing this, all other players except the one imitated must switch to the instrument which the leader was formerly playing. The one whose instrument is imitated must stop his motions and place his hands over his ears. Whenever the leader switches back to his original instrument, each player in turn must switch back to his. Anyone who plays his instrument while it is being imitated, or fails to switch to the leader's instrument when he switches to another, or anyone who fails to switch back to his own instrument when the leader switches back to his, must drop out of the game. The object is to see who can remain in the game the longest.

Another version of this game is to have a player who has made a mistake become the leader.

Marble Roll

DRAW CIRCLE, twelve inches in diameter, on the floor with chalk and get a dozen or two marbles.

Each player is allowed an equal number of marbles which he attempts to roll so that they will come to a stop within the circle. Players alternate rolls. Marbles within the circle after everyone has rolled his marbles, give the individual score. Marbles knocked out of the circle by opponents are not counted for their owner.

Card Toss

GET A TRAY, hat, box or wastebasket and a number of cards; any kind will do.

Use whichever of the receptacles you have procured and have players from a distance of 4 or 5 feet attempt to flip cards so they will land in the tray, hat or box. If two or more play, use different colored cards.

Line Toss

ONE DOZEN ordinary washers, coins, slugs, bottle caps, linoleum discs, or jar rubbers are all that is necessary for this game.

Draw a line on the floor, or if played on the rug, pick some part of the design and have the players attempt to toss two or three apiece, and the closest one to the line picks up all.

Funnel Ball

EQUIPMENT for this game is a small funnel and a tennis ball. The player stands near a wall, throws the ball towards the floor, so that it strikes the floor about three feet from the wall, bounces up, hits the wall, and rebounds toward the player. He then tries to catch it with the funnel. This will be quite difficult for a few tries, but after a little practice, it will be possible to catch the ball many times without missing, and it will make an interesting contest to see who can catch it the largest number of times. To score this game for competitive play, let each catch count a number of points agreed on in advance.

Clothespin Drop

SET A MILK BOTTLE on the floor and have the contestants stand erect holding a clothespin at the end of the nose. The idea is to drop the clothespin into the container. Each time the clothespin goes in, the player may score five points.

Section 2

quiet games

Did You Say THAT About Me?

ONE of the best games to play in an older group is "Did You Say That About Me?"

One person starts the game by retiring from the room, and while he is out of earshot, those left in the room say something about him to the person on their right. Any remark such as "As a lawyer, he would make a good plumber"; or "He is a ladies' man"; or "He is goofy"; or "He is handsome"; or "He has such beautiful blue eyes," or any other such statement. When each one has whispered a statement about the person who is out of the room, then all change chairs so that this one, when he returns, will not know who made the statement about him. When the game is in progress, it will be necessary to move before the statements are made, as the person who retires will remember how the persons were seated and will then know who made such a statement. When, however, this person comes back into the room, he goes to any person and says "What did you hear about me?" This person will then tell what he has heard—"I heard you always looked under the bed before you retired." He then goes to a person who he thinks may have said that and asks, "Did you say that about me?" This person, if he did not say it, replies, "No, but I heard that you did not drink coffee for breakfast because it kept you awake all day." And so the game continues until finally the person is found who made some remark. When a player has to admit that he made the remark, he then must go out and let the group make remarks about him.

Conundrum Baseball

Conundrum baseball is played by two groups in competition. The guests may be divided into two teams by two persons choosing sides. One team takes its place on one side of the room, and the other team takes its place on the other side of the room. A diamond is laid out by placing four books on the floor to correspond with the first, second, third, and home bases of a baseball diamond. The leader is the pitcher. One player from the team at bat takes his place at home base and is given a conundrum by the pitcher. If he can answer the conundrum, he advances to first base and another player is up "at bat." He in turn is asked a conundrum. If he can answer it, he advances to first base, while the player on first base advances to second base. A score can only be made after four conundrums have been answered correctly. Each time a conundrum is missed it counts as one out. When three conundrums have been missed, the side is retired and the other side is up "at bat." A list of suggested conundrums follows:

1. Who is the first woman mentioned in the Bible? *Genesis (Gene-sis)*.
2. What did Lot's wife turn to before she turned to salt? *She turned to rubber.*
3. Why is kiss spelled with two "s's"? *It always takes two to complete the spell.*
4. Why do doctors keep bad company? *The worse they are, the more often they go to the doctor.*
5. Why is the organ likely to burn in a church fire? *The engine cannot play upon it.*
6. What does a cat have that no other animal has? *Kittens.*
7. What is a good sign of cold weather? *A thermometer.*
8. Where can one always find happiness? *In the dictionary.*
9. What goes up when rain comes down? *Umbrella.*

10. When is a piece of wood like a monarch? *When it is made into a ruler.*
11. What is the first thing a man sets in his garden? *His foot.*
12. What is the oldest piece of furniture? *The multiplication table.*
13. What is the easiest breakfast to take in bed? *A couple of rolls.*
14. What is it that has neither flesh nor bone but has four fingers and a thumb? *A glove.*
15. What is the difference between a buffalo nickel and a quarter? *Twenty cents.*
16. When is a doctor most annoyed? *When he is out of patients.*
17. What animal comes from the clouds? *Rain, dear.* (*Reindeer.*)
18. What plant stands for the number "four"? *Ivy* (*IV*).
19. What is the relationship of a child to its own father when it is not its father's son? *Daughter.*
20. What city is drawn more frequently than any other? *Cork.*
21. What is it that occurs four times in every week, twice in every month, and only once in a year? *The letter E.*
22. What kind of cloth is a musical instrument plus a letter? *Organdy* (*organ-d*).
23. What words may be pronounced quicker and shorter by adding another syllable to them? *Quick and short.*
24. What ships are always within sight? *Hardships.*
25. How would you swallow a door? *Bolt it.*
26. Would you rather an elephant killed you or a gorilla? *Would prefer to have the elephant kill the gorilla.*
27. What is the center of gravity? *The letter V.*
28. Born the same time as the world, destined to live as long as the world, and yet never five weeks old. *The moon.*
29. What is the greatest surgical operation on record? *Lansing, Michigan.*
30. Why are a, e, and u the handsome vowels? *You can't have beauty without them.*
31. If Dick's father is John's son, what relation is Dick to John? *His grandson.*
32. If all the money in the world were divided equally, what would each one get? *His share.*

33. How many raw oysters could one eat on an empty stomach? *One. After the first, the stomach would no longer be empty.*
34. Why is a hen immortal? *Because her son never sets.*
35. When is a man obliged to keep his word? *When no one else will take it.*
36. What never asks questions and requires many answers? *Doorbell.*
37. What do ladies look for when they go to church? *The hymns (hims).*
38. Why is the letter "g" like 12 p.m.? *Because it is in the middle of the night.*
39. What is bought by the yard and worn out by the foot? *A carpet.*
40. Why is a beehive like a spectator? *Because it is a bee-holder (beholder).*
41. What is worse than raining dogs and cats? *Hailing taxis.*
42. What is it that you break by even speaking of it? *Silence.*
43. If a tree were to break a window, what would the window say? *Tree-mend-us (Tremendous).*
44. What grows the less tired the more it works? *Auto wheel.*
45. What is it that you may take away the whole and have some left? *The word wholesome.*
46. Why is it impossible to have a whole day? *The day breaks early in the morning.*
47. What makes more noise than a fire engine? *Two fire engines.*
48. Why is it absurd to call a dental office a dental parlor? *Because it's a drawing room.*
49. What is it about a house that seldom falls, but never hurts the occupant when it does? *The rent.*
50. What is it that is put on the table, cut, and passed, but never eaten? *A deck of cards.*
51. What is it that the man who made it does not need, the man who buys it does not use it for himself, and the person who uses it does not know it? *A casket.*
52. What was it that Adam never saw, never possessed, yet left two to each of his children. *Parents.*

53. Why are a fisherman and a shepherd not to be trusted? *Because they live by hook and crook.*
54. What kind of jam cannot be eaten? *A traffic jam.*
55. What do you always notice running along the street in a town? *The curb.*
56. Why is a chicken's neck like a dinner bell? *It is wrung for dinner.*
57. Why can you not expect a fisherman to be generous? *Because his business makes him sell fish.* (*Selfish.*)
58. Why is a vote in congress like a bad cold? *Because sometimes the ayes* (*eyes*) *have it and sometimes the noes* (*nose*).
59. A knight in shining armor had a pain. If you know when it was, you know where it was. *It was in the middle of the* (*k*) *night.*
60. What crosses water without making a shadow? *A sound.*
61. At what age should a man marry? *At the parson-age.*
62. Why is a committee of inquiry like a cannon? *It makes a report.*
63. Why is a wedding ring like eternity? *It has neither beginning nor end.*
64. What is a good thing to part with? *A comb.*
65. What is the best way to keep fish from smelling? *Cut off their noses.*
66. If it has two wheels it is a bicycle, and if it has three wheels it is a tricycle. What would you call it if it had five wheels? *A V-hicle.*
67. What always happens at the end of a dry spell? *It rains.*
68. Why is it that when you are looking for anything you always find it in the last place you look? *Because you always stop looking when you find it.*
69. Why is coffee like a dull tool? *It must be ground before it is used.*
70. Why are your nose and chin not so friendly with each other? *There are always words passing between them.*
71. If a blue stone fell into the Red Sea, what would happen? *It would get wet.*
72. What could be worse than to find a worm in an apple you are eating? *Finding half a worm.*

73. What letters are usually provoking? *T's* (*tease*).
74. What relation is a door mat to a door step? *A step farther* (*a step-father*).
75. Why is a woman like a hinge? *She is something to adore* (*a door*).
76. Which one of our Presidents wore the largest shoes? *The one who had the largest feet.*
77. When is money damp? *When it's due* (*dew*) *in the morning.*
78. Which is the more valuable, a ten-dollar bill or a ten-dollar gold piece? *The ten-dollar bill, because every time you put it in your pocket, you double it.*
79. Why is the letter "c" such a frigid letter? *It is in the middle of ice and makes old people cold people.*
80. What flies up and still is down? *A feather.*
81. What is it that can be right but never wrong? *An angle.*
82. When is a hat not a hat? *When it becomes a woman.*
83. Why can't one put on his left shoe first? *Whichever one he puts on first, the other is "left."*
84. What is the best system of bookkeeping? *Never lend them.*
85. What's the left side of a cake? *The side which is not eaten.*
86. Where did Noah strike the first nail in the Ark? *On the head.*
87. Why did Adam bite the apple Eve gave him? *He had no knife to cut it with.*
88. What does a lady become when she ceases to be pensive? *Ex-pensive.*
89. Who was the fastest runner in the world? *Adam—he was the first in the race.*
90. What did Adam and Eve do when they were expelled from Eden? *They raised Cain.*
91. What is the big difference between a cat and a bullfrog? *A cat has nine lives and a bullfrog croaks every night.*
92. What's the difference between a bum and a pillow? *The first is hard up, and the second is soft down.*
93. What was Joan of Arc made of? *Maid of Orleans.*
94. What is that which by losing an eye has nothing left but a nose? *Noise.*

95. If a lady falls, why cannot her brother help her up? *Because, how could he be a brother and assist her (a sister) too?*
96. Why do the Americans call English their mother tongue? *The father seldom gets a chance to use it.*
97. What fur did Adam and Eve wear? *Bear skin (bare skin)*.
98. What is the difference between some women and a mirror? *Some women speak without reflection; a mirror reflects without speaking.*
99. What part of a book do you sleep under? *Cover.*
100. Why does a sculptor die a terrible death? *Because he makes faces and busts.*

Question Baseball

QUESTION baseball is played like conundrum baseball described above. The only difference is that questions are used instead of conundrums, and scores are made every time one side answers four questions in one inning.

1. What is an Aurora Borealis? *Northern lights or "midnight sun."*
2. What was the name of the most noted Chinese philosopher? *Confucius.*
3. What is the meaning of the Latin expression found on many coins, *e pluribus unum? One out of many.*
4. What is Braille? *A system of raised dots to be read by the blind.*
5. Who was the editor of POOR RICHARD'S ALMANAC? *Benjamin Franklin.*
6. Who was the best known Indiana poet? *James Whitcomb Riley.*
7. What bird appears in the "Rime of the Ancient Mariner"? *Albatross.*
8. Who wrote THE INNOCENTS ABROAD? *Mark Twain.*
9. Who commanded the "Rough Riders" and in what war? *Theodore Roosevelt in the Spanish-American War.*
10. What are the catacombs? *The catacombs are underground tunnels in which the dead were buried, the most famous being in Rome.*

11. Who said, "I came, I saw, I conquered"? *Julius Caesar.*
12. Can you quote the next line? "Listen, my children, and you shall hear." *"Of the midnight ride of Paul Revere."*
13. Why is the Dead Sea so called? *The water is so salty that no fish can live in it.*
14. Who was the leader of the Protestant Reformation? *Martin Luther.*
15. How do kangaroos carry their offspring? *In a pouch on the under side of the body.*
16. For what is Downing Street famous? *The Prime Minister of England lives on this street in London.*
17. Who led an army of unemployed to Washington? *Coxey.*
18. What city is the capital of North Dakota? *Bismarck.*
19. What is a "fez"? *A brimless hat worn by the Turks and Moroccans.*
20. What city is called the city of churches? *Brooklyn.*
21. Who wrote BEN-HUR? *Lew Wallace.*
22. Who wrote "The Legend of Sleepy Hollow"? *Washington Irving.*
23. What is a gondola? *The name of a canal boat in Venice.*
24. On his first voyage to America, where did Columbus land? *The Island of San Salvador, West Indies.*
25. What city is called the city of magnificent distances? *Washington, D. C.*
26. Who founded the Colony of Georgia? *James Oglethorpe.*
27. What was the capital of the Southern Confederacy? *Richmond, Virginia.*
28. What is the Marseillaise? *The French national anthem.*
29. Who is a "cracker"? *A native of Georgia.*
30. For what purpose were the pyramids of Egypt built? *They were built for tombs of the ancient Egyptian rulers.*
31. Who was Fatima? *The daughter of Mohammed.*
32. What American general was convicted of treason? *Benedict Arnold.*
33. What is the Taj Mahal? *Famous building at Agra, India, and said to be the most beautiful building in the world.*

34. Can you repeat the next line, "But there is no joy in Mudville"? *"Mighty Casey has struck out."*
35. Who was the founder of Christian Science? *Mary Baker Eddy.*
36. What is a typhoon? *It means "war of winds" and sometimes causes the water to pile upon the ocean, sinking a ship.*
37. Who gave the Statue of Liberty to the United States? *France.*
38. Whose picture is on a one-dollar bill? *George Washington's.*
39. In what state are counties called parishes? *Louisiana.*
40. Name three great composers whose names begin with B. *Bach, Beethoven, Brahms.*
41. What prominent Frenchman assisted the Colonies in the Revolutionary War? *Lafayette.*
42. Three presidents were assassinated. Can you name two of them? *Lincoln, Garfield, McKinley.*
43. What city is called Gotham? *New York.*
44. Who is represented as holding the world on his shoulders? *Atlas.*
45. Where was Lincoln when he was shot? *At Ford's theater.*
46. What is a mirage? *It is an optical illusion in which we see something that does not exist, such as lakes on the desert.*
47. Who said "Give me liberty or give me death"? *Patrick Henry.*
48. What is the Golden Gate? *A strait, between low mountains, separating San Francisco Bay and the Pacific Ocean.*
49. What was the name of Abraham Lincoln's mother? *Nancy Hanks.*
50. What is the nineteenth amendment? *The amendment granting woman suffrage.*
51. What is the Fleur-de-lis? *It is the national emblem of France.*
52. What is the blue-grass state? *Kentucky.*
53. Who said, "Go west, young man"? *Horace Greeley.*
54. Who is nicknamed "Old Nick"? *The devil.*
55. What does the abbreviation *e.g.* means? *For example (exempli gratia).*
56. What fictional little girl was nearly devoured by a wolf which impersonated her grandmother? *Little Red Riding Hood.*
57. Who invented motion pictures? *Thomas A. Edison.*

58. Who spread his cloak over a mud puddle for a queen, and who was the queen? *Sir Walter Raleigh; Elizabeth I.*
59. Of what is Mecca the name? *The sacred city of the Mohammedans.*
60. What is indicated by a falling barometer? *The approach of stormy weather.*
61. What was Zachary Taylor called? *Old Rough and Ready.*
62. What does the name Alabama mean? *Here we rest.*
63. What two bodies of water are connected by the Suez Canal? *The Mediterranean and the Red Sea.*
64. What great military leader was called the "Little Corporal"? *Napoleon.*
65. What President did Congress impeach? *Andrew Johnson.*
66. What is the Fujiyama? *A mountain in Japan, held sacred.*
67. What city is called the city of brotherly love? *Philadelphia.*
68. Who was the founder of the Mormons? *Joseph Smith.*
69. What country is shaped like a boot, and what does it appear to be kicking? *Italy. It appears to be kicking Sicily.*
70. What was the sin and punishment of Lot's wife? *She looked back and was turned into a pillar of salt.*
71. In what game are pawns used? *Chess.*
72. Who was called the Sage of Monticello? *Thomas Jefferson.*
73. Of what was Excalibur the name? *The name of King Arthur's sword.*
74. Who was a noted Kentucky pioneer and explorer? *Daniel Boone.*
75. Who wrote PILGRIM'S PROGRESS? *John Bunyan.*
76. Where is the United States' national cemetery? *At Arlington.*
77. What river is known as the "Father of Waters"? *The Mississippi.*
78. When is Constitution Day and what does it commemorate? *September 17. The signing of the Constitution.*
79. Who was the Roman goddess of love and beauty? *Venus.*
80. What is the normal temperature of the human body? *98.6 degrees Fahrenheit.*
81. What are freshmen at Annapolis called? *Plebes.*

82. What are the first ten amendments to the U.S. Constitution usually called? *The Bill of Rights.*
83. Who founded Salt Lake City? *The Mormons.*
84. By whom was Napoleon defeated at Waterloo? *Wellington.*
85. Who wrote "Snowbound"? *John Greenleaf Whittier.*
86. What famous composer was deaf? *Beethoven.*
87. How is the date of Easter determined? *It is the first Sunday after the first full moon after the 20th of March.*
88. What is the Sistine Madonna? *Famous painting of the Virgin Mary by Raphael.*
89. Who created the famous character, Sherlock Holmes? *Conan Doyle.*
90. Which state of the United States was once an independent republic? *Texas.*
91. What country has no snakes and why? *Ireland. Tradition says Saint Patrick drove them out.*
92. On what island is the Statue of Liberty located? *Liberty Island (formerly Bedloe's Island)*.
93. What was the real name of Mark Twain? *Samuel Clemens.*
94. Who was the first chief justice of the United States? *John Jay.*
95. What is the capital of South Dakota? *Pierre.*
96. What famous volcano is near Naples? *Vesuvius.*
97. Who are the Seminoles and why were they so called? *Indians of Florida. The name means "Wanderers."*
98. What was Ponce de Leon seeking when he discovered Florida? *The fountain of youth.*
99. Who discovered the Pacific Ocean? *Balboa.*
100. What is the meaning of the Spanish word "manana"? *Tomorrow.*

You Have a Face

THE PLAYERS sit in a circle, and the player who starts the game turns to the one on his right and says, "You have a face," to which the player replies, "What kind of a face?" The first player must then reply with an adjective beginning with "a," so he answers "An attractive face." The next player then turns to the one on his right and says, "You have a face," and so the game continues. The second player must answer the inquiry "what kind of a face" with an adjective beginning with "b." For example, a bony face, and so the game goes on around the circle using adjectives beginning with consecutive letters of the alphabet.

Funny Pictures

A PICTURE frame about 16x20 is needed for this game. The person who is "It" takes his place behind the picture frame which has only the glass in it. The players then by asking questions or making funny faces seek to make "It" laugh or smile. A timekeeper keeps the time for each person, and the one who refrains from laughing the longest wins.

Grocery Store

THE GROUP is divided into two sides equal in number. These two lines stand facing the leader who has a number of letters face down on the table. The leader picks these letters up one at a time and calls them. The players attempt to give the name of some article sold in a grocery store which begins with that letter. For example, if the letter called was "b" one of the two persons at the head of the line who first said bacon or bread would win one point for his side. These two would then take their place at the back of the line, and the leader would pick up another letter. The side caught prompting should be penalized one point.

Alphabetical Progress

THIS GAME, Alphabetical Progress, may be played with a small group at a table. It may be played with three or four groups, placed around as many tables, or it may be played by a large group and may be a progressive game.

1. In playing with a small group at a table, the players are provided with pencils and papers. A pile of letters is placed on the table face down. The leader picks up a letter and calls the name of it. The player who first calls the name of a fruit beginning with this letter wins one point and marks it on his score card. So the game continues until the letters are used up. This game may be played by using the names of fruits, flowers, articles of dress, or any other objects.

2. This game may be played by three or four groups with four at a table. In this case the leader calls the letters for all the groups. Those who sit opposite each other are partners and if either suggests a word, the other has the privilege of scoring as well. In this case the two partners who have the highest score are the winners.

3. This game may be a very interesting progressive game. Let us suppose that we have forty-eight players seated at twelve tables. The tables are numbered from one to twelve, number one being the head table. The leader has a number of letters turned face down on a table. He picks these up one by one and calls the letter so that the whole group can hear. The leader should then call twelve letters in all before the players are allowed to progress. When the leader has called the twelve letters, the partners at each table who have made the highest score progress to the next table. The winners at table No. 1, the head table, do not progress but remain at this table as long as they win. Losers at table 1 go to the foot table, No. 12.

It will add to the interest of the game if players change partners every time they progress. In this case each of the players who progresses takes one of the players at the new table as a partner.

How Will You Travel?

THE LEADER tells the group that he is going on a journey and would like to have all the guests join him. The only requirement is that the guests select the proper means of travel. Only those who know the game will understand that the means of travel must begin with the same letter of the alphabet as the place to which the journey is to be made.

The leader may say, "I am going to take a trip to Atlanta. Would you like to join me?" The first player answers, "Yes." The leader then asks, "How would you like to travel?" If the first player answers, "By air," this would be correct and this player now becomes the leader. If the player should say, "By plane," this would be incorrect, and the leader would keep asking until some player gives a right answer. Each player giving a right answer becomes the leader, and the game continues around the room.

Any player who fails to travel by the right transportation is required to sit on the floor until his turn comes again. If by that time he has caught on to the game, he may have another try and, if he is correct, may take a seat in a chair again.

The players may choose any means of transportation—as, for example, bus, yacht, subway, rocket, walking, swimming, flying, bicycle, bobsled, skis, roller skates, and so on. No matter how crazy the transportation chosen, as long as it begins with the same letter as the destination, it is correct.

Battleship

THE GAME of Battleship represents a naval encounter in which two opposing fleets of four ships each are trying to sink each other. It is a game for two people, or for two couples playing as partners. Give each player a sheet of paper upon which are drawn two charts—10x10 blocks of 100 squares, numbered as shown below. Each chart represents an area of the sea where the ships are located.

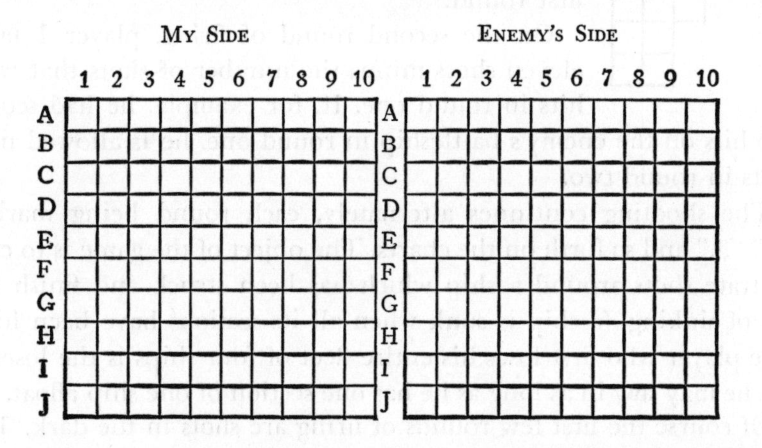

The player's own chart—marked "My Side"—is the defensive field, on which he must draw in his fleet—one battleship, one cruiser, and two destroyers. The battleship is four squares long, the cruiser three, and the destroyer two. In placing the fleet, the player must locate his ships so that each one is in a straight line. For instance, a battleship may be placed horizontally, vertically, or diagonally in a straight line; but to separate the battleship and place two sections in one place and two in another is not allowed. Players must not allow the others to see this defensive field.

The game starts with one player firing eleven shots at the "enemy." He shoots by calling the letter and number of the square he plans to hit on the enemy's side—F-5, J-7, etc. His opponent records these shots on his own defensive field, marking each square hit with a "1" to indicate round one of firing. At the same time, the player firing marks a "1" on his chart labeled "Enemy's Side," so that he can keep up with his own shots.

After the first player has shot eleven times, his opponent tells him how many hits have been made and on what vessel. Players keep track of hits on enemy ships by marking the "Hit" chart, indicating the round in which the hit was made.

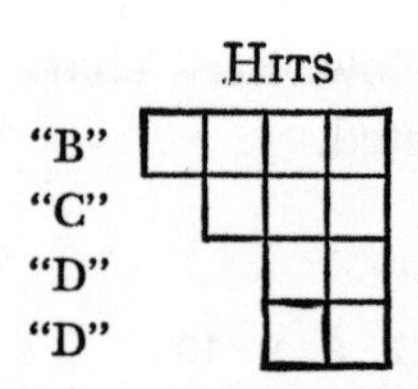

The second player now fires eleven shots. Each shot is still recorded with a "1" in the square struck, and the scoring is the same as player 1's first round.

On the second round of firing, player 1 takes eleven shots minus the number of shots that were hits in round one. If, for example, he had scored two hits on the enemy's battleship in round one, he is allowed nine shots in round two.

The shooting continues alternately, each round being marked "2," "3," and so forth on the charts. The object of the game is to concentrate shots around a ship which has been struck and finish the job of sinking (a ship is sunk when all its sections have been hit). The player who first loses his entire fleet of four ships is the loser—but he may stay in as long as he has one section of one ship afloat.

Of course the first few rounds of firing are shots in the dark. The skill comes later, in figuring where the enemy has placed his ships and concentrating fire in this area.

Personal Scavenger Hunt

THE PLAYERS are divided into two groups of equal number and are assembled in opposite corners of the room. Two chairs are placed near the center of the room.

The leader has made up two lists of objects which each group is to assemble. These lists may be identical, or they may consist only of an equal number of objects. Some suggestions for the list are: a pocket knife, photograph, toothpick, nail file, comb, cuff links, bobby pin, bunch of keys, compact, mirror, penny, five-dollar bill, a girl's shoe smaller than size six, a boy's belt, ball-point pen, a red hair.

When the play starts, the leader gives each group a list and tells them to assemble the objects. As the objects are found, they are placed on the chairs—one chair designated for each group. The group that assembles the largest number of the articles within a certain time limit is the winner. For a small group, five minutes should be enough time.

Spin the Plate

ONE of the old ones is Spin the Plate. The guests are arranged in a ring, kneeling. The hostess is the leader and starts the game off by numbering the players or giving them names of animals. She spins the plate and calls a number or a name. Unless the person who wears the name or has the number catches the plate before it falls to the floor, he must pay a forfeit. Redeeming the forfeits is the best part of the fun. A number of forfeits are suggested on page 54.

This game may be played without paying forfeits by having the player who fails to catch the plate retire from the game.

Jingle Bell

A SMALL bell with a tongue in it large enough to be held in the fingers is needed for this game. The players stand in a circle with their hands behind them and one player has the bell. When the game starts, the leader must close his eyes and count slowly to ten, the counts coming about a second apart. Upon the first count, whoever has the bell rings it vigorously and then takes the tongue in his hand and passes it behind his back either to the right or to the left. On the count of ten, the movements stop and the leader opens his eyes. He guesses who has the bell. Anyone caught with the bell must pay a forfeit and in addition must become the leader.

The Circus

ANOTHER game that may be used as a forfeit game is Circus. All the players sit in a circle and the first one starts the game by saying, "I went to the circus and saw an antelope." The next player on the right must repeat the statement and add something that he saw, and not only this, but it must begin with the second letter of the alphabet. For example, "I went to the circus and saw an antelope and a bear." The Third one may say, "I went to the circus and saw an antelope, a bear, and a clown." Each one in turn must repeat all that has been said before and add some object alphabetically. If he fails to do this, he must pay a forfeit.

This game may be made more difficult by requiring each one to add a descriptive word, as for example, "I went to the circus and saw an attractive antelope, a brown bear, or a clever clown."

You Name the Offspring

THE LEADER prepares in advance typewritten or mimeographed sheets for each guest with the following names typed on them. The name of the offspring is left blank, and the guests, working either singly or in couples, fill in the name of the offspring which these couples might have.

Mr. and Mrs. Mite.	Dina (dynamite)
Mr. and Mrs. Rot	Tommy (tommyrot)
Mr. and Mrs. Board	Bill (billboard)
Mr. and Mrs. Mander	Jerry (gerrymander)
Mr. and Mrs. Tock	Matt (mattock)
Mr. and Mrs. Anthemum	Cris (chrysanthemum)
Mr. and Mrs. Itosis	Hal (halitosis)
Mr. and Mrs. Iculate	Art (articulate)
Mr. and Mrs. Fi	Terry (terrify)
Mr. and Mrs. Mire	Ad (admire)
Mr. and Mrs. Vere	Percy (persevere)
Mr. and Mrs. Tor	Eddie (editor)
Mr. and Mrs. Tate	Hessie (hesitate)
Mr. and Mrs. Nasium	Jim (gymnasium)

Mr. and Mrs. Ware	Bee (beware)
Mr. and Mrs. Tastic	Fan (fantastic)
Mr. and Mrs. Tant	Milly (militant)
Mr. and Mrs. Grant	Emmy (emigrant)
Mr. and Mrs. Quill	John (jonquil)
Mr. and Mrs. Ficial	Benny (beneficial)
Mr. and Mrs. Mum	Minnie (minimum)

Give a token prize to the person or couple who gets the largest number correct.

This game is also good as an oral quiz. The leader might read the family names and ask the guests to hold up their hands if they are able to give the name of the offspring.

The guest can probably think of a number of other names to add to his list, and the leader may ask the guests to make suggestions.

Missing Nouns

THE GUESTS sit in a circle. Each person has chosen a trade or profession. The leader starts reading an article from a current newspaper, omitting the nouns as the article is read, except the noun which introduces the article. For example, he would read as follows: "The president asks early passage of his *program*." The leader instead of reading the noun "program" would stop when he came to it, point to one player and start counting ten. If the trade of that player was that of carpenter, he would be expected to say "saw" or "hammer" before the leader finishes counting ten. Anyone failing to respond must pay a forfeit and himself become the leader. The leader must not neglect to take a trade or profession for himself.

Shopping

THE PLAYERS may sit on the floor in a circle. The leader says, "You say you have been shopping. What did you buy?" This person must name an article within easy reach of himself and he cannot name the article more than once; that is, if the question goes around the circle and comes to him a second time, he cannot again name the same article. Another rule is that no one can name any object already named by another person. For example, if one person says, "I bought a rug," no one else can name a rug. In a short time it will be difficult to find any article to name. Whoever fails to respond, however, after a reasonable time must pay a forfeit.

Pawns Redeemed

IN PLAYING the game of forfeits, care should be taken not to prolong the game beyond a point of interest. Another precaution should be taken: the person who acts as the judge in redeeming the forfeits should be prepared in advance. He should have written on cards a number of penalties or stunts that may be done to redeem the forfeits.

The traditional manner of proceeding is to have the leader hold over the head of the judge the forfeit as they recite the following dialogue.

Leader, "Heavy, heavy hangs over your head."

Judge, "Is it fine or superfine?"

If the leader says, "fine," it means that the article belongs to a boy. The judge should describe a stunt suitable for a boy. If the leader says that the article is "superfine," that indicates that it belongs to a girl, and the judge should prescribe a stunt for a girl.

The list of forfeits given below should be carefully studied and to them might be added many others to be thought of at the time by the judge or gleaned from other sources.

Forfeits

1. Imitate a grasshopper.
2. Imagine you are Alice and tell something that happened to you in Wonderland.
3. Repeat exactly what each of three persons tells you.
4. Find a person that is not ticklish.
5. Brag about something you have accomplished.
6. Stand looking perfectly serious while the other guests try to make you laugh.
7. Kiss your shadow.

8. Drink a glass of water with a coin on your nose.
9. Describe a person in the room and say three nice things about him (*you have been told by the leader in advance the person you are describing is yourself*).
10. Place a candle in such a position that everyone in the room can see it except yourself (*it will have to be placed on your head*).
11. Imitate someone in the room whom the leader designates.
12. Compose a poem of at least two lines about someone present and recite it.
13. Push a penny across a table with your nose.
14. Lap up some milk out of a saucer.
15. Make an animated speech on the subject "prunes."
16. Say the alphabet backwards.
17. Beat time to the chorus of some popular song, and form the words with your lips without uttering a sound.
18. Hop around the room holding one foot in your hand.
19. Spear an apple with a pin and carry it across the room.
20. Pare an apple and keep the peel all in one length.
21. Sing a song and accompany yourself on an imaginary piano.
22. Count as far as you can on one breath.
23. Show how you usually act when you hit yourself on the finger with a hammer.
24. Shake hands with four persons; greet the first one with a solemn face, the second one with a smile, the third one with a grin, the fourth one with a frown.
25. Walk around the room on your hands and feet.
26. Imitate a typist at work.
27. Give an imitation of your favorite television entertainer.
28. Sing up and down the scale, but instead of using the notes, say "ha, ha, ha."
29. Pantomime the actions of Robinson Crusoe as he discovers Friday's footprints on the sand.
30. Peel an imaginary onion.
31. Make a sentence so that the first letter in each word is in alphabetical order. Illustration: A bear can drive every fearful girl heartsick.

32. Place one hand on the floor and run around it three times.
33. Imitate a donkey eating hay.
34. Hum a tune holding your nose.
35. Answer "yes" or "no" to three questions which are made up while you leave the room.
36. Imitate a baby and crawl across the room.
37. Try to make your face funnier than it is.
38. Say "six mixed biscuits made six sick" three times.
39. Imagine you are a circus clown and entertain the group.
40. Pretend you are taking a bath.
41. Pantomime Tom, the Piper's Son, stealing a pig.
42. Imagine you are a dog burying a bone.
43. Go to some person in the room and give six reasons why he should lend you a dollar.
44. Pantomime a cat watching a mouse hole.
45. Imitate a child that lisps saying, "round and round the rugged rock the ragged rascal rudely ran."
46. Show how a horse gallops, trots, and runs.
47. Repeat a nursery rhyme as you would if you had no teeth.
48. Imitate a doctor making a call.
49. Say, "Rubber baby buggy bumpers," three times, getting faster each time.
50. Tell the group the first thing you would do if you were to inherit a million dollars.
51. Tell a funny story.
52. Tell something amusing that you heard a child say.
53. Whistle your favorite tune.
54. Sneeze in three different ways.
55. Make a shadow picture on the wall with your hands.
56. Tip your hat in four different ways to as many guests.
57. Recite a Mother Goose rhyme with gestures.
58. Define the following words in sign language: accordion, goatee, spiral staircase.
59. Make a paper dunce cap and put it on the head of the most dignified guest.
60. Take the place of the judge and let forfeits be sold over your head.

This last one might be used a number of times. If the judge has this book in hand, it would be well to transfer his office to another after ten or twelve stunts. He should, of course, transfer the book as well.

Forfeits for Two Persons

1. Stage a dog fight.
2. Choose a partner and make him laugh with your antics.
3. Each eat five crackers and see which can whistle first.
4. Feed your partner a half glass of water with a spoon.
5. Have two compete in emptying baby bottles provided with the usual apparatus.
6. Have two compete in laughing contest to see which can laugh longer.
7. Have a boy give a girl a lesson in astronomy.
8. Select two persons for a talking contest. Give them such subjects as reducing, matrimony, etc.
9. Have a couple stand before the whole group, the girl saying the words of Yankee Doodle while the boy numbers them. As, Yankee, 1, Doodle, 2, went, 3, to, 4, and so on.

Proverbs

THERE are a number of very interesting games that can be played with proverbs. The following is a list of some of the most common proverbs:

1. A burned child dreads the fire.
2. A friend in need is a friend indeed.
3. A miss is as good as a mile.
4. A hedge between keeps friendship green.
5. Actions speak louder than words.
6. All work and no play makes Jack a dull boy.
7. Money makes the mare go.
8. A penny saved is a penny made.
9. Don't put the cart before the horse.
10. Two's company; three's a crowd.
11. Two heads are better than one.

12. He has an ax to grind.
13. Too many cooks spoil the broth.
14. A guilty conscience needs no accuser.
15. A stitch in time saves nine.
16. Haste makes waste.
17. A chip off the old block.
18. A fool and his money are soon parted.
19. A little pot is soon hot.
20. Birds of a feather flock together.
21. All that glitters is not gold.
22. In at one ear and out at the other.
23. It is a long lane that has no turning.
24. Make hay while the sun shines.
25. If the shoe fits, wear it.
26. Misery loves company.
27. There's no fool like an old fool.
28. Hitch your wagon to a star.
29. Practice makes perfect.
30. A word to the wise is sufficient.
31. Procrastination is the thief of time.
32. Every cloud has a silver lining.
33. Never count your chickens before they are hatched.
34. A little nonsense now and then is relished by the wisest men.
35. No news is good news.
36. Out of sight, out of mind.
37. He that is down need fear no fall.
38. Honesty is the best policy.
39. Well begun is half done.
40. Better late than never.
41. Variety is the spice of life.
42. Many hands make light work.
43. Time and tide wait for no man.
44. 'Tis an ill wind that blows no one good.
45. Still water runs deep.
46. Pretty is as pretty does.
47. It's a poor rule that won't work both ways.
48. Half a loaf is better than no bread.

49. Never put off until tomorrow what you can do today.
50. Time is short; art is long.
51. Hunger is the best sauce.
52. A good lawyer is a bad neighbor.
53. Better be alone than in bad company.
54. Poverty is no sin.
55. Friends are plenty when the purse is full.
56. He is wise who speaks little.
57. Lost time is never found again.
58. Promise little, but do much.
59. Out of debt, out of danger.
60. Better a slip with the foot than with the tongue.
61. He that can travel well afoot keeps a good horse.
62. Sloth is the mother of poverty.
63. A bad workman quarrels with his tools.
64. Do what you ought, come what may.
65. Time brings everything to light.
66. A heavy purse makes a light heart.
67. You made your bed, so you must lie on it.
68. A man's house is his castle.
69. Nothing is certain in life but death and taxes.
70. It's a sad house where the hen crows louder than the cock.
71. Happy is the man who has a hobby.
72. While there's life there's hope.
73. Lips however rosy must be fed.
74. Live and let live.
75. If fools went not to market, bad wares would not be sold.
76. It is never too late to mend.
77. Better a small fish than an empty dish.
78. Don't cut off your nose to spite your face.
79. A man of words and not of deeds is like a garden full of weeds.
80. If you want anything well done, do it yourself.
81. Absence makes the heart grow fonder.
82. Laugh and the world laughs with you.
83. The early bird catches the worm.
84. Nothing ventured, nothing gained.

85. If at first you don't succeed, try, try, again.
86. Discretion is the better part of valor.
87. Knowledge is power.
88. The pen is mightier than the sword.
89. Silence gives consent.
90. There is honor even among thieves.
91. A barking dog never bites.
92. Put a beggar on a horse, and he will ride to the devil.
93. Never look a gift horse in the mouth.
94. Beware of Greeks bearing gifts.
95. There's many a slip 'twixt the cup and the lip.
96. Faint heart never won fair lady.
97. It never rains but it pours.
98. One good turn deserves another.
99. Hell is paved with good intentions.
100. Save the pennies and the dollars will take care of themselves.

Pied Proverbs

GIVE out slips of paper on which are written or mimeographed the following pied proverbs and ask guests to decipher them.

1. Nife theerafs od ont kame inef sribd. *Fine feathers do not make fine birds.*
2. Oto yman kocos pilos eht thbor. *Too many cooks spoil the broth.*
3. Tricpace eskam fretecp. *Practice makes perfect.*
4. Lal si ton dolg taht tligtres. *All is not gold that glitters.*
5. Ghoenu si sa odog sa a seatf. *Enough is as good as a feast.*
6. A lolring etons tharseg on smos. *A rolling stone gathers no moss.*
7. A ribd ni het nadh si thowr owt ni eth husb. *A bird in the hand is worth two in the bush.*
8. Eh ghalus steb owh salugh salt. *He laughs best who laughs last.*
9. A toncedent mdin si a tulincona stafe. *A contented mind is a continual feast.*
10. Tinfroumess evern ecom sgyiln. *Misfortunes never come singly.*

Snapping Proverbs

DIVIDE the players into two teams of equal number and seat them facing each other. The captain of one team goes over to the other team, points at a member of that team, and starts counting. This player must give a proverb before the captain can count twenty. If this player succeeds, he then goes over to the other team and points out a player, who in turn must quote a proverb while he counts twenty. If a player fails to respond with a proverb before the count of twenty ends, he must go over to the opposing team as a captive, and the player who pointed him out has a chance at another player. A proverb once given may not be repeated. The game should continue until one side has captured all of the players of the other side.

Proverbs Suggested

GIVE GUESTS a list of the objects listed below and have them write what proverb the object should suggest. 1—A penny; 2—A link of chain; 3—An object made of brass; 4—A broom; 5—An apple; 6—A flower; 7—A paper sack; 8—A fork; 9—An acorn; 10—Half a loaf of bread; 11—A shoe; 12—A feather; 13—A cake of soap; 14—A stocking with a hole in it; 15—A stone. *Answer.* 1—A bad penny always come back. 2—A chain is no stronger that it weakest link. 3—All that glitters is not gold. 4—A new broom sweeps clean. 5—An apple a day keeps the doctor away. 6—April showers bring May flowers. 7—Don't buy a pig in a poke. 8—Fingers were made before forks. 9—Great oaks from little acorns grow. 10—Half a loaf is better than no bread. 11—If the shoe fits, wear it. 12—Fine feathers do not make fine birds. 13—Cleanliness is next to godliness. 14—A stitch in time saves nine. 15—A rolling stone gathers no moss.

Proverb Questions

ONE GUEST is sent from the room, and in his absence the rest decide on a proverb. When the guest returns to the room, he must determine what the proverb is by asking questions. The first one questioned must include in his answer the first word of the proverb, the second one questioned must include in his answer the second word of the proverb, the third one questioned must include the third word in the proverb. The questioner should be told how many words there are in the proverb so that he will know how many questions to ask. If the questioner discovers the proverb, the one from whom he got his clue in identifying it must retire and continue the game.

Illustrated Proverbs

FOR THIS GAME assemble a blackboard, chalk, eraser, and slips of paper on which have been written proverbs. The guests are divided into two groups, with each group selecting a leader and an illustrator. Such proverbs as the following may be chosen (see also the list of proverbs on page 57.

A hedge between keeps friendship green.
It's a long lane that has no turning.
Make hay while the sun shines
Half a loaf is better than none.
Every cloud has a silver lining.
Don't cut off your nose to spite your face.

When the action starts, the leader chooses one of the slips and gives it to the illustrator, who passes it around the players on his side so that they will know which proverb he is illustrating. As the illustrator draws on the blackboard, the players on the opposite team try to guess the proverb. Suppose the illustrator is using the proverb, "Half a loaf is better than none." He draws a half loaf of bread. The opposing players might guess, "A rolling stone gathers no moss." As this is incorrect, the game continues until the correct answer is given. The other team is then given a proverb and its illustrator goes to work.

Continue this game as long as the interest is maintained or until the supply of proverbs has been exhausted.

Boston Proverbs

BOSTON is said to be one of the most sophisticated towns. The following are proverbs said to have originated in Boston, they being some of the old familiar ones with a new dress.

1. Desiccated herbage submit to perturbation,

The while the radiant orb of day affords illumination.
Make hay while the sun shines.

2. A futile superfluity of culinary aid,
Destroys nutritious liquids from osseous issues made.
Too many cooks spoil the broth.
3. Your immediate environment submit to circumspection,
Ere you traverse some feet of space by muscular projection.
Look before you leap.
4. Inhabitants of domiciles of vitreous formation,
With lapidary fragments should ne'er perform jactation.
People who live in glass houses shouldn't throw stones.
5. Who counts, ere fractured are the shells, his bipeds gallinaceous,
Is apt to find his calculations utterly fallacious.
Don't count your chickens before they're hatched.

How Wise Are You?

PROVERBS are said to be wise sayings. One's wisdom is, therefore, to be judged by the number of proverbs he knows. Have the guests write down all the proverbs they can think of in fifteen minutes. The one writing the largest number should receive an appropriate prize.

Over

THIS, as well as the following stunts, must be done by two people who are confederates. In the game, "Over," one remains in the room, having in his hand a yardstick, a cane, or an umbrella. His confederate leaves the room. The one who remains in the room holds the object over the heads of different guests, each time says, "over." His confederate in the adjoining room repeats each time the word, "over." Finally the one in the room with the guests says, "over whom?" and the confederate in the adjoining room gives the correct name of the guest.

The one who remains in the room with the guests tells his confederate in advance over whose head he will hold the object by placing the end of it near the feet of the one who is to be next selected. This will not be noticed by the other guests if it is cleverly done.

What Time Is It?

THE mind reader must have a confederate who is familiar with the following code to assist him. The letters of the alphabet are the key letters to the hours of the clock, as A represents one, B, two, C, three, etc. The third word spoken by the confederate must begin with the key letter and tell the mind reader the hour that has been selected. The game would proceed somewhat as follows: The mind reader leaves the room and the group decides on an hour. Suppose it is ten o'clock. The mind reader returns and asks his assistant "What time it is?" He replies, "I don't just exactly know." The mind reader says, "Well, I know, it is ten o'clock." The third word used was "just" and J is the tenth letter of the alphabet.

Mind-Reading Stunt

THE MIND reader makes a statement that he can tell the owner of any small object such as a handkerchief, hairpin, or coin, by simply holding it in his hand. He must have a confederate of course, who works with him.

The mind reader leaves the room and his partner selects something from one of the guests for the experiment. When the mind reader returns he takes the article in his hand and his assistant asks, "What boy?" The mind reader immediately answers Walter Brown. This is the right answer, so he goes out again. When he comes back in the room, his partner hands him a handkerchief perhaps, and asys, "How now?" Some quick-witted guest may see through the mind reader and offer to try it out. If he has guessed that the first two words carry the initials of the owners of the articles, he will be successful with this stunt.

Car Salesman

ONE guest leaves the room while the salesman remains in the room. The guests decide on a make of automobile to be used. This may be done by writing the name on a piece of paper and holding it up so all can see. When the group has decided on a car, the salesman starts calling the names of makes of cars. Each time his confederate will say, "no," until finally the right one is mentioned. The confederate has been told in advance that it would be the first, second, third, or fourth car mentioned by the salesman. This was done by the salesman indicating by the number of fingers which car it will be. Either hand laid on the lap indicated that it would be the fifth car. The hand with the thumb concealed would indicate that it would be the fourth car; both hands the tenth car; and so on.

Crossed

THIS is a very old game, in fact so old, that it will perhaps be new to a great many people. The leader starts a pair of scissors around the circle of guests by saying, "I received these scissors uncrossed and I pass them to you crossed." The next person may know the game and say, "I received these scissors uncrossed and I pass them to you crossed." Each time the guest manipulates the scissors, opening or closing them. If a guest passes them incorrectly, the leader who is the judge asks him to sit on the floor. The trick is in the position of the feet or legs when the scissors are received. If the feet are uncrossed, the guest receives the scissors uncrossed. He may nonchalantly cross his feet before passing on the scissors, in which case he passes them crossed. This will be confusing to a guest who does not know the reason for the scissors sometimes being passed to him crossed while at the same time he received them uncrossed. Guests who are seated on the floor, if they think they have caught on, should have the scissors passed to them. If they receive them and pass them correctly, they should be allowed to sit in their chairs again.

Mystic Code

WHILE the mind reader is out of the room, the group selects a verb of action, as laugh, cough, sing, or dance. The confederate in the room is equipped with a cane or yardstick. When the mind reader returns, the assistant starts manipulating the can in many ways; finally he says, "Can't you all keep quiet?" Later on he says, "Get quiet please." Later on he says, "Hush." After a time the mind reader begins to cough. He has decided that the word selected was cough. His assistant told him the first letter of the verb by using a sentence, the first word of which began with the same letter as the verb. He was told the first vowel by his assistant tapping four times on the floor with the cane. He was told that the next letter was a vowel by the assistant tapping five times with the cane, and he was told the last two consonants by the beginning letters in the last two sentences. The vowel key is as follows: A, one tap, E, two, I, three, O four, U, five. Of course it is not necessary to choose a verb, any other word may be guessed by the mind reader.

Small Fruit as Clue

A CONFEDERATE of the leader is sent out of the room, and in his absence the group is asked to select some object far away. It might be, for example, Pike's Peak in Colorado, the Mississippi River, an orange in Florida, and African lion, or anything else. When the confederate is called back into the room, the leader asks questions, for example, "Is it the Gulf of Mexico? Is it a Cuban pineapple? Is it a strawberry? Is it Pike's Peak in Colorado?" The confederate answers "no" to all questions except the last. He had been told by the leader that the last was correct because the small fruit, strawberry, was his clue. Another small fruit may be used next time, such as blackberries, cherries, and others.

He Can Do Little

THE LEADER has a cane or a yardstick which he moves on the floor —he says, "I am drawing a picture of the man in the moon; he can do little who can't do this." The leader to confuse the guests may stand in any kind of funny position, as for example, pigeon-toed, or with arm akimbo. The trick, however, is in moving the cane or yardstick with the left hand. Usually, guests who try to imitate the leader will invariably use the right hand.

Blind Reading

THE leader tells the group that he has power to read from a folded paper with his eyes closed. He asks guests to write a short sentence on a slip of paper, fold it and hand it to him. When all papers have been written, the leader takes a folded paper, presses it against his forehead, closes his eyes, and reads, "Christmas comes on Saturday." Before he unfolds it he returns to the guests and says, "Who wrote that?" He has a confederate who acknowledges that this is what he wrote. Of course, "Christmas comes on Saturday" was not written on the piece of paper, and it was not his confederate's paper. The leader then unfolds the paper, looks at it, and fixes in mind just what the paper does say. When he presses the next paper against his forehead, he repeats the sentence that had been written on the one just before. In this way he is able to confuse the whole group.

This or That

THE LEADER remains in the room while his confederate retires. Four or five books are placed on a table, and the guests select one of these books. When the leader's confederate is called back in the room, the leader points to each book and says, "Is it this?" The confederate replies, "No." But when the leader points to a book and says, "Is it that?" the "that" is a cue for the confederate to say, "Yes."

Table Progressive Games

HERE IS A GAME that might be used to amuse a group for a whole evening. It will keep them moving about, permit each one to make the acquaintance of every other one, and keep the ice broken continually. Let us suppose that the group is large enough for twelve tables. Each player or each couple must go to each table and play the game set up there. The following games will suggest two types of progressive tables. In the first type, individual scores are kept and each individual works for his own score. In the second type of game suggested, couples work together. In all progressive games, however, a couple should not be permitted to work together in more than one game.

In the first group suggested below, the leader will seat two couples at each table. The two individual winners at each table will then progress by couples. That is, the boy who makes the highest score and the girl who makes the highest score would progress to the next table. If, however, they have been sitting opposite each other for this game, one of them should take a different side of the table for the next game. In the second type of game described below, where couples work together, when the winning couple progresses, one of them should take another side of the table so that each will have a different partner for the next game.

The hostess or leader should ring a bell or blow a whistle when the time limit for a game is up, or when it is time to begin a new game.

In both types of games described below, a scorecard is given to each player on which to record his points won. The points are scored as follows: first place fifteen points, second place ten points, third place five points, while no score is given for fourth place.

When players work on a game in couples, allow ten points to each for the winning couple and five points to each for the losing couple.

At the conclusion of the game the individual with the highest score should be given a suitable award.

The first nine games described below are suitable for a progressive game in which all players play the same game at the same time.

The last four games in this section, as well as some of those described just below, are suitable for a progressive game in which a different game is placed on each table, and a time limit is set for each game.

Five Points

SHEETS of blank paper are placed on each table, one for each guest. A small bowl of rice is placed on each table. Each guest is asked to take out five grains of rice, hold them about six inches above his paper and drop them. With a pencil he makes a dot where each grain of rice falls. The players are then asked to draw the figure of a man using the five points, one for the head, two for the feet, and two for the hands. It will be necessary to have a number of judges, and a judge should decide at each table the winners of first, second, and third places, and award them 15, 10 and 5 points respectively.

Alphabet Backwards

PLAYERS are supplied with blank sheets of paper and pencils. The leader tells them in advance that each table must determine its own winners. She tells them that she is going to assign them all a task, and the one who finishes first at his table must hold up his hand and declare himself the winner. The same thing must be done by those winning second and third place. The leader then announces that they are to write the alphabet backwards. (This does not mean that they are to perform the stunt of writing with their backs turned toward the table, but they are to begin with z and end with a.)

Down Town

WHEN the winners have progressed and every boy is sitting opposite a girl other than the one he had in the last game, you are ready to start Down Town. It will be necessary to have a time limit on this game of perhaps three or five minutes. When all are ready the leader announces that all are to write the names of the stores and business places on one side of the street in a certain designated block of the city. After the whistle blows, determine the winner at each table by the one who has the largest number correctly arranged, awarding 15, 10, and 5 points for first, second, and third. (It will be necessary for the leader to make a careful check of this block in advance so that he will have the correct answers.)

Automobiles

PROVIDE blank sheets of paper and pencils and ask guests to write down the names of different makes of automobiles. It would be permissible to permit the names of cars to be used which are now obsolete. It will be necessary to have a time limit and decide the winner from the one who has the largest number in a given time.

Harpooning Matches

THE LEADER places on each table a large box of matches and gives each player a pin. Using this pin as a harpoon, players must transfer matches from the box to a position in front of them. If a match drops on the table, it may be picked up with the fingers and put back in the box. When one box of matches is about to be exhausted, the leader blows the whistle and awards 15, 10, and 5 points to the three guests at each table who have the largest, the next largest, and the third largest number of matches.

Peanut Toss

ON THE TABLE place four shallow bowls—cereal dishes for example—one on each side of the table about eighteen inches from the middle.

Provide fifty peanuts, still in the hulls, for each of the four players. The players stand two feet from the table and toss the peanuts in an effort to land them in the bowl. The player that gets the largest number in is the winner. Players should be required to stand erect as the toss is made.

The States

SUPPLY guests at each table with pencil and paper and ask them to write the names of the states in the United States. The leader should ask the first one who finished to let the fact be known. This will be a signal for the game to stop and for each one to count the number of states he has written.

Blind Writing

ASK the guests to write four sentences on a blank slip of paper with the eyes closed. The judges should then select the best specimen at each table. First, second, and third place will receive 15, 10, and 5 points respectively.

Handful of Rice

THE LEADER places a small handful or tablespoon of rice in a small dish at each table. She tells the guests that each one is to guess the number of rice grains in the dish and then they are to count them to determine the winners of first, second, and third place.

In the games described above the players all score as individuals. In the following games couples work together and the winning couple at each table should score ten points each while the losing couple score five points each.

Checkerboard

A CHECKERBOARD is placed on the table and the couples are each given twelve pennies which they must pitch, turn about, on the checkerboard. Three points are awarded for every coin on a red space and five points for a coin on a black space. Coins that are touching lines must not be counted. The boy and girl in each couple then add their score to determine the winners, and instead of writing down the number actually made, they score themselves ten points for winners and five points for losers, by couples.

Floating Corks

ON A TABLE is placed a large pan of water on which a number of small corks are floating. This should not be a shallow pan so that the cork can easily be pushed against the bottom. The couples are each given a pin and must take a time about fishing out a cork. The cork must not be touched by hand, neither may it touch the side of the pan while being harpooned. This game is scored by keeping time. A judge stands by and times each couple. The couple doing it in the quickest time being the winner.

Moving Marbles

A BOWL with about two dozen marbles in it is placed on a table. Each couple is given two pencils and the boy and girl in the couple must take turn about using these pencils to pick up the marbles and transfer them to another bowl. A judge has been stationed at the table to keep time and he declares the couple who accomplishes this feat in the quickest time the winner.

Transferring Beans

ON THIS TABLE the leader has placed a bowl full of dried beans and a bottle. A judge, who is also a timekeeper, is stationed at the table. The boy and the girl in each couple are given teaspoons, and taking a teaspoon alternately they are to transfer the beans to the bottle while the judge keeps time. The next couple then has its turn and the couple accomplishing this in the quickest time is declared the winner.

Section 3

writing games

Tree Test

MIMEOGRAPH the following list of questions or make typewritten copies. If you do not wish to do this, you can ask the questions one at a time around the room and have the guests answer them orally.

1. What tree do we put away in summer? *Fir.*
2. What tree remains after a fire? *Ash.*
3. Under what tree would you seek shelter from the rain? *Umbrella tree.*
4. What tree gave a nickname to an American General? *Hickory.*
5. What trees are always sad? *Pine.*
6. If asked by your best girl whom you loved, what tree would you give for an answer? *Yew.*
7. The old story tree. *Chestnut.*
8. What trees are straight to the line? *Plum.*
9. The hero's tree. *Laurel.*
10. What tree is a good church man? *Elder.*
11. The quivering tree. *Aspen.*
12. What tree do you have in your hand? *Palm.*
13. The Garden of Eden tree. *Apple.*
14. What trees stick together? *Gum.*
15. What trees go hopping about? *Locusts.*
16. What trees are always well dressed? *Spruce.*

17. What tree is a part of a dress and a door? *Hemlock.*
18. What tree is a deep breath and a printing machine? *Cypress.*
19. What tree do we like stuffed? *Olive.*
20. What tree is a body of water? *A Bay.*

Presidential Riddles

1. A beautiful flower; grass country. (*Roosevelt, Rosevelt.*)
2. A legendary King. (*Arthur.*)
3. Whose name was first called? (*Adams, Adam's.*)
4. A nickname for John; human male child. (*Jack-son.*)
5. Not false; persons of the male sex. (*True-man, Truman.*)
6. Prolongation of the backbone of an animal's body, usually hanging loose; either. (*Taylor, Tail-or.*)
7. Compact and solid; a suffix meaning performing the act of. (*Hard-ing.*)
8. To cleanse with water; a suffix meaning performing the act of; two thousand pounds. (*Wash-ing-ton.*)
9. Mentally disordered; a vowel; male offspring. (*Mad-i-son.*)
10. Abbreviation for the second day of the week; the collected mass of eggs of fish. (*Mon-roe.*)
11. The rail around a ship's stern; add the letter "t." (*Taft, Taff-t.*)
12. Chilly; behead the word ridge. (*Cool-idge.*)
13. To be attached strongly to; the solid portion of the surface of the globe. (*Cleveland, Cleave-land.*)
14. To penetrate with a pointed instrument. (*Pierce.*)
15. To attach with a link. (*Lincoln, Link-on.*)
16. To give or confer in response to a request. (*Grant.*)

Find the Sting

1. A sting that cures fatigue—*Resting.*
2. A sting that cures hunger—*Feasting.*
3. A sting that tidies your room—*Dusting.*
4. A sting that makes you laugh—*Jesting.*
5. A sting that cooks your meat—*Roasting.*
6. A sting that browns your bread—*Toasting.*
7. A sting unwise people indulge in—*Boasting.*

8. A sting that spoils your tools—*Rusting.*
9. A sting that makes you read a book through—*Interesting.*
10. A sting that tries—*Testing.*
11. A sting that adapts—*Adjusting.*
12. A sting that shopkeepers dislike—*Trusting.*
13. A sting that we observe in Lent—*Fasting.*
14. A sting that cooks are always doing—*Tasting.*

Nothing but the Truth[1]

GIVE each guest papers on which the following questions are typewritten or mimeographed and tell them that they are to grade themselves after answering the questions given below. If a person tells nothing but the truth, a score of 295 is possible. The one, however, who receives the highest score should be acclaimed the biggest prevaricator and should receive a prize. The one who receives the lowest score should be declared the most truthful or the most honest and should likewise receive a prize. The list of questions follows:

1. If you had cut down the cherry tree as Washington did, would you have told the truth to your father about it? *Score 20 for Yes.*
2. If you were on a crowded bus and the conductor failed to collect your fare, would you remind him and pay the fare? *Score 15 for Yes.*
3. If arrested while exceeding the speed limit, would you tell the cop the truth? *10 for Yes.*
4. Would you return coins from a pay telephone when the operator presses the wrong button, and you get back more than you should after having failed to complete a call? *10 for Yes.*
5. Would you exaggerate the size of a fish you caught? *10 for No.*
6. If you found a pocket-book in the street, would you try to find the owner? *20 for Yes.*
7. Would you, in a college examination, give information to a friend who might fail? *10 for No.*
8. Would you, on a similar examination, accept aid from a friend? *20 for No.*
9. If you were in the real estate business would you call the at-

[1] Adapted from *American Magazine.*

tention of a possible purchaser to a leaky roof or smoky fireplace? *25 for Yes.*

10. In applying for life insurance would you give correct answers to all questions? *20 for Yes.*
11. Would you use a hotel towel for a shoe rag? *10 for No.*
12. Would you carry off a hotel towel for a souvenir? *10 for No.*
13. If you were returning from Europe, would you attempt to smuggle in purchases that you knew were subject to duty? *20 for No.*
14. Would you return excess change given you by a clerk in a department store? *20 for Yes.*
15. Would you minimize your obligations when attempting to get a loan from the bank? *25 for No.*
16. Would you lie out of an invitation already accepted if a more attractive one came later? *25 for No.*
17. Would you make a larger donation when the plate is passed at church if you knew someone was watching you? *25 for No.*

The Museum

PLACE the objects as listed below on a table in a room adjoining the room where the party is held. Give guests sheets of paper on which the subjects are written and let them supply the answers. Give a prize to the one that guesses the largest number correctly.

	Subject	*Answer*
1.	Hidden tears.	Onion.
2.	Bygone days.	Last year's calendar.
3.	A drive through the wood.	A nail in a block.
4.	We part to meet again.	A pair of shears.
5.	Tax on tea.	Some tacks on a box of tea.
6.	Home of Burns.	Electric iron.
7.	The greatest bet ever made.	Alphabet.
8.	Way-worn traveler.	An old shoe.
9.	My own native land.	Small pile of dirt.
10.	House the Colonel lived in.	English walnut hull.
11.	Light of other days.	A candle.
12.	Ruins of China.	Broken dish.

13.	Broken heart.	A candy heart, broken.
14.	Sweet sixteen.	Sixteen pieces of candy.
15.	The four seasons.	Four spices.
16.	A line from home.	A clothes line.
17.	Kids at rest.	Kid gloves.
18.	A perfect foot.	12-inch ruler.
19.	Something to adore.	A key or doorknob.
20.	Something that can't be beat.	Hard-boiled egg.
21.	Olivet.	An olive seed.
22.	The horse fair.	Oats.
23.	The world's fair.	Pictures of girls.
24.	A book that is never read.	A blue, green, or yellow book.
25.	One that is going to be licked.	A lollipop.

Identify the Pen

Prepare the following list of questions, leaving the answers blank, and have the guests write the answers:

1. What pen is part of a clock? *Pendulum.*
2. What pen is undecided? *Pending.*
3. What pen is a coin? *Penny.*
4. What pen is self-imposed suffering? *Penance.*
5. What pen confines criminals? *Penitentiary.*
6. What pen is nearly surrounded by water? *Peninsula.*
7. What pen is thoughtful? *Pensive.*
8. What pen has five sides? *Pentagon.*
9. What pen goes to many old or wounded soldiers? *Pension.*
10. What pen cuts? *Penknife.*
11. What pen is in want of necessities of life? *Penury.*
12. What pen writes? *Pencil or pen.*
13. What pen is a weight? *Pennyweight.*
14. What pen is a State? *Pennsylvania.*
15. What pen is an herb? *Pennyroyal.*
16. What pen is a good writer? *Penman.*
17. What pen must we pay for doing wrong? *Penalty.*

18. What pen would you be if you were broke? *Penniless.*
19. What pen was the beginning of the Christian Church? *Pentecost.*
20. What pen pierces? *Penetrate.*
21. What pen is used as a souvenir for towns, colleges, etc.? *Pennant.*
22. What pen is a large web-footed sea bird? *Penguin.*
23. What pen is a powerful drug? *Penicillin.*
24. What pen is the science of punishment of crime? *Penology.*
25. What pen is a house on a roof? *Penthouse.*

Found on Most Any Table

HAVE the following questions written on slips of paper and ask the guests to supply the answers:

1. An important baseball man—*Pitcher.*
2. Found at the home base in baseball—*Plate.*
3. A term by which the clergy is often referred to—*Cloth.*
4. What a sailor is often called—*Salt.*
5. Also found in the road—*Fork.*
6. Used by the golfer when driving off—*Tea (tee).*
7. Used on the 4th of July—*Crackers.*
8. Also used in windows—*Glass.*
9. What men like to do in the alley—*Bowl.*
10. Given at the 25th wedding anniversary—*Silver.*
11. What a young couple does in the moonlight—*Spoon.*
12. What the earthquake makes—*A jar.*

What Ad Is?

PREPARE the following list of questions on typewritten or mimeographed sheets of paper, leaving the answer blank.

1. A mathematical ad? *Addition.*
2. An ad that is a tool? *Adze.*
3. An ad that is grown up? *Adult.*
4. An ad that sticks? *Adhesive.*
5. An ad that is a wise observation? *Adage.*
6. An ad that is a musical term? *Adagio.*
7. An ad that goes forward? *Advance.*

8. An ad that regards with approval? *Admire.*
9. An ad at the mercy of wind and wave? *Adrift.*
10. An ad that announces or publishes? *Advertise.*
11. An ad that says, "Good-bye"? *Adieu.*
12. An ad that offers an opinion? *Advice.*
13. An ad that embellishes? *Adorn.*
14. An ad that loves intensely? *Adore.*
15. An ad that is excessive praise? *Adulation.*
16. An ad that comes? *Advent.*
17. An ad that is a part of speech? *Adverb, Adjective.*
18. An ad that is a Naval Officer? *Admiral.*

T-plus

PREPARE the following list on typewritten or mimeographed sheets, leaving the answer blank for the guest to fill in.

1. T before a man-like animal forms a narrow band of cloth. *Tape.*
2. T before a beverage forms a story. *Tale.*
3. T before your Father's sister forms a sarcastic reproach. *Taunt.*
4. T before craft forms a small pie. *Tart.*
5. T before showers forms a line of cars. *Train.*
6. T before foolhardy forms rubbish. *Trash.*
7. T before request forms labor. *Task.*
8. T before a lubricant forms work. *Toil.*
9. T before a gun forms something trivial. *Trifle.*
10. T before regret forms sincerity. *True.*
11. T before everything forms height. *Tall.*
12. T before rest forms "to annoy." *Tease.*
13. T before mistake forms fright. *Terror.*
14. T before humor forms "to taunt." *Twit.*
15. T before something paid for release forms an opening over the door. *Transom.*
16. T before finish forms watchfulness. *Tend.*
17. T before competent forms a piece of furniture. *Table.*
18. T before embrace forms a criminal. *Thug.*

19. T before a worthless plant forms a river of Scotland. *Tweed.*
20. T before a contest of speed forms a faint mark. *Trace.*

A Search for Ants

PREPARE papers on which you have the following questions given and have guests apply the answer with a word ending in "ant."

What ant is:

1. Remote — *Distant.*
2. Courteous — *Gallant.*
3. A fruit — *Currant.*
4. To authorize — *Warrant.*
5. One who works for another — *Servant.*
6. One engaged in rural labor — *Peasant.*
7. Officer in charge — *Commandant.*
8. To breathe quickly — *Pant.*
9. One of large proportions — *Giant.*
10. A resident — *Tenant.*
11. A bird — *Pheasant.*
12. A flag — *Pennant.*
13. To be sorry — *Repentant.*
14. To be overbearing — *Arrogant.*
15. What everyone should be — *Pleasant.*
16. An ornament — *Pendant.*
17. What some schoolboys play — *Truant.*
18. Quick and pert of speech — *Flippant.*
19. Overreaching natural bonds — *Rampant.*

A Host's Name

SUPPLY the guests with blank sheets of paper and ask them to write the letters in the name of the host or hostess in a vertical row. Ask them then to make a word that contains each one of the letters consecutively, beginning from the top, and to make these words in such a way that they will form a sentence. The one who has the most success in producing a sensible or humorous sentence should be given a prize. The following is an example of how this would work out if the host's name were Paul Jones.

Please
Ask
MaUd
Long
AJax's
Other
Name
whEn
Sick

English Exercise

THE LEADER supplies the guests with sheets of paper on which have been written ten letters of the alphabet. Space should be left after each letter so that the guest can fill in the rest of the word. Guests are then asked to make a complete sentence—each word of which must begin with the ten letters they have, in the order they have them. The player who makes the best or funniest sentence should be given a prize.

Banker's Contest [2]

FILL in the blank spaces with terms used in banking.

There was a banker's daughter whose chief ...... was her pretty face. She would often .... her ...., but her father was not able to .... her bad habit. He decided to .... that he would .... her .... and would never make .... to her .... if she did not .... her ways.

Her ability to spend .... was her chief .... and it was hard to keep a .... in the .... to her .... He told the .... that the next time she drew a .... on him he must .... on it. This .... had a quicker effect than all his remonstrances and its .... to .... she mended her ways in a .... of the .... she would otherwise have done.

Her father .... and now she shows good

[2] Adapted from *Good Housekeeping Magazine.*

.... in her .... and counts her ...., never fails to make her .... and is in .... with the .... and ....

Asset — overdraw — account — check — teller — cancel — checking account — deposit — credit — stop — money — liability — balance — bank — credit — cashier — draft — stop-payment — drastic — action — dollars — dimes — quarter — time — resumed — payment — cents — banking — business — cancelled — checks — payments — good — standing — President — bookkeeper.

Familiar Numbers

GIVE guests slips of paper on which the following has been mimeographed with the numbers which are in *italics* left blank. Guests are to fill in the blanks.

1. Just as sure as *two* and *two* are *four.*
2. The *eighteenth* amendment was repealed.
3. The *seven* wonders of the world.
4. The house of *seven* gables.
5. Engine, engine number *nine,*
Running on Chicago line.
6. The *twentieth* amendment is the "Lame Duck" amendment.
7. Possession is *nine* points of the law.
8. Ho, ho, *fifteen* men on a dead man's chest.
9. The *sixteenth* amendment was the income tax amendment.
10. The spirit of *seventy-six.*
11. She was one of the *four hundred* of society.
12. Friday the *thirteenth.*
13. The *nineteenth* amendment was the woman suffrage amendment.
14. Into the jaws of death rode the *six hundred.*
15. *Fifty-four forty* or fight.
16. The first *hundred* years are the hardest.
17. *One, two,* buckle my shoe.
18. *Twelve* men good and true.
19. The *seven* ages of man.

20. A *ten* o'clock scholar.
21. The *fourth* dimension.
22. Leap year gives us *twenty-nine.*
23. *Three, four,* close the door.
24. Come *one,* come all.
25. The *ten* Commandments.
26. *Twenty thousand* leagues under the sea.
27. Come *seven,* come *eleven.*
28. A stitch in time saves *nine.*
29. *Ten* nights in a barroom.
30. *Three* blind mice.
31. *Two's* company, *three's* a crowd.
32. The *sixth* sense.
33. He arrived at the *eleventh* hour.
34. *Five, six,* pick up sticks.
35. The animals went in *two* by *two.*
36. The *thirteen* original colonies.

Bible Rhymes

THE leader reads the Bible rhymes, and guests are asked to write the name of the Bible character described in each of the fifteen verses.

1. Who divided waves before the rod
 That to a serpent turned,
 When Egypt's king upon his throne,
 The Hebrew prophet spurned?

2. What gospel prophet cried aloud
 "You'll die unless you turn;
 This nation shall to bondage go;
 But a remnant shall return?"

3. Who was a wise, much married king
 That built a temple great,
 But when the union he would save
 God said, "It is too late"?

4. Who was the first of mighty kings
 Who ruled fair Canaan's land,

He disobeyed and met defeat
And died by his own hand?

5. Who was a prince of Judah's line;
A king he longed to be;
But death came to him as he hung,
His head caught in a tree?

6. Who was a ruddy, fair-haired boy
With staff and harp and sling
But ere the sun of life went down
Was Israel's greatest king?

7. Who was a son of the desert,
Bold, fearless, determined, free,
But he lost his head when a maiden
Danced for the king to see?

8. What man was strongest in his time,
Whose power none could withstand,
But when his head was shaven
He died in a foreign land?

9. Who of all in the wide, wide world
Missed life's one earliest joy?
He was the only man on earth
Who never was a boy.

10. Who sailed away o'er the mountaintops
E'er the days of the aeroplane,
But then was given a heavenly sign
That would never happen again?

11. Who, hidden beside the brook,
Was fed by the birds unseen;
He feared not the prophets of Baal,
But fled from before the queen?

12. Who was the favorite of our Lord,
With him on the mountain high,

And alone on the Isle of Patmos
'Twas said he should not die?

13. Who was a fisherman of Galilee
And toiled while others slept
But when the cock at morning crew
He bowed his head and wept?

14. Shipwrecked and beaten with many stripes,
Hungry, and faint, and cold,
He persecuted the church in youth
But died for it when old?

15. Who was a Hebrew captive
That braved the great king's ire,
But when they tried to roast him
He was not hurt by fire?

ANSWERS: (1) *Moses.* (2) *Isaiah.* (3) *Solomon.* (4) *Saul.* (5) *Absalom.* (6) *David.* (7) *John the Baptist.* (8) *Samson.* (9) *Adam.* (10) *Noah.* (11) *Elijah.* (12) *John.* (13) *Peter.* (14) *Paul.* (15) *Either Shadrach, Meshach, or Abednego.*

Bible Questions in Verse

1. Who played a harp to please King Saul?
2. What city saw the birth of Paul?
3. What man of Alexandria was an eloquent preacher?
4. Who sat at the feet of Gamaliel, the teacher?
5. What prophet was by ravens fed?
6. Who raised Dorcas from the dead?
7. What prophet did wicked children mock?
8. Who answered Simon Peter's knock?
9. What name did Jesus to Simon give?
10. Where did Simon the Sorcerer live?
11. What creature was first to leave the Ark?
12. What worker with Paul was an uncle of Mark?
13. What people dry shod passed through the Red Sea?
14. Who was almost persuaded a Christian to be?

ANSWERS: (1) *David.* (2) *Tarsus.* (3) *Apollos.* (4) *Paul.* (5) *Elijah.* (6) *Peter.* (7) *Elisha.* (8) *Rhoda.* (9) *Peter.* (10) *Samaria.* (11) *Dove.* (12) *Barnabas.* (13) *Jews.* (14) *Agrippa.*

Books of the Bible Contest

ANSWER with the names of books of the Bible the following questions either read orally or given out on slips of paper.

1. Ruled by the Caesars. *Romans.*
2. A king who authorized the revision of the Bible. *James.*
3. What a man wants when he is out of employment. *Job.*
4. What a person does when he is in a play. *Acts.*
5. What a man makes when he cannot write his name. *Mark.*
6. Wise sayings. *Proverbs.*
7. A transparent material. *Mica* (*Micah*).
8. What the mathematician uses. *Numbers.*
9. A kind of hay. *Timothy.*
10. Crowned heads of many states. *Kings.*
11. Written events. *Chronicles.*
12. What those who preside over courts are called. *Judges.*
13. Slang for a man who brings bad luck. *Jonah.*
14. A great surprise. *Revelation.*
15. A name originally applied to the Jews. *Hebrews.*

Parts of the Body

ANSWER the following with parts of the human body.

1. A strong box. *Chest.*
2. Something made by whips. *Lashes* (*eye lashes*).
3. Part of a shoe. *Tongue.*
4. What the soldier carries. *Arms.*
5. Part of a tree. *Limb.*
6. Steps of a hotel. *Inn steps* (*insteps*).
7. Heard in Congress when a vote is taken. *Ayes and Nos* (*eyes and nose*).
8. Scholars. *Pupils.*
9. Two musical instruments. *Drums.*
10. Two places of worship. *Temples.*

11. Two measures. *Feet and hands.*
12. What every builder must have. *Nails.*
13. A kind of fish. *Sole* (*soul*).
14. A shell fish. *Mussel.* (*muscle*).
15. Little white things in the head that bite. *Teeth.*
16. Two baby cows. *Calves.*
17. A number of small animals. *Hares* (*hairs*).
18. Two stately trees. *Palms.*
19. A member of the deer family. *Hart* (*heart*).
20. Two articles used by a blacksmith. *Hammer and anvil* (*in ear*).
21. Two flowers. *Tulips.*
22. A kind of leather. *Raw hide.*

Disguised Animals

HAVE guests supply the answers to the following Disguised Animal questions:

1. What animal do you think of when you go into an empty room? *Bear* (*bare*)
2. What animal do you think of when you hear a fish story? *Lion* (*lyin'*)
3. What animal do you think of when you see a pilot at the wheel of a vessel? *Steer*
4. What animal do you think of when you see a key used to help students with Latin and algebra? *Pony*
5. What animal do you think of when you hear someone boasting? *Bull*
6. What animal do you think of when you see an adjustable wrench? *Monkey*
7. What animal do you think of when you see slabs of unforged iron? *Pig*
8. What animal does a Scottish clan make you think of? *Camel* (*Campbell*)
9. What animal do you think of when you lick an envelope? *Seal*
10. What animal do you think of when you

are making bread? *Doe (dough)*

11. What animal does an expensive article make you think of? *Deer (dear)*
12. What animal do you think the most of? *Ewe (you)*
13. What animal never grows old? *Gnu (new)*
14. What animal does a mole's house make you think of? *Burro (burrow)*

The Wife's Dress

ASK guests to give the name of the cloth that would be appropriate for the dress of the wives of men of the following occupations:

1. Woodcutter's wife. *Corduroy*
2. The musician's wife. *Organdy*
3. Baseball player's wife. *Batiste*
4. Dairyman's wife. *Cheesecloth*
5. Cal's wife. *Percale*
6. Banker's wife. *Cashmere or gold cloth*
7. Fisherman's wife. *Net*
8. Fat man's wife. *Broadcloth*
9. Tennis player's wife. *Lawn*
10. Baldheaded man's wife. *Mohair*

Proper Footwear

WHAT material should be used for proper footwear for the following:

1. A clergyman. *Cloth*
2. A tourist. *Rubber*
3. For a baby. *Kid*
4. For a dairyman. *Calf*
5. For a book agent. *Canvas*

Letter Words

THE GUESTS are given a mimeographed sheet with the following questions. They are to fill in the blanks with letters that sound like the words.

1. Two letters that mean poorly dressed. *C-D* (*Seedy*)
2. Two letters that mean cold. *I-C* (*Icy*)
3. Two letters that mean vacant. *M-T* (*Empty*)
4. Two letters that mean jealousy. *N-V* (*Envy*)
5. Two letters that are a written composition. *S-A* (*Essay*)
6. Two letters that mean to surpass. *X-L* (*Excel*)
7. Two letters that mean superfluous. *X-S* (*Excess*)
8. Two letters that describe a snake's eyes. *B-D* (*Beady*)
9. Two letters that mean to rot. *D-K* (*Decay*)
10. Two letters that mean it is not difficult. *E-Z* (*Easy*)
11. Two letters that are a vine. *I-V* (*Ivy*)
12. Two letters that are a tent. *T-P* (*Tepee*)
13. Two letters that are a kind of cloth. *P-K* (*Pique*)
14. Two letters that are a girl's name. *K-T* (*Katy*), *L-C* (*Elsie*)
15. Two letters that are an attractive girl. *Q-T* (*Cutie*)
16. Double letters that mean comfort. *EE* (*Ease*)
17. Double letters that mean intelligence. *YY* (*Wise*)
18. Double letters that mean to worry or irritate. *TT* (*Tease*)
19. Three letters that are a mournful poem. *L-E-G* (*Elegy*)
20. Three letters that mean overpowering emotion. *X-T-C* (*Ecstasy*)
21. Three letters that are a girl's name. *M-L-E* (*Emily*)
22. Three letters that mean a foe. *N-M-E* (*Enemy*)
23. Three letters that mean capacity for vigorous activity. *N-R-G* (*Energy*)
24. Five letters that mean fit or suitable. *X-P-D-N-T* (*Expedient*)
25. Two letters and the number 8 that mean a drug. *O-P-8* (*Opiate*)

Dictionary Girls

THE LEADER should give the guests the following questions typewritten or mimeographed. As this is a rather difficult game, it being necessary for the guests to deduce the answers, it will probably be necessary for the leader to help them out by giving them the answer to about every fifth one. It will be difficult enough for the guests to answer the remaining ones.

1. A disagreeable girl. — Annie Mosity (*animosity*)
2. A sweet girl. — Carrie Mel (*caramel*)

3. A very pleasant girl. Jennie Rosity (*generosity*)
4. A smooth girl. Amelia Ration (*amelioration*)
5. A seedy girl. Cora Ander (*coriander*)
6. A clear case of girl. E. Lucy Date (*elucidate*)
7. A geometrical girl. Polly Gon (*polygon*)
8. Not orthodox. Hettie Rodoxy (*heterodoxy*)
9. One of the best girls. Ella Gant (*elegant*)
10. A flower girl. Rhoda Dendron (*rhododendron*)
11. A musical girl. Sarah Nade (*serenade*)
12. A profound girl. Mettie Physics (*metaphysics*)
13. A star girl. Meta Oric (*Meteoric*)
14. A clinging girl. Jessie Mine (*jessamine*)
15. A nervous girl. Hester Ical (*hysterical*)
16. A muscular girl. Callie Sthenics (*calisthenics*)
17. A lively girl. Annie Mation (*animation*)
18. An uncertain girl. Eva Nescent (*evanescent*)
19. A sad girl. Ella G. (*elegy*)
20. A great big girl. Ellie Phant (*elephant*)
21. A warlike girl. Millie Tarry (*military*)

Ring Contest

Have the ring questionnaire mimeographed with the answers to be supplied by the guests.

1. The ring of a tiresome speaker. *Bo-ring*
2. The ring that pleases the singer. *Enco-ring*
3. The sinner's ring. *Er-ring*
4. The ring that the deaf person misses. *Hea-ring*
5. The ring that pleases the political speaker. *Chee-ring*
6. The hero's ring. *Da-ring*
7. The trigger man's ring. *Murde-ring*
8. The traveler's ring. *Tou-ring*
9. The ring of the cat. *Pur-ring*
10. The shepherd's ring. *Shea-ring*
11. The tea server's ring. *Pou-ring*
12. The lion's ring. *Roa-ring*
13. The ring that ruins clothing. *Wea-ring*

14. The ring one takes the dog out for. *Ai-ring*
15. The ring of "young charms." *Endea-ring*
16. The questioner's ring. *Inqui-ring*

Alliteration [3]

AN AMUSING pencil and paper game is to write a short story using only words beginning with the same letter. An example using S is given. "Sarah Saunders saw some sifted sugar, so she snatched same surrepitiously. Soon someone searched seacoast seeking Sarah. She silently scuttled southward securing sanctuary. Soon she sat secluded, secretly self-satisfied." Another variation is to use two letters. Example using S and L. "Sally Lunn sought life. She liked specious looking Sam. Long Sam loved Sally languishingly. She landed Sam lately."

Nut Contest

HAVE the guests answer the following questions with the name of a nut. The one who gets the largest number might be declared the biggest nut.

1. What nut is a nickname once given to a president? *Hickory*
2. What nut is the color of an eye? *Hazel*
3. Where we like to go on a hot day. *Beech*
4. What nut is a trunk or a box? *Chestnut*
5. What nut is a popular beverage? *Coconut*
6. What nut is a spring vegetable? *Peanut*
7. What nut is a penalty for wearing tight shoes? *A-corn*
8. What nut is a South American country? *Brazil*
9. What nut is a barrier? *Walnut*
10. What nut is made out of cream? *Butternut*

A Hive of Bees

ANSWERS to the following begin with "be."

1. A light *Beacon*
2. Main timber *Beam*

[3] Adapted from *Good Housekeeping Magazine.*

3. An animal	*Bear*
4. To throb	*Beat*
5. Pleasing	*Beautiful*
6. Deportment	*Bearing*
7. Part of a church	*Belfry*
8. To signal	*Beckon*
9. A kind of tree	*Beech*
10. A vegetable	*Beet*
11. Flesh of an animal	*Beef*
12. To start something	*Begin*
13. An insect	*Beetle*
14. To puzzle	*Bewilder*
15. Advantageous	*Beneficial*
16. Closing invocation	*Benediction*

A Tea Party

Answers to the following end with the syllable "ty."

1. The soul of wit	*Brevity*
2. The best policy	*Honesty*
3. Never faileth	*Charity*
4. Possession of gossips	*Curiosity*
5. Gives power and light	*Electricity*
6. A pretty girl's temptation	*Vanity*
7. A criminal's dread	*Captivity*
8. The four hundred	*Society*
9. Everlasting	*Eternity*
10. Freedom	*Liberty*
11. The spice of life	*Variety*
12. Pleasing to the eye	*Beauty*
13. Quick at repartee	*Witty*
14. Safe from harm	*Security*
15. Sober reflection	*Gravity*
16. Great speed	*Velocity*

An Ice Contest

Prepare typewritten or mimeographed sheets with the following definitions of words that end in "ice." Let the players guess the word.

1. An ice that the world would be better without (four letters). *Vice.*
2. An ice that is easier to give than to take (six letters). *Advice.*
3. An ice that lures (six letters). *Entice.*
4. An ice much mentioned in the scriptures (nine letters). *Sacrifice.*
5. An ice that occurs three times (six letters). *Thrice.*
6. An ice that is cut (five letters). *Slice.*
7. An ice that repeats itself (five letters). *Twice.*
8. An ice that gives a piquant flavor (five letters). *Spice.*
9. An ice seen at weddings (four letters). *Rice.*
10. An ice fixed by the merchant (five letters). *Price.*
11. An ice that is dainty (four letters). *Nice.*
12. An ice feared by the ladies (four letters). *Mice.*
13. An ice that directs traffic (six letters). *Police.*
14. An ice we get out of oranges (five letters). *Juice.*
15. An ice that makes one yellow (eight letters). *Jaundice.*
16. An ice that ties end together (six letters). *Splice.*
17. An ice that is sometimes called "bones" (four letters). *Dice.*
18. An ice that desires to inflict injury or suffering (six letters). *Malice.*
19. An ice that bites (four letters). *Lice.*
20. An ice that is a projection that finishes a wall (seven letters). *Cornice.*

To Be Found in the Word, "Violets"

1.	Part of a house	*Tile*
2.	Found in every garden	*Soil*
3.	A Biblical character	*Lot*
4.	Part of a lady's attire	*Veil*
5.	A foreign fruit	*Olive*
6.	A musical instrument	*Viol*
7.	What we all wish to do	*Live*
8.	The opposite of good	*Evil*
9.	Wicked	*Vile*
10.	Part of the human body	*Toe*
11.	To make fast	*Tie*

12.	Hard work	*Toil*
13.	Land surrounded by water	*Isle*
14.	Necessary for a building	*Site*
15.	A false statement	*Lie*
16.	To answer a puzzle	*Solve*

I Am And U Are

1.	I am the rainbow	*Iris*
2.	U agree with all	*Unanimous*
3.	I am exceedingly cold	*Icicle*
4.	U match the rest	*Uniform*
5.	I am an object of worship	*Idol*
6.	U are only one	*Unit*
7.	I am a climbing plant	*Ivy*
8.	U store learning	*University*
9.	I know who others are	*Identify*
10.	U sing with others	*Unison*
11.	I am brief	*Item*
12.	U are needed in the kitchen	*Utensil*

Chrysanthemums

Answers to the following will be found in the word, Chrysanthemums.

1.	A musical part of a church service	*Anthem*
2.	A domestic animal	*Cat*
3.	To hurry	*Hasten*
4.	An article of dress	*Hat*
5.	An organ of the human body	*Heart*
6.	An insect found in the woods	*Ant*
7.	City of Greece	*Athens*
8.	An abbreviated Christian name for a man	*Sam*
9.	What few women keep	*Mum*
10.	What all healthy people do	*Eat*
11.	A technical term in dress making	*Hem*
12.	What we like our critics to remember we are	*Human*
13.	Used in sandwiches	*Ham*

14.	What an actress aspires to be	*Star*
15.	To assemble troops	*Muster*
16.	A fable	*Myth*
17.	Tenderness toward an offender	*Mercy*
18.	Necessary to kindle a fire	*Match*
19.	A small house	*Shanty*
20.	Close friends	*Chums*
21.	Found in a dairy	*Churn*
22.	An autumn flower	*Aster*
23.	An odor	*Scent*
24.	To punish	*Chasten*
25.	A map	*Chart*

Golf Terms

ANSWER the following questions with terms used by golfers. Supply guests with papers on which have been written the questions and have guests write the answers.

1.	A portion of a meal	*Course*
2.	A chauffeur	*Driver*
3.	A Latin prefix meaning before	*Pro*
4.	An Irish color	*Green*
5.	A social assembly	*Ball*
6.	A drink from China	*Tee (tea)*
7.	What tea is kept in	*Caddy (caddie)*
8.	Rural term for aimless work	*Putter*
9.	What we use to catch mice	*Trap*
10.	To put in peril	*Hazard*
11.	Round cavities	*Holes*
12.	Separate parts of a musical work	*Score*
13.	A table utensil	*Spoon*
14.	What we would call an impudent person	*Brassie*

A Family of Twelve Sons

CAN YOU guess the boys' names? (Twelve words ending in son.)

1.	A poisonous weed	*Jimson*

2. Harmony — *Unison*
3. A motive or cause — *Reason*
4. Any human being — *Person*
5. Venom — *Poison*
6. Disloyalty — *Treason*
7. To accustom — *Season*
8. The flesh of a wild animal — *Venison*
9. A small plum — *Damson*
10. A clergyman — *Parson*
11. A criminal offense — *Arson*
12. A prayer or supplication — *Orison*

Transpositions

In each sentence one blank is filled with the transposition of the other. All the blanks contain words of six letters.

1. The young artist evidently possesses ....
(*Latent, Talent*)
2. The school boy got into a .... through his ....
(*Scrape, Capers*)
3. The school .... walked by the side of the ....
(*Master, Stream*)
4. The .... stopped swimming for want of ....
(*Bather, Breath*)
5. My friend had to .... and so we ....
(*Depart, Parted*)
6. If anyone .... my private apartment, I will .... it.
(*Enters, Resent*)
7. The pretty girl with the .... as she walked.
(*Dimple, Limped*)
8. Does the .... at the gateway .... the intruders?
(*Porter, Report*)
9. The bad boy .... his answers from others' ....
(*Steals, Slates*)

A Floral Bouquet

1. Oh, tell me the flower that is queen of them all. *Rose.*
2. And the flower dedicated to brides. *Orange blossoms.*
3. The flower that stands up so stately and tall. *Lily.*
4. And one that's a color besides. *Pink.*
5. The flower that's a parent, loving and fond. *Poppy.*
6. The flower that's just made to kiss. *Tulips.*
7. The flower that's a weapon from over beyond. *Spanish Bayonet.*
8. One worn by a dainty young miss. *Lady's-slipper.*
9. The flower with eyes so snappy and bright. *Black-eyed Susan.*
10. The flower that soothes the sad heart. *Heart's-ease.*
11. The flower that blooms only at night. *Night-blooming Cereus.*
12. The one that we say when we part. *Forget-me-not.*
13. The one that Br'er Fox draws on when he walks. *Fox-glove.*
14. The one that the Chanticleers use. *Coxcomb.*
15. A flower that won't tell when she talks. *Daisy.*
16. The one that's the dropping of dews. *Dewdrops.*
17. The flowers that ring as they wave in the breeze. *Bluebells.*
18. The flowers that tell you the time. *Four-o'clock.*
19. The flowers that bloom on southern trees. *Magnolia.*
20. And the flower of morning sublime. *Morning-glory.*
21. The flower that Johnny can use when he writes. *Jonquil.*
22. The flower you wear in your hat. *Prince's feather.*
23. The flower that blossoms on bright moonlight nights. *Moon-flower.*
24. And the one that's the end of a cat. *Cattail.*
25. The vine you blow on to make a loud noise. *Trumpet.*
26. And the one that blooms close to the ground. *Arbutus.*
27. The one that's unpleasant when thrown by small boys. *Snow-ball.*
28. And the one's that in sweetness abound. *Honeysuckle.*
29. The one that Joseph's brothers were attending of old. *Phlox.*
30. And the one that does preach night and day. *Jack-in-the-Pulpit.*
31. The one that makes you think of the cold. *Snowdrop.*
32. And the one that's a dude, blithe and gay. *Dandelion.*
33. One worn by those disappointed in love. *Bleeding heart.*

34. One a boon to the bachelor lone. *Bachelor's Buttons.*
35. Some often fall from the heavens above. *Shooting-stars.*
36. Some like precious metal has shown. *Goldenrod.*
37. The ones that are now called bachelor girls. *Old-maids.*
38. And what they'd all do if they could. *Marigold.*
39. A kiss token from the home of the squirrel. *Mistletoe.*
40. And a tree that blooms in the wood. *Dogwood.*

Missing Letters

A DASH (—) represents the missing letters.

1. Ma — (First in every home.) *Mat.*
2. L — — e (Couldn't live without it.) *Life.*
3. — — le (The more you take from it the larger it gets.) *Hole.*
4. — oo — (It's all over the house.) *Roof.*
5. Lo — — (Found in the suburbs.) *Lots.*
6. — ra — t (Gives a cold, cures a cold, and pays the doctor.) *Draft.*
7. — r — — s (That for which women spend too much money.) *Dress.*
8. L — n — s (Near to every girl's heart.) *Lungs.*

Impromptu Stories

CUT a dozen headlines out of the newspaper, or take large captions out of a magazine. Then cut out each individual word. Jumble all the words together, and, picking them out at random, give three different words to each player present. Each must then make up a story, using the three words given him to form the plot of the story. The person distributing the words should announce whether the story is to be long or short, funny or serious.

Writing Telegrams

PLAYERS are given telegraph blanks or blank sheets of paper and told to write down the name of a person present, fold the paper, and pass it to the guest on the right. The next person again writes the name of a guest, folds the paper, and passes it to the player on his right.

The leader then calls out ten letters of the alphabet and each guest writes these letters on his folded paper, leaving room to fill in words. The players must write a ten-word telegram, each word beginning with the letters given and in the order in which they were given, making the telegram as humorous as possible.

When the telegrams are completed, they are once more passed to the right. Each player then unfolds the paper and reads out the telegram, the sender, and the receiver. The person whose name was first written on the paper is the sender and the second name is the receiver.

Consecutive Letters

THE GUESTS have been supplied with blank sheets of paper, and they are told by the leader to write down any ten consecutive letters as they come in the alphabet. After this has been done, the guests are asked to write a sentence, about someone in the group, using these ten letters and later to read the sentence for the amusement of the group. The result might be somewhat as follows: "Maud Never Opens Places Quite Right, She Tries Using Vim."

Definitions Game

PROVIDE guests with pieces of paper and instruct them to write certain words to be defined later. Such subjects as love, marriage, school-teacher, and others, would be conducive to such definitions as those desired. It goes without saying that humorous definitions are wanted.

When one guest has written his subject, he passes the paper on to the next player. This one is then asked to write the definition. After the definition has been written, the player folds the paper concealing his definition, but leaving the subject exposed. The paper is then passed to the player on the right who writes a definition, folds the paper, and passes it on. When three or four definitions have been secured for each subject, ask the guests to read them aloud.

Some such results as the following might be expected: Love, "An itching around the heart which you can't scratch." "The joy of entwining arms." "The old maid's fondest wish." Or Marriage: "The hardest knot to untie." "The disease a bachelor never gets." "Hitched up."

Writing Contests

THE following writing contests require no equipment except paper and pencil and are full of interest.

1. Ask the guests to write the names of the countries of the world and give a small prize to the one who can write the longest list in five minutes.
2. Have the guests write the names of the capitals of the states of the United States.
3. Have the guests write the names of the presidents of the United States.

What Son?

GIVE the guests papers with the following questions written on them which must be answered with words containing "son" or "sun."

1.	Various or several	*Sundry*
2.	A famous evangelist	*Billy Sunday*
3.	A device for measuring time	*Sundial*
4.	What son wrote "Idylls of the King"	*Tennyson*
5.	What son is a short lyric poem	*Sonnet*
6.	What sun browns your skin	*Sunburn*
7.	What sun is a kind of apoplexy	*Sunstroke*
8.	What son started the spoils system	*Jackson*
9.	What sun is a flower	*Sunflower*
10.	What sun is the first day of the week	*Sunday*
11.	What sun is an old-fashioned hat	*Sunbonnet*
12.	What son is the name of a plum	*Damson*

Autobiography

EACH player is given a slip of paper and asked to write the numbers from one to seventeen on the lefthand side. The leader of the game reads the statements listed below on the lefthand side, and the players fill in the corresponding numbers on their sheets of paper, giving answers appropriate to the statement read by the leader.

When the papers are all properly filled in, the players write their names on the backs of the sheets, and the sheets are collected by the leader.

Of course, the players do not realize that they are writing their own biographies and are rather startled when the leader, using the key in the righthand column, reads as follows:

Joseph Brown was born "1898" at "Philadelphia," was educated at "Yale," and so on.

1. A famous date	1. Year of birth
2. A city	2. City where born
3. A favorite college	3. Where educated
4. Yes or no	4. Married or not
5. If No. 4 is answered in the affirmative, state a number; otherwise leave blank	5. If married, number of children
6. A method of earning a living	6. Occupation
7. How much money constitutes a good bank balance	7. Yearly income
8. Automobile license number	8. Yearly expenditures
9. Three numbers	9. Size of hat, shoes, and gloves
10. A descriptive adjective	10. Personal appearance
11. Two colors	11. Color of eyes and hair
12. A fault seen in others	12. Worst fault
13. An outdoor activity	13. Favorite sport
14. A fruit	14. Favorite food
15. A political party	15. Political affiliation
16. A slang expression	16. Favorite expression
17. Any short remark	17. Comment when this was read

The Vowel Game

SUPPLY each player with pencil and paper. The regular vowels a, e, i, o, u, are used, and beginning with "a" each player writes as long a sentence as he can, using no word that contains a vowel other than "a," but repeating that vowel as often as he wishes. For example, a sentence containing "a" might read as follows: "At last Jack Sprat can catch all bad gray cats, lanky rats, black bats, and arty ants at Harry's ranch."

Give the players five minutes, or any other amount of time agreed upon, to write their sentences. When the time is up, the players read their sentences, and the first point is won by the player having the longest good plain English sentence. All of the vowels are used in this way, and the person winning the most points wins the game.

Interviews

ALL OF THE GUESTS are given a number and told that those who receive odd numbers are to act as newspaper reporters; those who receive even numbers are the Famous Ones. There is to be one editor for every ten reporters, and one person is to act as Editor-in-Chief as final judge to award the final prizes. Each Famous One is interviewed by the reporter whose number is just below his, so that Famous One Number Two is interviewed by Reporter Number One; Famous One Number Four is interviewed by Reporter Number Three, and so on.

The reporters are given pencils and slips of paper on which the following questions have been written.

1. What is your name?
2. If you could change it, what would you choose?
3. Why did you choose the profession or occupation you are engaged in?
4. Give your idea of a perfect woman (or man).
5. What is your idea of complete honesty?
6. If you were president, what would be your first act?
7. What do you think of the city you live in?

A suitable award should be made to the reporter securing the best interview. The Famous One granting the interview might also be awarded.

Literary Sandwiches

1. Example: The leader announces: "I know a word of five letters, the first is "s" the last "e." Insert a vehicle (three letters) and have a fright— (s *car* e).

The following list here given may be used, but impromptu ones from any guest present make the game more interesting.

2. S——— e. Insert a label and have a vehicle—(S *tag* e).
3. H——— t. Insert an organ of the body and have another organ of the body—(h *ear* t).
4. S——— e. Insert a small steel instrument and have the backbone—(s *pin* e).
5. S——— e. Insert a kind of meat and have disgrace—(s *ham* e).
6. F——— s. Insert a falsehood and have annoying little insects —(f *lie* s).
7. T——— k. Insert "to move swiftly," and have a chest—(t *run* k).
8. C——— s. Insert a rule and have a cat's weapon of defense (c *law* s).
9. S——— t. Insert a jolly sailor boy and have to begin—(s *tar* t).
10. S——— k. Insert a small seed food and have to utter—(s *pea* k).
11. S——— d. Insert a light brown color and have a small table—(s *tan* d).
12. W——— h. Insert a small animal (rodent) and have anger —(w *rat* h).
13. T———— s. (Six letters) Insert soft water and have lines of cars—(t *rain* s).
14. G———— s. Insert to wander and have groups of trees—(g *rove* s).
15. S——— e. Insert a weight and have a rock—(s *ton* e)
16. T——— b. Insert a buzz and have a part of the body—(t *hum* b).
17. T———— y. Insert to corrode and have reliable—(t *rust* y).
18. H———— y. Insert anything and have vain—(h *aught* y).
19. S———— e. Insert always and have harsh—(s *ever* e).

Section 4

outdoor games

Steal the Bacon

STEAL the bacon is a favorite game for young people, especially such groups as Boy Scouts and Girl Scouts. As many as twenty-four could participate in one game. Two persons choose and form two sides of twelve each. They line up as follows:

1 2 3 4 5 6 7 8 9 10 11 12

BACON

12 11 10 9 8 7 6 5 4 3 2 1

The two sides stand about twenty feet apart. Any object may represent the bacon, such as a block of wood, a stone, an old hat. The referee calls the numbers and decides points in dispute. When the game starts, the referee calls a number, for example, number two, whereupon the numbers two from each side make a run for the bacon. The person who secures it makes one point for his side. The game should continue until at least each one has had a chance to grab for the bacon.

Crows and Cranes

"CROWS and Cranes" is a game which is entirely active but will provide lots of entertainment for a group of young people. There is no equipment required except a coin and a leader for the game.

Following are the directions for the leader:

Divide the group into two equal sides. Name one of the teams "Crows" and the other team "Cranes." Line the two teams up four or five feet apart facing each other. Flip the coin and if it lands heads-up call "Crows." Upon the calling of "Crows," the "Crows" must turn in flight, with the "Cranes" after them. If any of the "Cranes" succeed in touching a member (or members) of the "Crows" before he crosses a given line (this line may be from twenty to sixty feet behind the original line) he is considered as a captive of the "Cranes" and must aid the "Cranes" when play is continued. If the coin should land tails-up, the "Cranes" must turn in flight with the "Crows" chasing them and endeavoring to capture the "Cranes." Continue flipping the coin, each time calling "Crows" or "Cranes." The team succeeding in capturing all members of the other team is declared the winner.

Rabbit

The players are divided into groups of threes and are scattered into groups around the playground. Two of the three form a "home" by facing each other and joining hands. The third one will be the "rabbit" and will simply stand in this house.

In addition to these groups of threes, there should be two extra players, a homeless rabbit and a hunter. The hunter starts the game by chasing the homeless rabbit around and around in and out the groups. When the rabbit has grown tired, he may go into one of the homes, and at once the rabbit who was already there must leave, and this rabbit is chased by the hunter. When the hunter catches a rabbit, the two change places, the hunter becoming the rabbit, and the rabbit becoming the hunter.

Snake and Crab Race

This is a race in which all participate simultaneously. Divide the group into two teams of equal number and have the team members stand one behind the other, all those behind the first player having their hands on the shoulders of the player in front of them. When the signal is given, all must run in this fashion, without taking their hands off the shoulders of the player ahead, to the goal line about twenty-five yards away. When the last player in each group crosses the goal line the race is finished, and the team that has its last player over first is the winner.

All now return to the starting point and get ready for the second phase of the race. They take the same positions, with their hands on the shoulders of the player in front, but this time they must hop instead of run. The side that gets its last player over the line first is the winner.

In the third phase of the race the players line up one behind the other. This time each player must grasp his left ankle with his right hand. When the signal is given, all run to the goal, still keeping in their line. If it is desirable to make this game very difficult, have a fourth race and require all players to run in line to the goal holding the right ankle with the right hand and the left ankle with the left hand.

Goal

ARRANGE the players in a circle and have them stand with their legs wide apart. Secure a large ball for this game such as a football or backetball. One player stands in the center with the ball and tries to score a goal by rolling the ball between the outstretched legs of some player in the circle. Those who are in the circle may only defend the "goal" by using their hands to prevent the ball passing between their legs and must not at any time of the game bring their legs together. Unless the ball is coming toward a player, he should have his hands on his hips. When the player in the center scores a goal, the player on whom the score is made must take his place in the center and must stay there until he succeeds in scoring.

Cops and Robbers

HAVE the players arranged as for a grand march and bring them down into rows of eight. Arrange these rows with spaces of 2½ feet between each row and the players an arm's length from each other. All the players join hands and face the leader. When the leader blows the whistle, the players turn half way around and join hands with the players now in line. The leader blows the whistle again, and the players turn back into their original position.

In the meantime a cop and robber have been chosen and placed at opposite ends of the room. The cop is to chase the robber who may dodge through the various lines. However, the robber is not to break through the line, and whenever the whistle is blown the direction of the lines is changed, so that sometimes the robber is aided and sometimes hindered in evading the cop. When the cop catches the robber, the leader should give three short blasts on the whistle and allow each one to choose another to take his place.

Toe and Nose Tag

THE players stand in a circle, three of four "Its" are within the circle. When the leader blows the whistle and the game starts, any "It" may tag anyone in the circle. If a player is tagged while not holding his toe with one hand and his nose with the other, he must be "It" and the one who tagged him will take his place in the circle. If there are not more than twelve in the circle, one "It" would be sufficient while for a circle of forty or fifty, there ought to be at least four. While this game is extremely funny for about ten minutes, it will soon grow tiresome.

Aquatic Sports

IT IS ESSENTIAL when picnics are planned and water is available for swimming that a program of water sports be arranged. There will always be a few expert swimmers and divers who will enjoy displaying their talents before the spectators. It would be of interest also to demonstrate lifesaving methods before the whole group. The following are some suggested aquatic sports:

Water Scramble

GREASE a watermelon and float it on the water. Divide the group into two equal sides, and charge each side to attempt to bring back the watermelon to his goal.

Ball Between Knees

HAVE a swimming race and require each swimmer to carry a rubber water ball between his knees as he swims to the goal and back. If the ball is dropped, the swimmer must recover it and swim back to the place where it was lost, replace it, and continue.

Live Duck Race

ANOTHER mad scramble game in the water is a live duck race. The duck's wing feathers should be cut so that it cannot fly, and it should be held in the center of the pool by the leader until the signal is given to the two sides to try to bring in the duck. The duck is then released, and the scramble is on. One side may be able to bring in the duck, but quite likely neither side will succeed, and the duck will win the race.

Swimming with Candle

EACH swimmer is given a lighted candle and, holding it in his hand, he must swim to the goal and back. If the candle is extinguished, he must drop out of the race. The winner would be the one who first returns to the starting point with his candle still burning.

Water Tug-of-War

A LONG rope is put in the water and the contestants, having been divided into two groups of equal number, stand on the shore. Two persons hold the ends of the rope by treading water at a depth that is slightly over their heads. When the signal is given, both groups plunge into the water, and each group takes hold of its end of the rope and tries to pull the rope in its direction, beyond a designated goal on its side. The other group, of course, tries to do the same thing. The game is similar to a tug-of-war on land except that the players must swim as they pull.

Drowning Man

ANCHOR three blocks of wood or three large cork floats in the water, about twenty-five feet from the edge of the lake or pool. These floats should be about five inches square and should be anchored about three feet apart. The floats or blocks represent the head and two hands of a drowning man. Each player, or each member of a team, if the group has been divided into teams, is given three chances to ring the blocks by throwing an eighteen-inch life preserver over them. Attach the life preserver to a rope to facilitate drawing it back. The player must make three throws in not more than ninety seconds. If he rings one of the blocks the first time, he is given a score of ten; the second throw, a score of five; and the third throw, a score of two.

Swimming Pole Push

DIVIDE the swimmers into two groups of equal number. An effort should be made also to divide them according to size and swimming ability. A pole about twelve feet long or a board is needed for this game. Place the pole in the water at the center of the pool and line up one team on one side and the other team on the other side of the pole. When the signal is given, each side tries to push the pole forward. The side that is able to advance the pole fifteen feet wins the game.

Twin Swimming Race

PAIR off two girls against two girls or two boys against two boys for the twin swimming races. First have the breast stroke with the front swimmer locking his legs around the body of the back swimmer. Both may use their arms but only the back swimmer may use his legs. The crawl may be done the same way. The backstroke is done with the contestants in the same position except they swim on their backs. In the alligator race, the back swimmer places his hand on the hips of the first swimmer. In the Siamese twin swim the two swimmers must lock their inside arms and legs.

Hand Propelled Boat Race

IN water where boats may be used, two or more boats may be entered in a race in which the boats are propelled by swimmers using their hands instead of paddles. One, two, or four persons may be put in each boat. They are required to paddle the boat with their hands only.

Swimming Race

In order that the good swimmers may display their talent, have a real swimming race. This may be divided into several races, for example, a breaststroke race, a backstroke race, a crawl. There should be at least one freestroke race in which contestants may use any stroke they desire. Prizes should be given to the winner in each case.

Backstroke Spoon and Ball Race

Select a number of backstroke swimmers and give each one a tablespoon and a small rubber ball. At a given signal they are to put the handle of the spoon in their mouth, lay the ball on the bowl of the spoon and swim toward the goal. If the ball rolls out, the swimmer must stop and replace it.

Retrieving Corks

Secure a large number of corks. Divide the swimmers into two groups of equal number and line them up on each edge of the pool. The corks are dumped into the water in the center of the pool; and when the signal is given, all swimmers dive in and attempt to retrieve as many corks as possible. When all of the corks have been gathered, all players swim back to their side of the pool; and the corks are counted to determine the winner.

Water Hoop Relay

Divide the group into two, three, or four teams for a water relay. Line them up one behind the other on the shore of the lake or the edge of the swimming pool. Place four hoops in the water, trying to arrange them in front of each group. They will probably not stay in place but that should make no difference. When the signal is given, the front one in each line plunges in, swims to the hoop, slips it over his head, down over his body and off his feet, leaving it in the water for the next player. He swims back again, touching off the next swimmer in his group. So the relay continues until each one in each group has had a chance. The first group to finish is the winner.

Swimming Singing Relay

DIVIDE the group into two or more teams for a relay race. When the signal is given, the first one in each group plunges into the water and swims across the pool and back, at the same time singing at the top of his voice a song which has been previously selected by that group as its theme song. It will probably be very humorous to watch a player try to swim and sing while other swimmers are singing another song. When the first player finishes, he touches the next.

Water Skirt Relay

THIS is a relay race in which a contestant in each group must put on a girl's skirt over his bathing suit before getting into the water. Wearing this skirt, he must swim across and back and climb out of the pool. The next contestant must then don the girl's skirt, wet though it be, and swim across the pool. The funny part will be to watch the boys getting into the wet skirt.

Board Race in Water

SECURE some large boards, preferably a two-by-eight about ten feet long. Select one contestant from each group and have them race to a goal on the boards. Two wooden boxes of equal size may be used in place of the boards.

Stone Carry in Water

HAVE a swimming race in which the contestants are required to carry three small stones on the back of their left hand and keep the stones there until they swim to a goal and return.

Hand on Ankle Race in Water

HAVE a race in which the contestants are required to swim to a goal and back with the left hand holding the left ankle.

Locked Arms Race in Water

HAVE a race in which couples compete by the girl locking her left arm into the boy's right arm. Coupled together in this fashion, they must race to a given point.

Water Football

DIVIDE the group into two teams and let the captains choose goals by flipping a coin in the usual manner. The ball is thrown up in the center of the pool, and members of both teams endeavor to take the ball to their goal. The other side, of course, tries to prevent this and at the same time tries to make a touchdown for themselves. Six points are given to the team which is able by swimming or passing to touch the side of the pool which is their goal. Every time a touchdown is made, the teams change goals. This will give one team the shallow end of the pool for only part of the time. It will be necessary for the leader to establish certain rules with reference to guarding.

Sack Swim

SOME burlap sacks are needed for this stunt, and they may be obtained from almost any grocery store. This might be a straight race or a relay. In either case contestants must step into the sack, pull it up around the waist, knot it in, and swim to a goal and back, wearing the sack.

Under Water Tag

ONE player is "It." If he tags any player when the player is not "safe," that player must take his place and become "It." A player to become safe must dive under the water and remain there while "It" is near him. If "It" can follow him until he has to come up, he can then tag him.

Backstroke Umbrella Race

ANOTHER good backstroke stunt is an umbrella race. Swimmers line up at the starting point and swim to a goal a short distance away. Each one must carry an open umbrella.

Water O'Grady

O'GRADY in the water is very much like this popular game which boys play on land. Each command by the leader, to be legitimate, must be preceded by "O'Grady says." If a command is obeyed without being preceded by "O'Grady says," the one who obeys it must drop out of the game. Line the boys or girls up on the edge of the pool and proceed somewhat as follows: "O'Grady says: attention," "O'Grady says, 'hands up,' " "dive." Whoever obeys the command to dive would be counted out.

Water Polo

CHOOSE five men on a side. The referee stands about the middle of the shallow end of the pool. The players hang on to the side of the pool, one team on either side. When the referee throws the ball into the middle of the pool, the game starts. The object is for one team to get the ball and swim back and touch its goal, which is its side of the pool, with the ball. Of course, the opposing team has designated some of its players to swim to the opponents' side and guard the goal. A goal is made when a player is able to hold the ball against his side of the pool. Play in fifteen-minute halves, the side making the largest number of goals in that time wins.

Water Follow the Leader

FOLLOW the leader played in water is more fun than follow the leader played on land. There are so many things that the leader can do, as for example: Dive the different kinds of dives; swim in several different ways; swim under water; plunge for distance; dive from the diving tower; and so on.

Water Pom Pom Pull Away

THE player who is "It" stations himself in the middle of the pool and calls out "Pom pom pull away." All other swimmers must plunge in and swim across the pool. Whenever "It" tags one of them, this one also becomes "It" and helps tag the others. When all who were not caught have crossed the pool and climb out, all the "Its" in the water call again, "Pom pom pull away." It is quite likely that all of them will be caught this time. When all have been caught, the game starts again by the one who was first caught becoming "It."

Canoe Paddling Race

GET two canoes of approximately the same size and have a canoe paddling race. Lay out a goal in the water, which might be a canoe anchored in the middle of the river or lake, and require the contestants to paddle the canoe around this goal. Try it first with one paddler in each boat, one race for girls and one for boys. Then try it with two boys in each canoe, then two girls, and finally with a boy and a girl in each boat. There should be a judge or judges, as the races may have very close finishes.

Ball Capture

A GAME that is always a lot of fun on the beach or in a pool is ball capture. It may be played with a rubber ball of most any size. A ball about four inches in diameter is best. The party is divided into two groups of equal number, and the ball is thrown high into the air by the leader. No scores are made but the object is to see which group can keep the ball. Players are not allowed to snatch the ball out of the hand of a player on the other team and may only obtain it by intercepting a pass while the ball is in the air or recovering a fumble.

Sea Shore

HERE is a game to be played on the beach. The leader goes around and whispers to each player the name of some object commonly found on the beach. For example, sand, pail, shells, bather, tide, cabana, umbrella, blanket, water. All the players then sit down, and the leader starts telling a story about something that happened on the seashore. Whenever one of the objects for which the players are named is mentioned, that player must stand up, turn around twice, and sit down again. Should the word seashore be mentioned all must stand up, turn around twice, and sit down again.

Ice Water Relay

PLAYERS in bathing suits form two lines on the beach with an equal number in each line. Two large flat pans of ice water have been provided and, at a signal from the leader, these must be passed back over the heads of the players until they reach the players at the rear of the line. These must then run to the front and start the pan of ice water again. The game is over as soon as the man on the front at the beginning of the game reaches the back of the line and makes the run to the front. The group that finishes first is declared the winner, but the funny part will be watching players squirm when the ice water is spilled on them.

Bumping

HERE is a game that may be played on the beach or on soft ground. Pair off your guests and select a pair to do the bumping. Players in this game should be limited to boys, as it will be too rough for girls. Each boy draws up his left leg and throws his arms across his chest. When the signal is given, they hop toward each other "and shoulder charge" in an effort to knock each other off his balance. As soon as the left foot touches the ground, or one of the arms is unfolded, that player is out, and another may take his place. After these two have contested, the winners of the first two contests may be matched. This game may be made into a tournament by eliminating all those who were bumped out on the first round and then matching the winners. It would be well to have a consolation tournament for those who were knocked out in the first round.

Chinese Wrestling

CHINESE wrestling, like bumping, is suitable for a tournament. Divide the players into pairs and match them two at a time. Each wrestler stands on one leg, his left, the other being stretched forward and folds his arms across his chest. Each wrestler hops forward and tries to unbalance his opponent with his right leg. No kicking or charging is allowed, and one player is declared winner if he forces the other to touch his right foot to the ground. This game should be played on a grassy lawn or soft ground.

Cross Tag

TAG games are perhaps the oldest form of outdoor games. Cross tag is like the ordinary tag with but one difference. If "It" is chasing someone and another player runs between him and the one he is chasing, he must immediately cease to chase that one and chase the player who crosses before him. There is plenty of variety in this game as good runners will always dare to cross the path of the hunter.

In this as in other tag games certain rules should be in force. No tagging back should be allowed. Whenever a player is tagged, he should be required to tell whom he has decided to chase. No one should be allowed to help the runner by interfering with the chaser. In this game of cross tag after all players have crossed twice, "It" should be allowed to tag anyone.

Object-passing Tag

THE group selects some object which is passed by handing it from one to the other. This may be a ball, handkerchief, or stone. One can only be tagged when he has this object in his possession. Another player must take it as soon as it is offered to him, and if he refuses to do so, he immediately becomes "It."

Japanese Tag

As in all tag games, "It" pursues the rest of the players and tries to touch one of them. When one has been touched, he must keep his hand on the spot where he was touched and pursue the others. His hand cannot be freed from this spot until he has tagged someone else. The idea is to tag people in inconvenient places, on the ankle, on the knee, and so forth.

Pose Tag

BEFORE the game starts, "It" takes some funny position. He might put his hands up over his eyes, or stand at attention, or parade rest, or in any other position. When all have seen this position, "It" starts chasing the others. The only way a player can avoid being tagged is by striking the same position that "It" did in the beginning. This may be difficult to do if someone strikes a very humorous position and everyone else is laughing. When one is tagged, he becomes "It" and strikes a new pose, and so the game continues.

Capture the Ring

On a clothesline tie a number of curtain rings about two inches in diameter. These should be tied about two feet apart and a thread that is easily broken should be used to tie them on, as a sewing thread. They should be tied about eighteen inches from the clothesline and should hang about four or five feet over the water in the deep part of the pool. Six persons at a time play. Each one is given a long pole, such as a bamboo fishing pole, eight or ten feet long. The object is to spear the rings and capture them. Of course, everybody will be spearing at them at the same time. The one who collects the largest number is the winner. This may be played in teams, five on each side.

Black Fagots

Black Fagot is an outdoor game based on the old familiar game, Jack Straws. It would be especially interesting to groups around a bonfire, on hikes, picnics, and outings of various kinds.

An armful of fagots is held about a foot from the ground and allowed to fall. The first player takes out with a crook as many fagots as possible, without disturbing the remainder. If any of the fagots not being hooked by the player moves the slightest, the player's turn is ended. After counting the score, the fagots are then gathered and dropped for the next player. The number of fagots removed by each player constitutes the individual score.

Peg

Select nine sticks, two feet long, sharpened at one end, for the pegs. Arrange the pegs, pointed ends in the ground, in the shape of a diamond, each peg being two feet from its nearest neighbor.

Divide the players into two equal sides using all the boys and men on one side and all the girls and women on the other. The boys then choose a girl to be the First Lady, who is to lead their opponents, and the girls choose a First Gentleman, who is to command the men. With three short clubs in her hands, First Lady, standing on a line twenty feet from the apex of the diamond made from the pegs, tries to knock down all the pegs with three consecutive throws with the clubs. The score is recorded and the pegs reset.

It is then the turn of the First Gentleman who takes three clubs and tries to perform the same feat.

When all have had a turn, the individual scores are compared, and the right arm of each man or boy is bound with a handkerchief to the left arm of the girl or woman whose score most nearly approaches his own. Then the First Lady and the First Gentleman choose sides, taking a couple at each choice.

In the order of their score, the couples now take turns pitching clubs at the pegs. The men, of course, must use their left hands, and the women their right hands to throw the clubs, which they do simultaneously.

When each couple has had a turn, the scores are again counted and compared, and the couples bound into groups of fours, the fours, into sixes, until each side is a continuous line, the man on the end using his left hand and the woman on the end using her right hand to make the final score. New teams are formed each time by the method described at the first coupling.

Stone Throw

DRAW twelve concentric circles upon the ground or upon the sand at the beach. The center circle should be about three feet in diameter and each other circle should have a radius of about two feet more than the circle within it so as to make rings about two feet wide. If the game is played on grass the circles might be made with whitewash. Number the rings from outside to center, the center circle being number twelve and the chief goal at which all will throw. There should be two sets of twelve stones, distinct in color or size in order that the stones may be distinguished from each other.

The game is played by players one at a time throwing all twelve of their stones, one at a time, into the circles, standing at a distance of about twelve feet from the outside circle.

The first player makes an effort to pitch two stones into the center circle. He then tries to pitch two each of the other stones into the higher numbered circles. The rule is that not more than two stones may count in any circle for one player. One stone may count in any circle as long as it remains there alone. If, however, the next player throws a stone into a circle in which the first player has only one stone, the first player's score for that stone is thereby cancelled and it is removed from the ring. No stone touching a line counts and should, therefore, be removed.

When number one has finished throwing his stones, number two then has his turn. If number two throws a stone into a circle in which number one has only one stone, that will cancel that score for number one. Number two's first object should be to place two stones in each of the highest numbered circles, and of course by doing this he will thereby cancel the score of the first player if he only has one stone in such circle.

After number two has finished throwing, number one is ready to mark his score which will be made up as follows: A score equal to the number of the circle for each of two stones in it (even though player number two has one or more stones in the same circle). No score is made if player number one has more than two stones in one circle, as the third stone thrown into a circle by him has cancelled his score for that ring. Player number one may also mark a score equal to the number of the ring for each single stone thrown in by him which has not been cancelled by player number two throwing a stone into such ring.

After number one has marked his score his stones are removed from the rings and number three has a turn, competing against number two. When all players have had a try, number one will have to throw again in an effort to cancel part of the score of the last player who throws.

After all have had a try, two or more of those making the highest scores may be matched.

The game is most enjoyed when the players keep these three things in mind: (1) Protect stones from capture by keeping more than one stone in the circle. (2) Work toward the center. (3) Capture the stones of the opponents.

Section 5

games to make and play

THERE is rightfully much emphasis today on creative recreation. In this chapter there will be found instructions for the making and playing of sixty such games.

In the case of Churches, Y. M. C. A.'s, Boys' Clubs, Summer Camps, and others, it would be a good thing to have a workshop with a competent person in charge to teach members of the group how to make the games described in this chapter and other games.

In this chapter the compiler is presenting games that can be made by anyone. Some of these are made of regular available articles found in the home or in institutions or from boxes or pieces of wood that can be secured from any store. Instead of using the usual purchased articles, make use of the odds and ends found in most homes. Instead of checker men why not use bottle caps or golf tees? For tossing articles use linoleum blocks or rubber heels or jar rubbers.

Lines and diagrams on face of board games are most permanent and effective if one follows these directions:

1 Shellac face of board.
2 Use black drawing ink with size pen desired for names and lines.
3 After ink has dried thoroughly, cover with another coat of shellac or varnish. Varnish gives best results as a finish

but be sure to use shellac for the first coat, because ink will not stick to varnish very well.

Our readers will note the lack of strict rules accompanying the descriptions of the various games. It is the belief of the compiler that rules should be made to fit the occasion, the place, and the skill of the persons participating. If ten feet is too far for a toss game for the age participating, move it closer. If the individuals are not able to hit the target from a fifteen-foot distance, bring them up to a line where they are able to score often and easily.

Games in this chapter may be used in different ways.

First, a game-creation night—buy or secure the materials and have the group plan to make a half dozen of these games in one evening. This in itself is a good type of social activity.

Second, make these games for a permanent game room or institutional use where people may play when they have ten or fifteen minutes' leisure.

Third, use these games as a progressive game party by having a large number of the games set up in the room and then groups of four move from one game to the other as you would in a foursome of golf. New partners at each game may be available by two of each foursome moving forward and the other two moving backward, i.e., from ten to nine instead of ten to eleven.

Fourth, these games provide splendid pre-party activity, with one or two people playing at various games as the larger number is arriving.

Fifth, make games for home and family recreation.

Sixth, people want to play games that can be played in a short time without necessity of change of clothes. Many of these games are adaptable to this use at homes, churches, playgrounds, and schools.

Let everyone experience the joy of creation and the fun of playing games they have made.

Can Toss

PROCURE two one-pound coffee cans and a beanbag or tennis ball.

Players stand opposite each other, the can in one hand and the other hand behind them. They then attempt to toss the ball or beanbag back and forth between them using only the can with which to catch and toss.

Box Hockey (Regular)

HOW TO MAKE

ONE GATE

TWO GATES

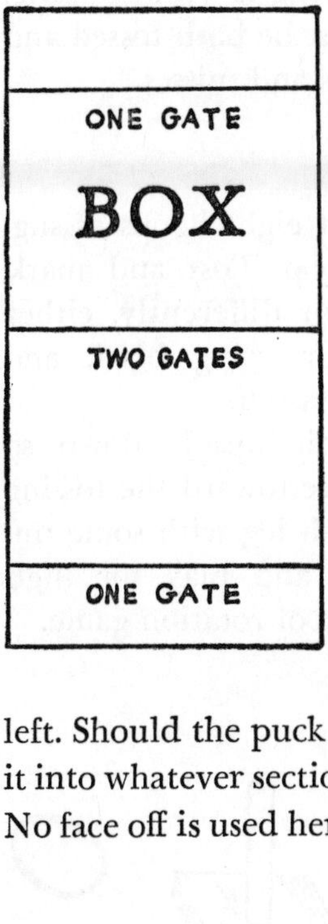

ONE GATE
BOX
TWO GATES
ONE GATE

Using ordinary 2 in. pine wood, construct a sturdy box 6 ft. long and 3 ft. wide with sides about 10 in. high. Prepare two partitions which will fit in the box and cut in the bottom of each a little doorway about 6 in. sq. Anchor these partitions firmly at either end of the box about 6 in. from the end wall. Prepare a third partition and cut two gateways in it the same size as the end ones. Anchor this partition securely in the middle of the box. Get several sections of old broom sticks. Saw some cross-sections from an old baseball bat for pucks and you are ready to start.

HOW TO PLAY

Place the puck on the top of the middle partition. Opponents stand on either side of the box and face off with their sticks as in regular hockey, tapping the bottom of the box and their opponents' sticks three times in succession; after grounding the sticks the third time the battle is on and the sky is the limit. Each person tries to hit the puck through the gate in the end partition to his left. Should the puck fly out of the box, it is put in play by dropping it into whatever section of the box it was when it was caused to go out. No face off is used here.

Box Hockey (Table)

CONSTRUCT a box as described for regular Box Hockey but make it 36 in. long, 18 in. wide, and 6 in. deep. Use 7/8 in. wood for this if possible.

Play as in the larger game, using smaller sticks and a cross section of an old broomstick for the puck.

Cane Toss

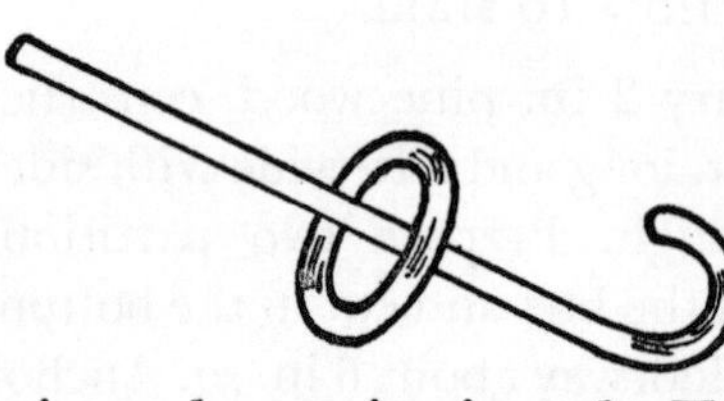

TAKE a 30 in. length of old garden hose. Whittle a small wooden plug which will fit snuggly into one end of the hose. Draw the other end up and fasten by tacking through the rubber into the wood. Tape the point and your ring is ready. Two ordinary canes complete the equipment.

Attempt to pass the ring back and forth spearing it with the cane. Ring must not be touched by the hand and must be both tossed and caught with the cane. Score according to catches and misses.

Chair Toss

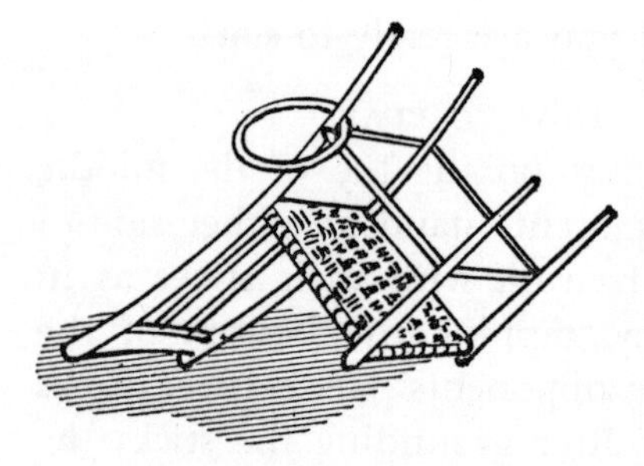

PREPARE about eight hoops as suggested for Hoop Toss and mark two sets of four differently, either by painting or using black and white tape to fasten.

Turn a chair upside down so that the legs are toward the tossing line. Label each leg with some numerical value and play for high score, or label legs from 1 to 4 and play as a type of rotation game.

Hoop Toss

PROCURE four lengths of very heavy sash cord about 20 in. long and fashion each into a ring or quoit by bringing the ends together and taping the joints securely. Get two 8 in. squares of heavy plank; bore hole in the center of each and set an 8 in. peg securely in place.

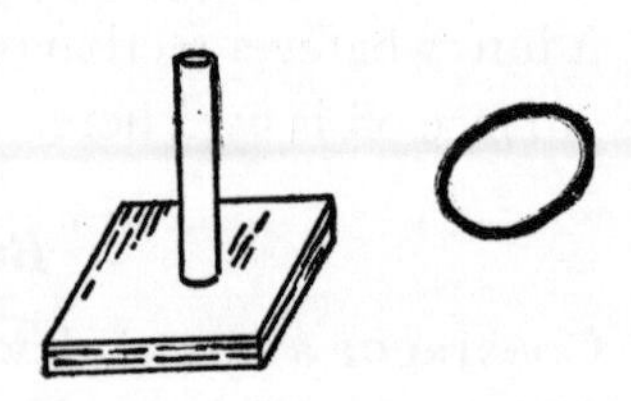

Play as in horseshoes except that ringers count five points, leaners three points, and closest hoop one point. Embroidery hoops may also be used.

Ring Tennis

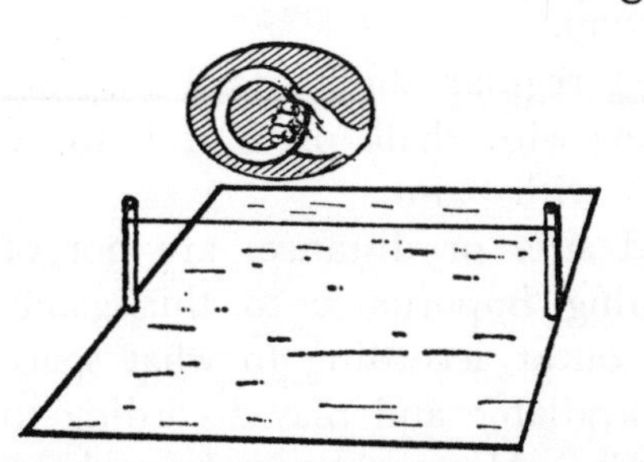

Make a quoit or ring about 6 or 8 in. in diameter as per the suggestions for Hoop Toss, using garden hose or heavy rope. Find some way to stretch a piece of clothesline about five feet from the floor and, if it is possible, mark off with chalk on the floor a court on each side of the rope according to what space is available. If it is not deemed advisable to put chalk marks on the floor disregard boundaries and just play for errors as suggested under direction for playing.

The game is played by tossing the quoit back and forth across the rope. Each player must catch the quoit with one hand only without allowing it to touch either his body or the floor. He must then return it immediately back across the rope, using a side arm motion only. Score by errors committed.

Paddle Tennis

This is a fine game for backyards, basements, gymnasiums, or play areas and may be laid out according to whatever space is available. Simply mark out the playing court of regular proportions patterned after a standard tennis court and adapted to the size of space available. Some sort of a barrier or net should be used which is 24 in. high. This may be made from an old tennis net. Paddles with 8 in. surfaces may be fashioned from 3-ply wood.

Play as in regular tennis except that an underhand "service" must be used. An old tennis ball which has become "dead" is the best to use.

Shuffleboard (Regular)

For this game, you will need to make four shuffleboard pushers and eight wooden discs. Pushers may be made from a broom or mop handle, or from any other wooden pole about 3/4 inches in diameter.

The curved end of the pusher may be made from short lengths of a wooden barrel hoop or nail keg hoop.

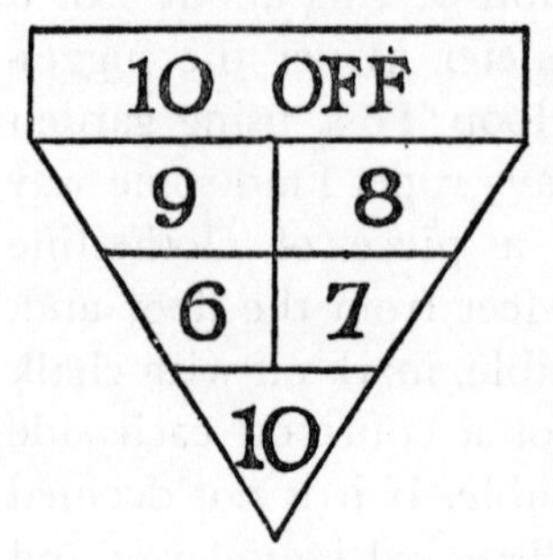

Mark off regular shuffleboard diagram on the floor with chalk or, if it is to be permanent, with paint.

Standard sizes or distances are not of overwhelming importance to this game. Build the outfit according to what space you have available and play according to regular rules. Many set-ups have been found to be very successful even though they were only a half or third the regular size. Game may even be played on a table top using miniature pushers.

Tether Ball (Outdoor)

TETHER ball is a game for two or four players. If there are four, those who stand in opposite triangles are partners. The object of the game is to wind the rope holding the ball around the upright pole, above a line about six feet from the base; using tennis rackets or paddles.

Many ways have been used to set up the pole for this game but the following will be found to be both usable and convenient. Get a section of 1¼ in. pipe ten feet long. Holes through which to tie the rope should be drilled in the top of this pipe. Or, the end of the pipe could be plugged with wood and a large screw eye inserted through which the rope could be tied. Get another section of pipe 30 or 36 inches long and just large enough to slip over the piece of longer pipe. Drive the shorter piece of thick pipe into the ground so that it will be flush with the surface; this will serve as a socket into which the long piece of pipe is set for play, and if it should be desirable to dismantle the game temporarily, the long piece may be simply lifted out of the socket and returned when desired very easily.

Take an old tennis ball and cut two very small slits in it on opposite sides. The rope leading to the top of the pole may then be pushed through these slits and tied, but it is recommended that a piece of leather thong be used to actually tie the ball and lead away for about 16 in. from it to the rope. This will not wear out nearly as easily as will clothesline or other rope. More elaborate methods of making a net to hold the ball are possible, but the way suggested above works just as well and replacements when necessary may be made very quickly by removing the thong and pushing it through the slits of another ball with a screw driver. This is a good use for old tennis balls.

For this outside game it is advisable to mark off the playing area into quadrants by means of two lines which intersect at the base of the pole and extend about 8 feet in each direction. Players take their positions in opposite quadrants and may not step out of their boundary lines. Play may thus be carried on vigorously without danger to either. Such boundary lines are important for safety sake. Further zest may be added to this game by scoring one point for the opponent each time that the ball hits the player on any part of his body except the forearm or hand holding the racket. Five points should then be allowed for winding the ball up and the single points added as they are scored during the play. If the rope becomes wound around the racket or arm or a player, his opponent is allowed a free swing at the ball when tossed.

Beanbag Board

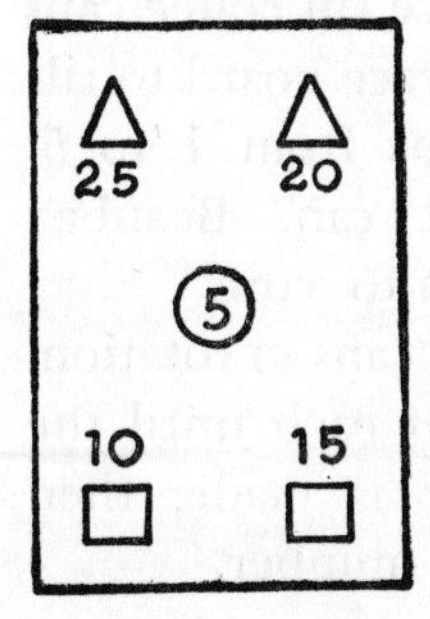

CUT a piece of ⅜ or ½ in. five-ply wood 24 by 36 in. Cut holes in it as shown and label each hole with values as indicated. If desired a prop may be fastened to the back of the board by means of a hinge and regulated to the right angle by a piece of cord or light chain.

Play either for high score, using values as shown, or try for the holes in rotation from 5 to 25.

Bag Post Office

PLACE partitions in an ordinary box so it resembles a letter box. 12 or 16 small sections make a good unit. Designate each box with a humorous name of some family relation such as Aunt Polly and Uncle Hiram, and so on. Six beanbags are used to toss.

Bags are tossed so they fall into various sections of the box. Each bag represents a letter to some member of the family. Score may be arranged in different values from one hundred points for a letter written to Mother or Dad on down to minus one hundred points for a mother-in-law letter.

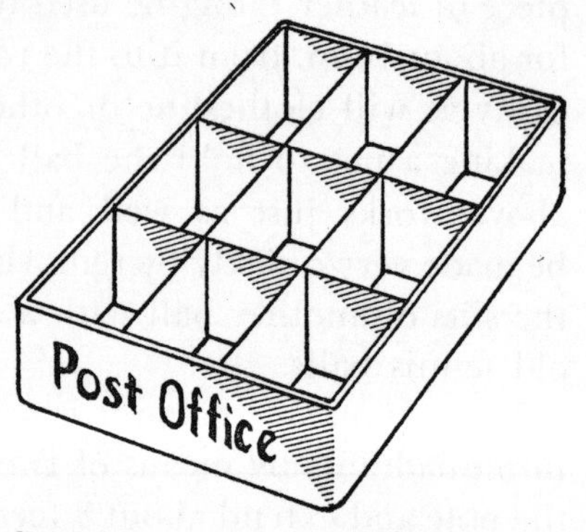

Beanbag Store

PREPARE a set of partitions as suggested for Bag Post Office. Label each section with some well-known part of a good meal. Then prepare menus containing five or six items of food, picked from the names marked on the partitions of the box. Six beanbags complete the equipment.

Each player is given a menu which he attempts to fill by tossing bags into corresponding sections of box. As each item is filled, he checks it on his list. Player completing menu in the least number of tosses wins.

Beanbag Toss

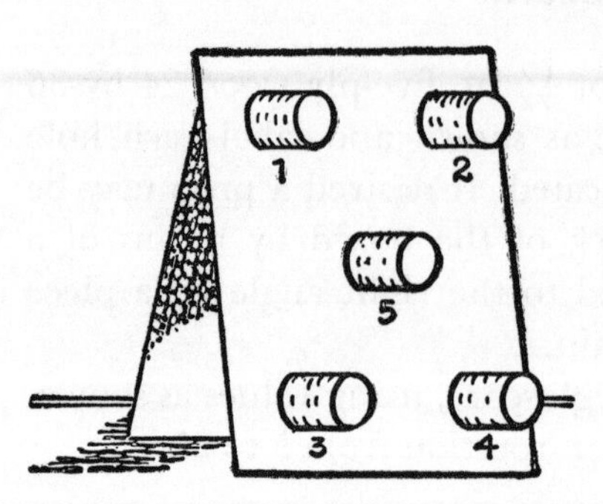

USE board. Nail five tin coffee cans on heavy board. Brace board to tilt upward. Label cans from 1 to 5. Toss beanbags at can. Beanbag must remain in can to score.

Toss beanbags at cans in rotation. Continue tossing at each until the particular number is made, then pass on to the next number.

Can 'Em

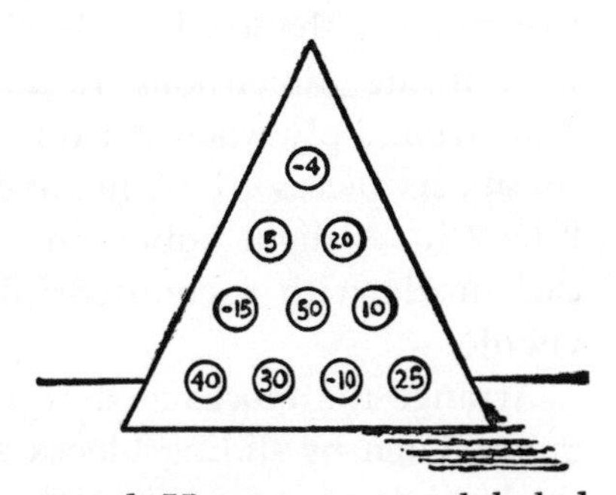

GET ten one-pound coffee cans and, using stove bolts and washers, fasten them on a piece of plywood cut to the shape of a triangle 24 in. on a side. Make a half dozen small beanbags, label each can with some particular value.

Attempt to toss bags into the cans and compute total scores from bags remaining in cans after all six are tossed. Have some cans labeled with minus values to add to uncertainty.

Pyramid Solitaire

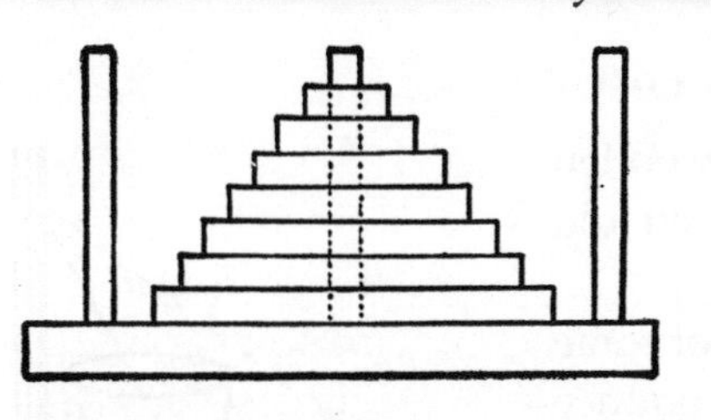

USE a board 16 inches long and 6 inches wide to make the playing field. Place three upright pegs 6 inches high in the center of the board. The two end ones should be 3 inches from the end of the board, and the center one should be 8 inches from each end. These are to hold the pyramids as they are built. Make seven wooden squares with holes in them to fit over the pegs. Make the first one 1½ inches square, and increase the size of the others by ½ inch until the last one is 4½ inches square.

At the beginning of the game, all squares are on the middle peg with the largest at the base and the others arranged by size with the smallest at the top. The object of the game is to remove all the squares from the middle peg to either one of the outer pegs and arrange them in the same order as they were on the middle peg. The squares must be moved one at a time to either outside peg, but a large square must never be placed on top of a smaller one. This can be done—but it is very difficult.

Shifting Block Puzzle

CONSTRUCT a shallow box about $\frac{1}{2}$ in. deep with inside dimensions $10\frac{3}{4}$ by $8\frac{1}{2}$ in. Now from 3-ply wood cut out one piece 4 in. sq., six pieces 4 by 2 in., and two pieces 2 by 2 in. A slight hollow in the center of each made with a counter-sink bit is advisable.

Arrange the blocks as shown in the diagram. Then by sliding blocks around in the box, attempt to move the large 4 in. square block from the upper right-hand corner to the upper left-hand corner. No blocks may be picked up.

N.B. This is accomplished, in general, by a clockwise shifting of the blocks.

Basket Toss

GET A corrugated pasteboard box, wooden box, or wastebasket and a half dozen old tennis balls.

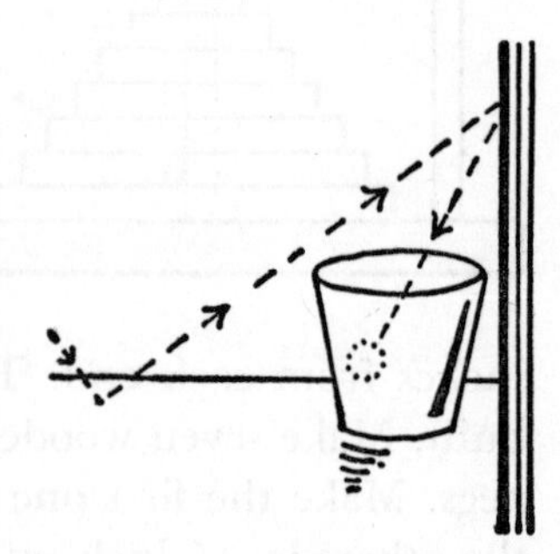

Place the box about 6 in. in front of some flat wall. Stand back and attempt to bounce the balls so they will strike the floor first, the wall second, and then drop into the box. A single volleyball or basketball may be used for this game.

Muffin Pan Bounce Ball

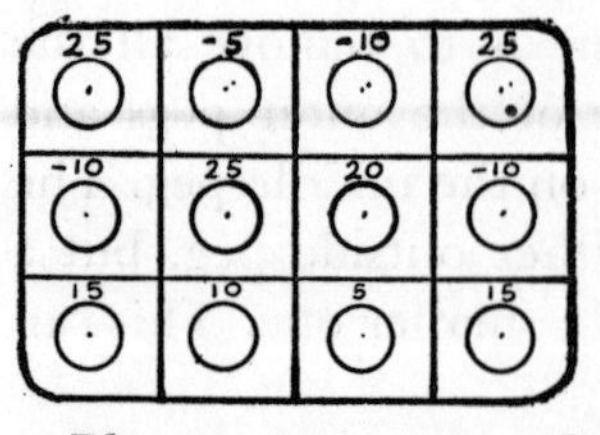

GET AN ordinary muffin pan with dozen cups. With small pieces of adhesive tape, mark different values both plus and minus, as is suggested by diagram and stick them near the edge of each cup. Five ping-pong balls complete the equipment.

Place pan on one end of a bare table near a wall if possible. Players stand at other end of table and attempt to bounce the balls so they will stop in the cups. Score is counted as indicated in the diagram.

Peg Solitaire

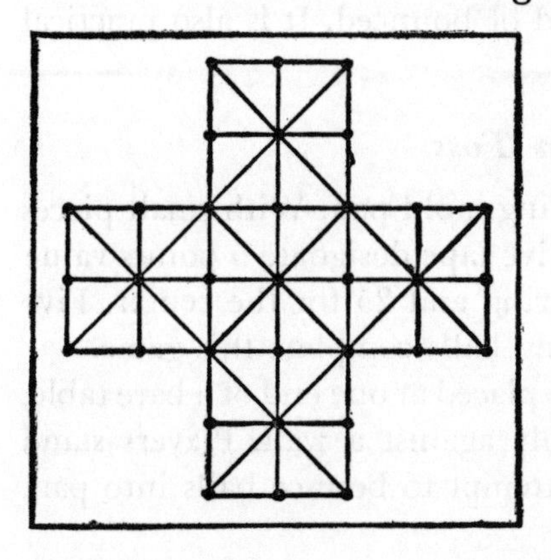

CUT A BOARD approximately 12 inches square and mark out a diagram as shown. At the line intersections drill holes just large enough to hold the shaft of a golf tee loosely. Thirty-two golf tees are necessary to play this game.

The object of this game, which is played by one person at a time, is to remove pegs by jumping so that at the end of the game there is only one peg left on the board. This game may be played in turn by several people or at the same time by several in competition, if each is supplied with a board, comparative score being figured by the number of men left on each board when it is no longer possible to jump a man.

Egg Carton Bounce Ball

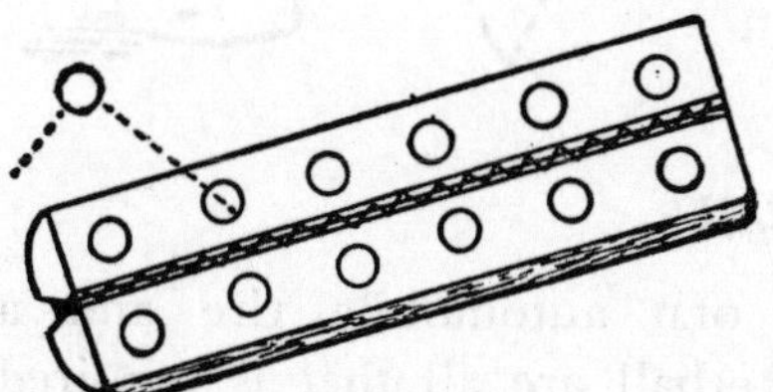

PROCURE an ordinary egg carton. Fold the halves back so that they will lie flat on the table and label each compartment as was suggested in Muffin Pan Bounce Ball.

Attempt to bounce ping-pong balls so they will come to a stop in some division of the carton. Score according to values indicated.

Pan Toss

PROCURE three pans of different sizes which will fit inside of each other and still allow some space between the rims. Label each pan some value from 5 to 25. Five or six ping-pong balls complete the equipment.

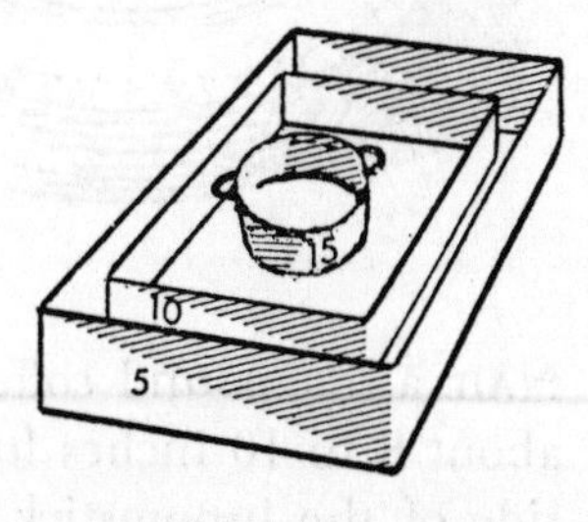

Bounce the ping-pong balls so they will hop into the pans. Score according to value indicated. Soft balls made of yarn, or cotton practice golf balls may be used and tossed instead of bounced. It is also practical to use marbles.

Ring Pan Toss

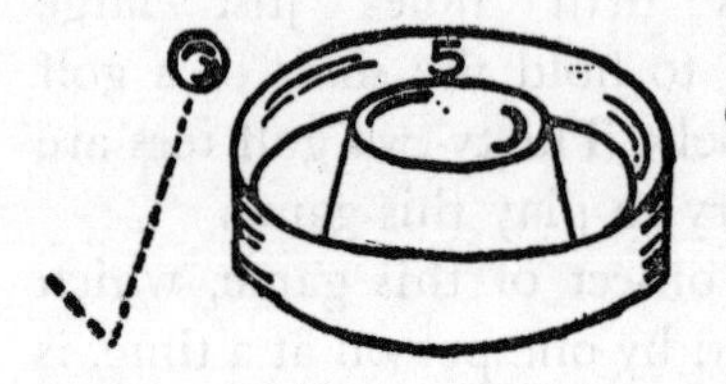

GET A ring mold pan. With small pieces of adhesive tape designate 5 points value for the ring and 25 for the center. Five ping-pong balls complete this game.

Pan is placed at one end of a bare table, perferably against a wall. Players stand at the other end of the table and attempt to bounce balls into pan, scoring according to values shown.

Tennis Bounce Ball

USE ANY type of box, or wastebasket, or container that may be handy, with a dozen or so tennis balls to bounce.

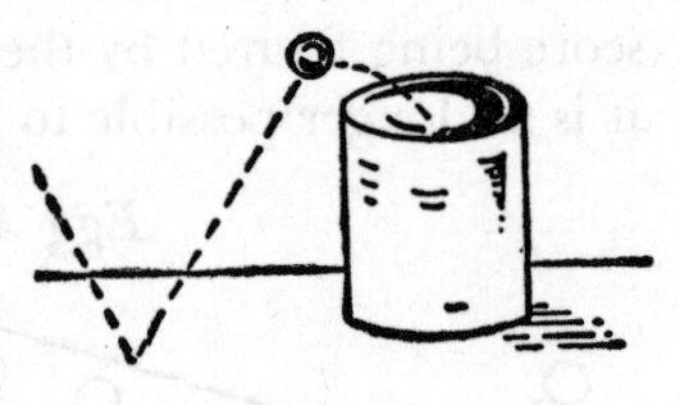

Attempt to bounce balls into box. Count the total number which remain in the box.

Tire Ball

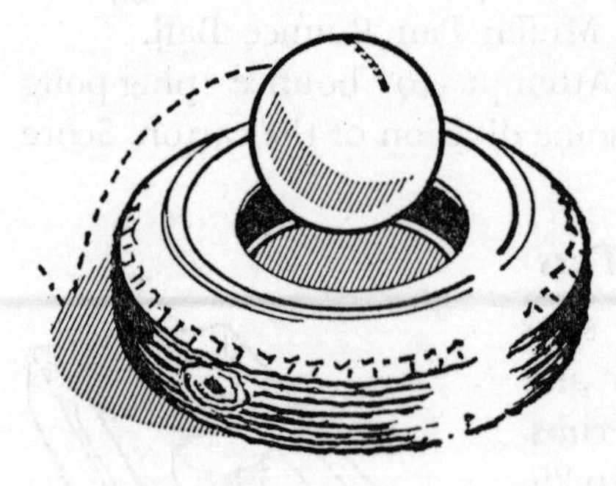

AN OLD automobile tire and a basketball are all that is required for this game.

Lay the tire flat on the floor and stand back from 5 to 6 feet and bounce the ball so it will come to rest within the tire. Score according to successful tries.

Cup Ball

NAIL a one-pound coffee can to the end of a section of broomstick about 8 to 10 inches long. Attach a string about 3 feet long to the side of the broomstick with a screw eye, and tie the other end of this string to an old tennis ball in which holes have been cut. Hold the stick in the right hand and toss the ball into the air with the left hand. Attempt to catch it in the coffee can.

Each player should be given ten chances, with one point scored for each catch.

Ball Spear

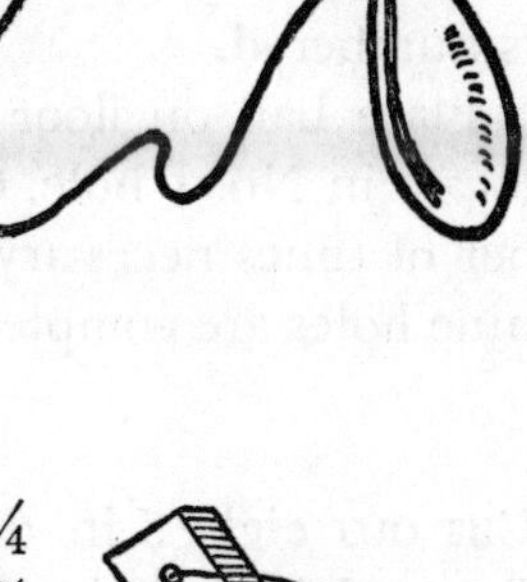

GET A small wooden ball about 2 or 3 in. in diameter and bore a hole completely through it as large as can be safely done without splitting. Attach a cord to the ball by means of a small screweye and the other end to a spear such as illustrated.

Flip the ball into the air and attempt to catch it on the spear.

Lapel Needle

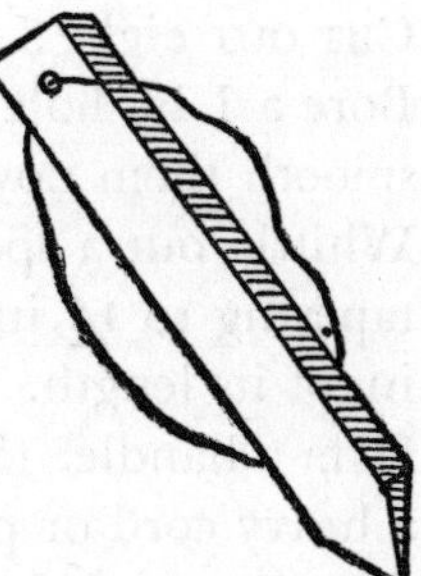

USE A piece of wood 1/4 inch in diameter, or 1/4 inch square and about four inches long. Point at one end and make a hole in the other end. String a cord through the hole and tie it so that the entire length of the loop is about 1/2 inch less than the length of the needle. Place the loop over the top of the lapel of a person's coat, pull down the lapel and stick needle through the button hole in the lapel, thus fastening the needle on the lapel. Put it on a friend's lapel and challenge him to get it off.

Dart Archery

CUT A piece of 3-ply wood 24 by 36 in. and draw five concentric circles with radii of 4, 8, 12, 16, and 20 in., respectively. Paint the center circle yellow or gold; second, red; third, blue; fourth, black; and outside, white. If desired label them 9, 7, 5, 3, 1, which are the values used in regulation archery.

Six darts are provided for each player which he throws in turn. If more than one person throws at a time, darts should be painted some distinctive color in sets of six each.

Paddle Golf

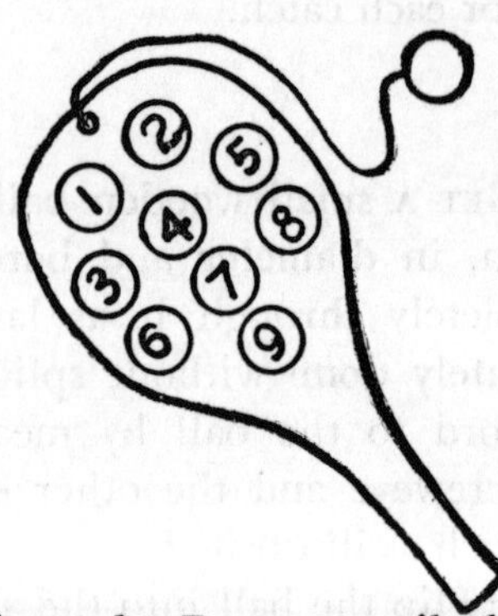

MAKE A paddle out of 3-ply wood a little larger than ping-pong paddle and large handle with two extra pieces of plywood. Make nine holes in paddle 1¼ in. in diameter. Attach cord at end of paddle with the ball at the other end of a 2-foot string. Each hole is numbered.

Place ball on floor and jerk up to locate in No. 1 hole. Count the number of times necessary to lift before hole is made. Repeat until all nine holes are completed. Record total for nine holes.

Ring Spear

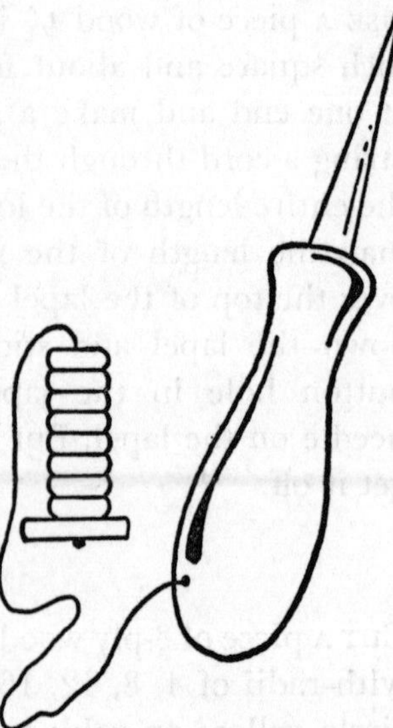

CUT OUT eight 3 in. discs from 3-ply wood. Bore a 1 in. hole in the center of each and smooth them down nicely with sandpaper. Whittle out a spear about 12 in. long and tapering to ½ in. in diameter for about 5 in. of its length. The rest may be carved to form a handle. (See the diagram.) Procure a heavy cord or preferably a leather thong. Attach one end to the spear at the thick end. Put the thong through the hole in the discs and attach a short crossbar 2 or 3 in. long at the other end.

Take the spear by the handle. Allow the thong to hang down with eight discs resting on the crossbar. Now swing or flip them into the air and see how many you can spear. Take turns or allow each person ten turns and count the total number of rings each spears.

N.B. This is an old Indian game and a model more like the one they use can be made by saving sections of round steak bones, cleaning them and polishing well, and using these for the rings on the thong. Somewhat smaller spear will have to be used.

Block Anagrams

MAKE six cubes out of wood. 1 to 1½ in. cubes will work best. Mark on six sides of each one the letters of some six-letter word which has no duplication of letters. A pound coffee can from which to roll them completes the equipment.

Roll block out of can and after rolling attempt to form word from letters showing on the top of the block. Five points for each letter used in a word. No letter may be used more than once. Deduct 10 points each time three letters of a kind show. One hundred points make a good game.

Put And Take

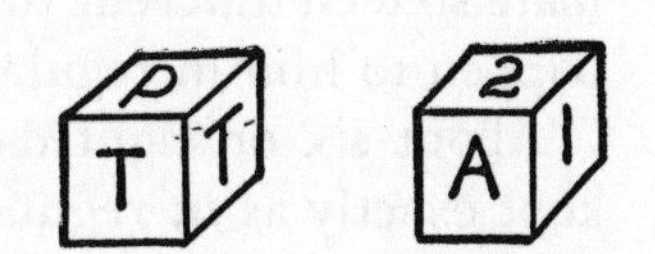

MAKE TWO wooden cubes about 3 inches square. Label three sides of one with letter P and the other three sides with the letter T. On the second cube mark the figures 1, 2, 3, and 4 on four of the sides and the letter A on each of the two remaining sides. Use beans or matches for counters. Each player is given 25 counters, and 25 are placed in the "pot."

Roll the two cubes out of a large coffee can and add or take away counters from the "pot" as indicated by the cubes. P stands for "put"; T stands for "take"; A stands for "All." Play five times around the circle of players and at the end of that time, the person with the largest number of counters is the winner.

Dart Mathematics

CUT A section of 3-ply wood 24 by 36 in. and lay out the diagram as shown. Procure six darts for throwing. Paint one of the six darts a distinctive color.

Toss darts at board and compute total score from where they stick. Count double value for the odd-colored dart.

Dart Baseball

CUT BOARD 24 by 36 in. and inscribe on it a circle 20 in. in diameter. In the center of this inscribe a smaller circle 2 in. in diameter. Now drawing radiating lines from the small circle to the larger circle's circumference, divide it into sixteen equal quadrants. Label the small circle "home run" and the sixteen divisions name after the approximate sixteen different things which a batter or base runner can have happen to him in regular baseball.

About six or eight darts are needed to play this game. Score is kept exactly as in regular baseball and play is governed by regular baseball rules. Players alternate being "at bat" and toss their darts until their side is retired.

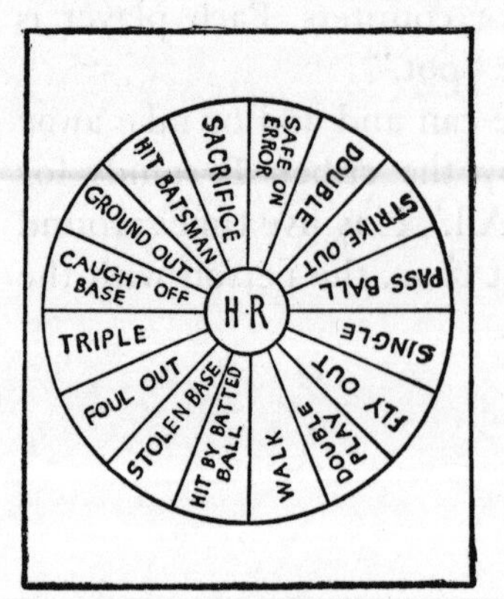

1. Single
2. Double
3. Triple
4. Strike out
5. Walk
6. Foul out
7. Fly out
8. Ground out
9. Caught off base
10. Hit batsman
11. Stolen base

12. Safe on error
13. Pass ball
14. Sacrifice
15. Hit by batted ball
16. Double play

N.B. In case a dart shows some situation which could not happen, i.e., a stolen base when no one is on base, such a dart is disregarded and play continues. Darts striking lines count for the worst of the two situations in question. If very fine lines are used, much of this will be avoided.

Disc Toss

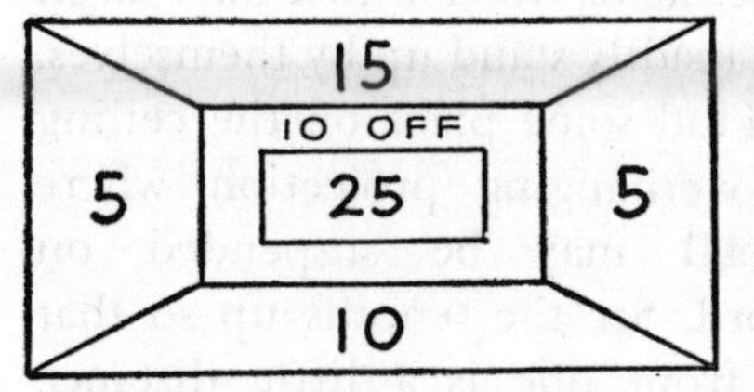

Cut 10 or 12 three-inch discs out of linoleum, using two colors if possible; if not, mark half to differentiate them from the others. Draw diagram as suggested with chalk on the floor or table top.

Players are divided into two teams and each team is given different colored discs. They attempt to toss the discs onto the diagram, and the score is computed according to where the discs stop. Line discs count for the smallest values which they touch. The teams throw alternately and score is kept by teams.

Rolling Home

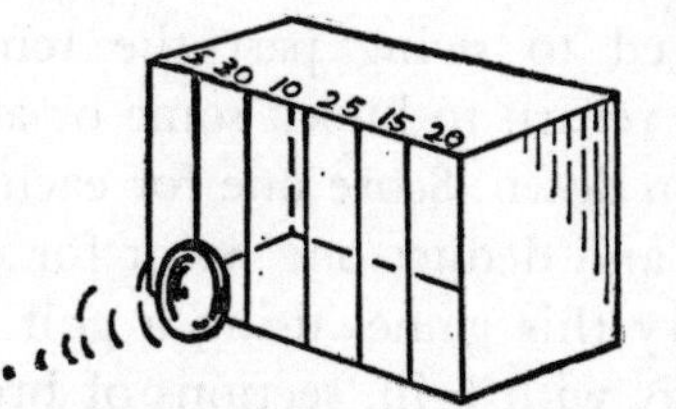

Take any wooden box and nail narrow slats across the face of it 2 or 3 in. apart, according to the size of the box. Designate values for the slots or openings thus formed between the slats. Half dozen 8 or 10 in. discs such as hot pads or even ordinary paper plates may be used.

Attempt to roll the discs so they will enter one of the slots of the box. Score as indicated.

Spot

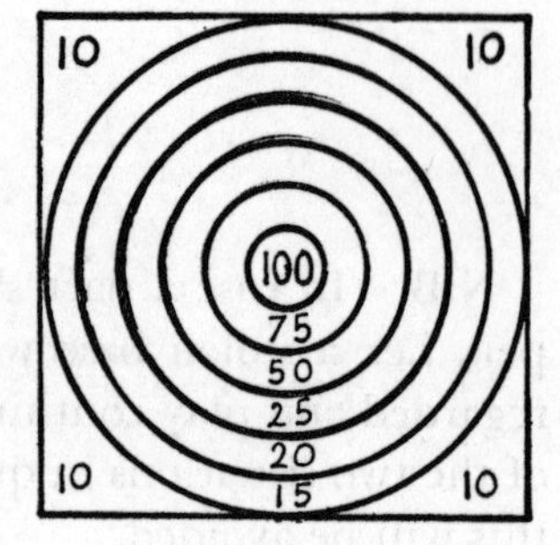

Cut a piece of plywood 24 in. square and lay out the diagram as shown. Use several large, flat, rubber sink stoppers to toss.

Toss the flat stoppers on to the board which has been laid flat on the table or floor or, perhaps, tilted a bit. Count the highest value touched by any edge of the stopper.

Swing Ball Tenpins

Use Indian clubs, tenpins, or thick sticks of wood which have been well flattened on one side so they will readily stand up by themselves. They should be about 12 in. long. Find some place on the ceiling or overhanging projection where a ball may be suspended on a cord. Set the tenpins up so that the front one is a little distance away from the ball as it hangs from the ceiling. A basketball, volleyball, or large indoor baseball may be used.

The players stand some distance behind the tenpins and hold the ball in their hands with the rope taut. Ball is then released and caused to swing past the tenpins and return to knock some or all of them down. Score one for each pin knocked down on this return swing and deduct one point for each pin upset on the forward swing. Try this game, using a golf ball suspended from a string in a doorway with 6 in. sections of broom handle for pins.

Golf Putting

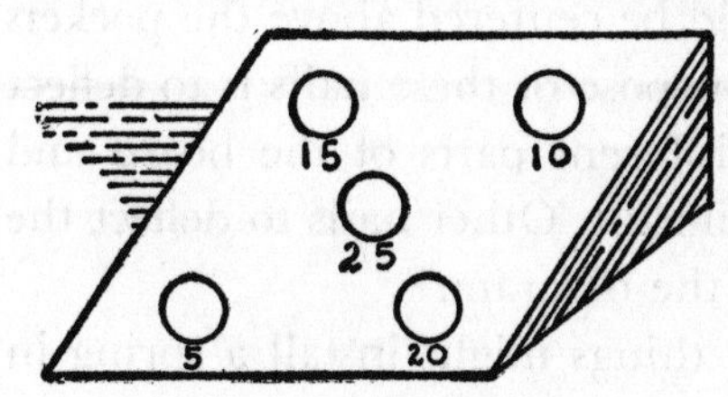

USE ordinary golf putter and regular golf balls. Make inclined board with holes little larger than golf balls.

Putt and score according to hole through which the ball falls. Players may use circle drawn in with chalk on rug in lieu of board.

Thumbo

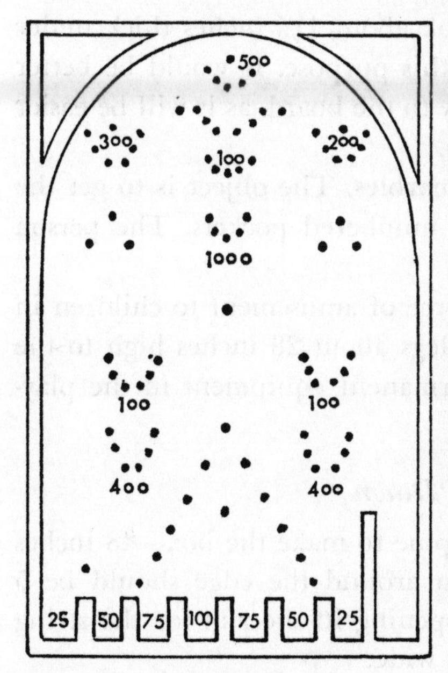

CUT A piece of ¾ inch plywood 24x36 inches and nail strips around all four sides, making a rim which will stand up about 1 inch above the edge of the board. At one end nail strips ¾ inches square as shown on the lower end of the diagram. The one on the right, which is the place to tee off the marbles, should be about 6 inches long. The others, six in number, need to be only 2 inches long. These are the pockets to catch the marbles. These should be spaced about 2¼ inches apart and the pockets should be numbered—from right to left—25, 50, 75, 100, 75, 50, 25.

To make the curved arch at the top end of the board, take a thin strip of soft wood that will bend and steam it to make it more pliable. Bend it in the form of the arch, as shown, and nail it securely to the top of the board. Using 4 penny finish nails or brass nails of similar size, create various pockets at different places on the board as shown in the diagram. Label these with numbers 100, 200, 300, 400, 500, 1000 as shown on the diagram.

Three nails should be placed on the curve made by the arch, about ½ inch inside the arch. These should be centered above the pockets numbered 200, 300, and 500. The purpose of these nails is to deflect the marble so that it will roll to different parts of the board and making scoring the high numbers difficult. Other nails to deflect the marble may be placed as shown on the diagram.

A person who is adept at making things might install a spring in the lower right-hand slot to propel the marbles. The marbles may be shot, however, by flipping with the thumb or finger so that they will travel toward the curve and until they strike one of the nails.

When the play starts, the arched end of the board must be elevated. This may be done by placing a book about 1½ inches thick under this end, or providing a block for this purpose. It would be better not to attach this block permanently to the board, as it will be easier to carry around if it is in two pieces.

Each player shoots eight or ten marbles. The object is to get the marbles to stop within the higher numbered pockets. The person with the highest score is the winner.

This game will be a constant source of amusement to children in the home. It would help to attach legs about 28 inches high to the board—making it a part of the permanent equipment in the playroom.

Spin 'em Down

Use three-ply wood or lightweight pine to make the box—48 inches long and 19 inches wide. The rim around the edge should be 5 inches high. At one end leave an opening in the rim for the string and for the top, which is 2½ inches wide.

Cross pieces divide the box into four main divisions, as shown in the diagram. The two end sections are further divided into three small sections each, as shown.

Tenpins may be made from any round sections of wood—dowels, broomsticks, and so forth. These should be 4½ inches high. Place the tenpins in the box as illustrated by the black dots on the diagram.

Wrap the handle of the top with string. Placing the top inside the

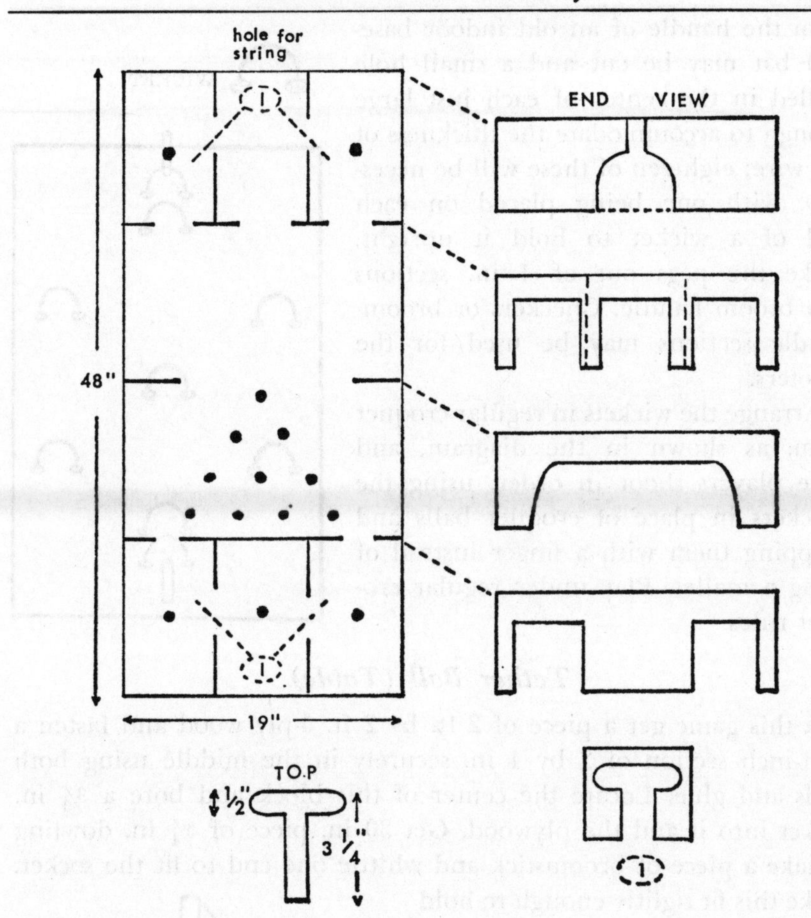

box, and bracing it against the rim, give the string a sharp pull—as you ordinarily would in spinning a top. The top will spin on a wobbling course through the box, striking some of the tenpins.

Score one for every pin knocked down in the large section of the box and five for every pin down in the small end sections.

Table Croquet

THIS game may be planned either for a large board where wickets are placed permanently or for a table top or on the floor. Cut nine pieces of heavy wire and bend each in the form of an arch. Sections from the handle of an old indoor baseball bat may be cut and a small hole drilled in the center of each just large enough to accommodate the thickness of the wire; eighteen of these will be necessary, with one being placed on each end of a wicket to hold it upright. Make the pegs out of 4 in. sections of a broom handle. Checkers or broom-handle sections may be used for the shooters.

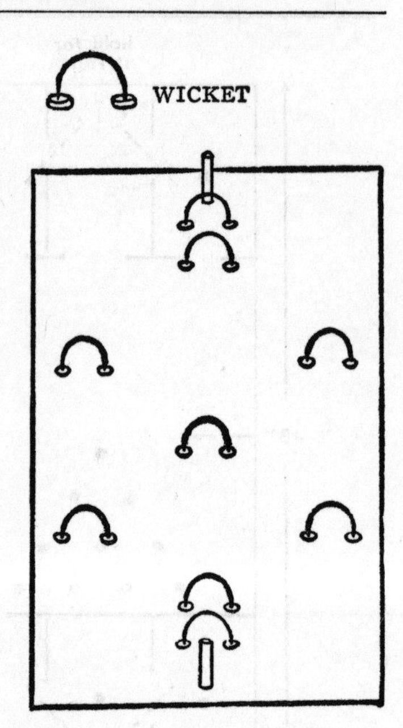

Arrange the wickets in regular croquet form, as shown in the diagram, and have players shoot in order, using the checkers in place of croquet balls and snapping them with a finger instead of using a mallet. Play under regular croquet rules.

Tether Ball (Table)

For this game get a piece of 2 ft. by 2 ft. 5-ply wood and fasten a four-inch section of 2 by 4 in. securely in the middle using both nails and glue. Locate the center of this block and bore a ¾ in. socket into it and the plywood. Get 30 in. piece of ¾ in. dowling or take a piece of broomstick and whittle one end to fit the socket. Make this fit tightly enough to hold the pole securely but not so tightly that it cannot be dismantled when desired. Either make a small ball of yarn or get a cotton practice golf ball; fasten one end of stout twine, such as plumb line, to the ball and the other end to the top of the pole, allowing the ball to hang about 2 in. above the block. Wind a narrow piece of tape around the pole about 12 in. from the top.

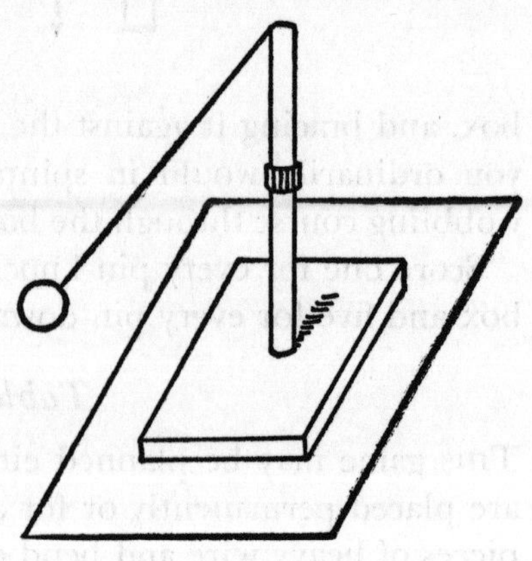

To play this game place it on a small table between two persons. Then the ball is started swinging around the pole by one who is called the server. His opponent attempts to cause the ball to be wound in the opposite direction. The first person to wind the string completely around the pole in his chosen direction, above the tape marker, is the winner. It is possible to play this game either with the bare hands or by using small ping-pong paddles.

Snap Shuffleboard

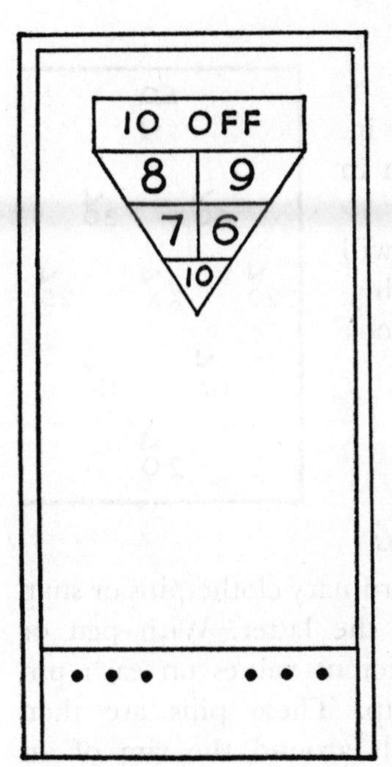

TAKE a piece of 10 or 12 in. board about 20 or 36 in. long or a piece of plywood the corresponding size. Nail strips along both sides and one end to form a railing. Three in. from open end draw line to be used as shooting line. At the closed end draw the shuffleboard diagram and use checker men or sections of broom handle for shooters.

The game is played by two people, each having four shooters. These are shot alternately by placing them on the shooting line and snapping them with the finger. Scoring is made according to what section of the diagram the shooters stop at the end of the game. After both players have completed their four shots, all counters on lines, which do not score, are removed and remaining counters totaled for final score.

Megaphone Ring Toss

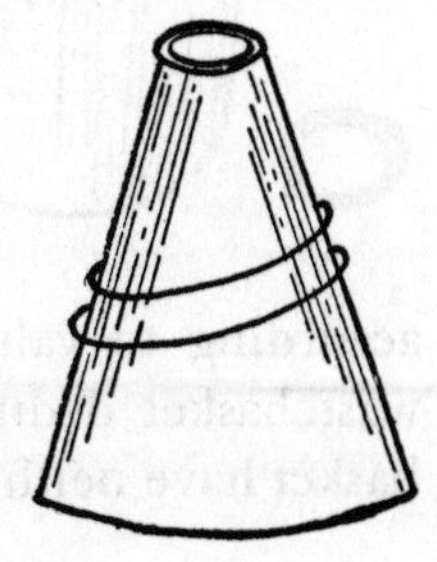

A GOOD sized cheerleader's megaphone and a half dozen rope rings, such as those described in Hoop Toss (page 122) or ordinary embroidery rings, form the necessary equipment for this game.

Set the megaphone on the floor with the small end up and attempt to toss the hoops over it.

Milk Bottle Toss

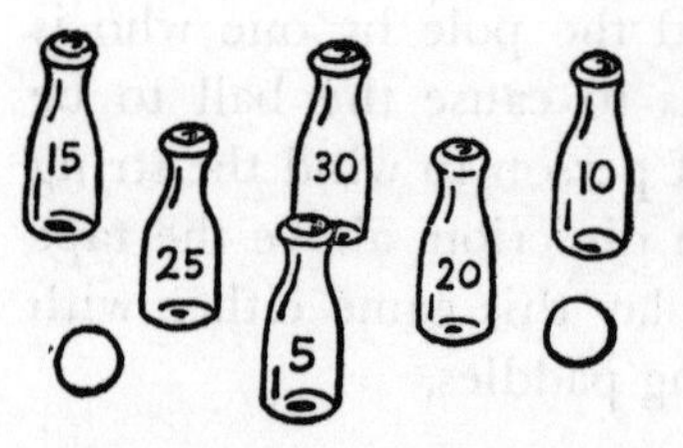

GET five or six pint milk bottles and six embroidery hoops. Put a strip of adhesive tape around the neck of each bottle and mark on it values as suggested in the diagram.

Attempt to toss rings over bottles. Set up in some manner such as in diagram and score as bottles are rung.

Ring Toss

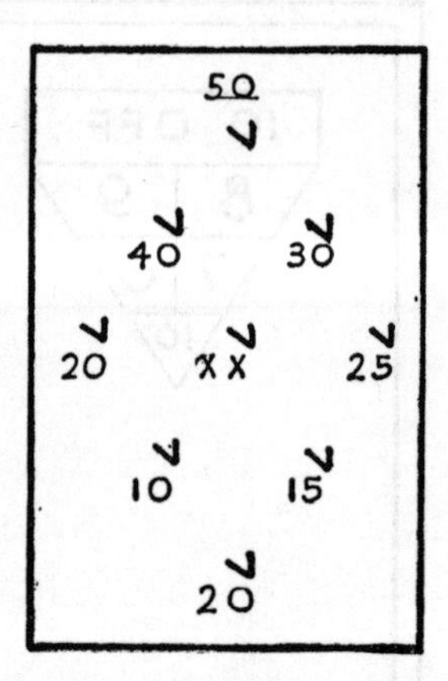

PREPARE a board of 3-ply wood 24 by 36 in. Place screw hooks in this board as shown in the diagram and label them as suggested.

Attempt to toss jar rubbers so that they will catch on hooks and compute scores accordingly. Any rubber sticking on the middle hook labeled XX subtracts 50 from total score.

Clothespin Toss

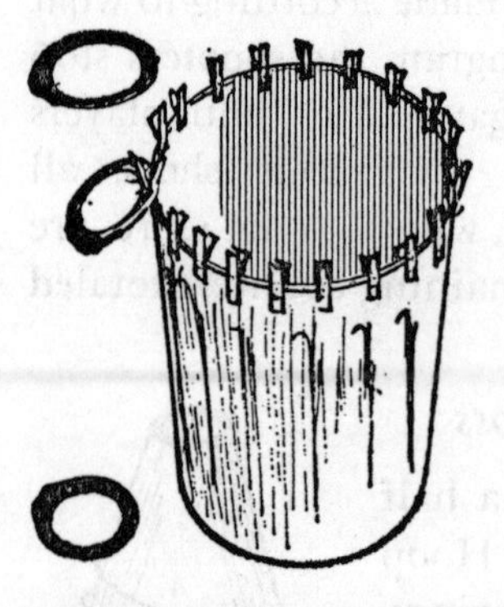

GET two dozen ordinary clothespins or snap pins, preferably the latter. With pen or pencil mark different values on each pin from five on up. These pins are then stuck at intervals around the rim of an ordinary wastebasket. Jar rubbers are used for tossing.

Players are provided with an equal number of jar rubbers which they attempt to toss over the pins around the edge of the basket. Rings falling on pins are counted according to value marked on the pins. Rings falling within the wastebasket deduct ten from total score. Rings falling outside the basket have neither a minus nor a plus value.

Ring Pan

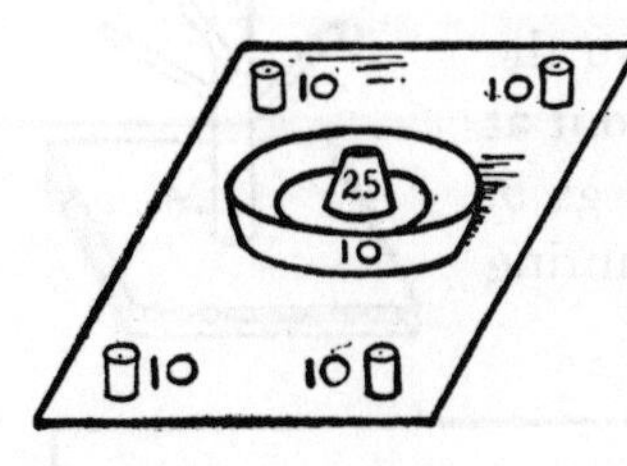

Get an angel food cake pan and fasten it in the middle of a 15 in. sq. piece of plywood. Set four spools in the corners and label as shown. Use jar rubbers to toss.

Attempt to toss jar rubbers for score as indicated, counting minus ten value for rubbers which go into the pan without encircling the center. Subtract five for each rubber which remains on the board without encircling a spool.

Peg Quoits

Cut a section of 3-ply wood 24 by 36 in. and lay out diagram as shown. Nail three strips along the back of the board and drill holes for the pegs through the board and into the strips which will form an additional reinforcement. Make eight pegs 4 in. long from ½ in. dowel rod and set them in holes located as shown in the diagram. Make several rope quoits as described in Hoop Toss.

Stand back 8 or 10 feet and attempt to toss the rings onto the pegs.

Rubber Tire Horseshoes

Get an old automobile tire and with a knife or ordinary hand saw cut cross sections from it. Make a pair of pegs such as described in Hoop Toss or simply take two chairs placed some distance apart and use one particular leg of each for your peg. Table legs will serve the same purpose.

Have each player use two of the rubber horseshoes and play as in the standard game, except that ringers must of necessity slide onto the peg instead of falling from above.

Tree Quoits

INSTEAD of the usual single pole coming from the base attach to single pole three pegs coming out at different levels, like a hall tree. Number pegs 5, 10, 15, and top 25. Play as regular quoits, counting different scores for different pegs.

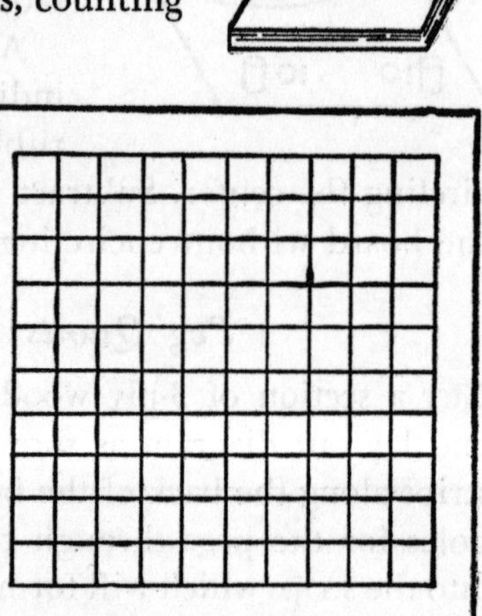

Five-in-a-row

DRAW a checker board with ten squares on a side and each square being about 1½ in. Get a supply of pop bottle caps and you're ready.

The players alternate laying down their men in any fashion they choose. The object is to get five men in a row in any direction. Whoever does this first wins.

Make Him Take It

CUT a small piece of wood about 6 in. square. Drill holes as is shown in the diagram and insert golf tees.

Game may be played by two people who alternate picking up pegs. A player may pick up as many pegs as is desired from any row preferred, *but* from only one row at a turn. Object is to make your opponent pick up the last peg. This game can be played without a board by using coins, matches, stones, etc., laying them out in rows of three, four and five on a table; however, the board is much more convenient.

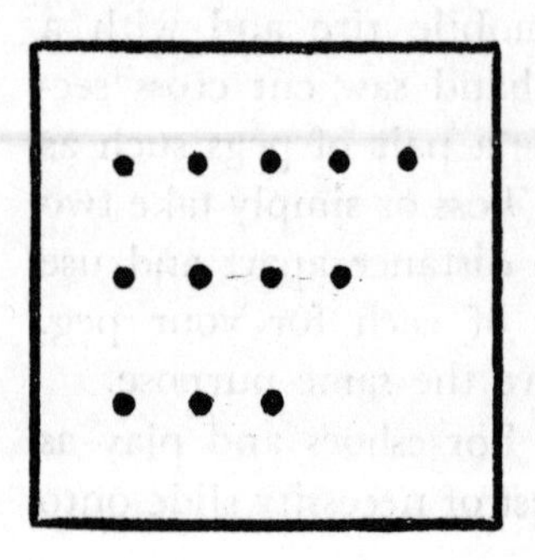

N.B. After playing a bit, notice that if you can force your opponent to play when pegs are left so as to form two rows of four each, two rows of three each, three rows of one each, or three rows containing one, two, and three, respectively, he will lose. Keep this in mind.

Three-in-one

CUT a piece of wood 12 in. square either out of 3-ply wood or regular 7/8 in. pine (end of orange crate makes an ideal piece for this game). Lay out the diagram as shown and drill holes at intersections of lines. Two colored sets of golf tees of nine each are used as men.

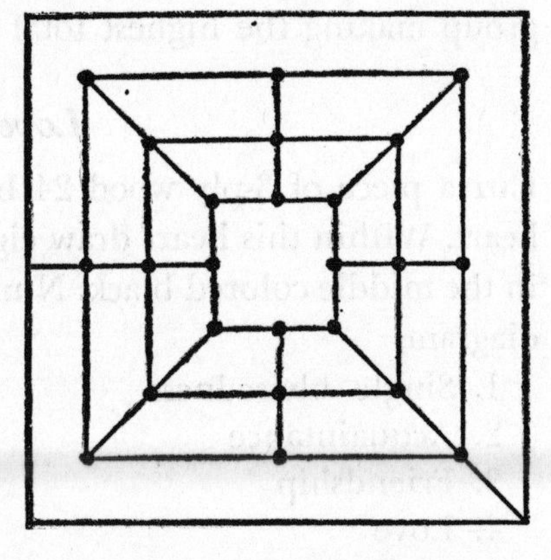

This game has an old historical background and many complicated rules but may be played very simply by playing under the following suggestions. Players alternate setting men down on the board and attempt to get three in a row in any direction along a line. Any player accomplishing this has the privilege of removing one of his opponent's men from the board, providing it is not a member of a three-in-a-row combination. After all men are placed, players may shift them one space at a time along any line attempting to form new combinations of three. The player wins who succeeds in either "bottling up" his opponent or in removing enough of his men to render him helpless.

Bull Board

BULL	10	BULL
2	9	4
7	5	3
6	1	8

LAY out a bull board on the floor with chalk, as indicated in the diagram at left. Bull board may be played by pitching pennies or by pitching discs made from beaver board or linoleum. If pennies are used, the board should be laid out about 12 by 16 inches. If discs are used, the board should be about 3 feet by 4 feet, and the discs should be about 3 inches in diameter. In either case the players should stand from 8 to 10 feet away when they toss the discs or the penny. The disc or penny must land wholly within the square. If it lands in a space marked "bull," it cancels all the previous scores. When two persons play, they may shoot alternately and the first one who scores a total of one hundred wins. When one group competes against another group of an equal number, each player may have one, two, or three shots, and the group making the highest total score wins.

Lover's Golf

CUT a piece of 3-ply wood 24 by 36 in. and on it inscribe a large heart. Within this heart draw eight small plain hearts and one heart in the middle colored black. Number and label these as shown in the diagram.

1. Single blessedness
2. Acquaintance
3. Friendship
4. Love
5. Courtship
6. Proposal
7. Engagement
8. Marriage

Black Heart—Refusal.

Players toss darts at board, attempting to strike the smaller hearts in numerical order. Each person is allowed three tosses per turn and must keep trying for each heart before progressing to the next. Player first striking number eight in its proper order is the winner. Player striking the black heart must begin all over again.

Dodo Board

A DODO BOARD should be about 2 feet square. It may be drawn on a door panel in the recreation room or gymnasium. Nails are driven in 4 inches apart vertically and horizontally making twenty-five in all. These nails are slightly bent up on the end. The game is played with fruit jar rubbers which may be purchased at almost any grocery store. Players get twelve tosses and make the amount indicated under the nail. If anyone rings "dodo," the center hook, this cancels all the score up to this point, and the player must begin all over again. The one who first makes 100 points wins.

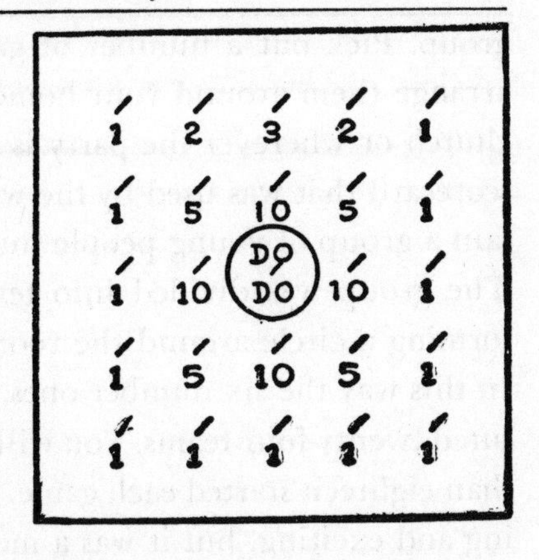

Off-center Ball

TAKE AN old tennis ball and cut a small hole in the cover. Pour in a little melted sealing wax or tar and weight with a few "BB" shot. Allow to harden and cover hole with piece of tape. A dozen golf tees complete the equipment.

Lay two good-sized books flat on the floor in a V shape with opening to right of the player. (See illustration.) Set the tees up in some uniform manner within the opening between the books. The off-center ball may with a little practice be sent rolling in an arc so that it will go out beyond the books and circle around to knock some of the pins down. Score according to the number of pins knocked over. Play on the floor is best for this game and skill in rolling the ball is well worth cultivating as many amusing variations may be worked out.

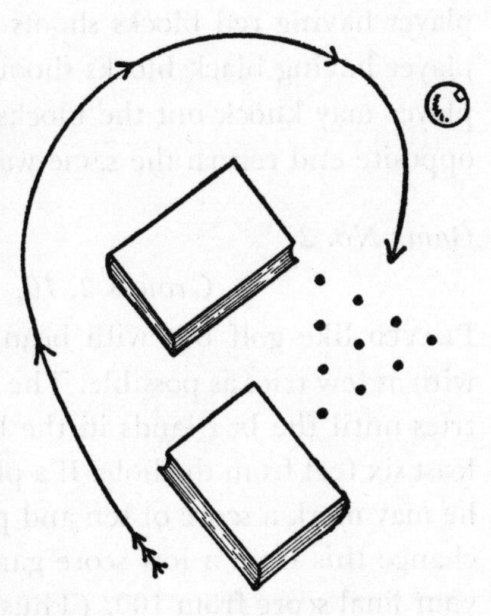

Skill Game Party

ONE of the finest ways to entertain a group is with a skill game party. It is possible to use such a party for either a small group or a large group. Pick out a number of games as described in this book and arrange them around your home or in the recreation room of your church or wherever the party is to be held. Below is given a sample scorecard that was used by the writer for a skill game party to entertain a group of young people numbering about a hundred and fifty. The group was divided into teams of six each. This was done by forming a circle around the room and counting off by twenty-fours. In this way the six number ones, six number twos, and so on, constituted twenty-four teams. You will note by the scorecard that not more than eighteen started each game. This party not only proved interesting and exciting, but it was a means of getting acquainted for many of the group. A sample of the rules and scorecard follows:

Skill Game Party Rules and Scorecard

Game No. 1 *Shuffleboard*

Groups 1, 9, 17 start this game

Not to be played in the usual way. Each player has eight shots. The player having red blocks shoots all four first and counts score. The player having black blocks shoots all four and counts score. Neither player may knock out the blocks of the other player. Players on the opposite end return the same way. Final Score———.

Game No. 2 *Beanbag Golf*

Groups 2, 10, 18 start this game

Played like golf but with beanbags. Each player tries to hole out with as few tries as possible. The score for each hole is the number of tries until the bag lands in the hole. All last shots must be from at least six feet from the hole. If a player does not succeed in ten throws, he may mark a score of ten and pass on to the next hole. In order to change this from a low score game into a high score game, subtract your final score from 100. (Thus, if a player scores 24, his final score would be 76; if he scores 60 his final score would be 40)

Score — Holes 1—2—3—4—5—6—7—8—9—. Total score ——
100 minus score ——.

Game No. 3 *Beanbag Boards*

Groups 3, 11, 19 start on this game

EACH player has eight shots at the board. Score the amount won as indicated on the board. FINAL SCORE ———.

Game No. 4 *Dodo*

Groups 4, 12, 20 start on this game

EACH player must stand behind the mark and he has eight throws. He makes the score indicated over the pin. If a player rings DODO or center pin, it cancels all of his score up to that point. If, however, he has other rings he has not thrown, he may score with these.

SCORE ———

Game No. 5 *Funnel Ball*

Groups 5, 13, 21 start on this game

BOUNCE the ball against the floor so that it will strike the wall from below on the rebound and catch it in the funnel. Each player has eight tries and may score five points for each catch.

FINAL SCORE ———.

Game No. 6 *Can Catch*

Groups 6, 14, 22 start on this game

PLAYERS try to catch the ball in the can. Each player has eight tries. The player must hold the end of the handle. Each catch counts 5 points. FINAL SCORE ———.

Game No. 7 *Clothespin Drop*

Groups 7, 15, 23 start on this game

HOLD the clothespin on the end of your nose and stand erect. Drop the pin in an effort to drop it in the container. Each time it goes in the player may score 5 points. FINAL SCORE ———.

Game No. 8 *Target Dart*

Groups 8, 16, 24 start on this game

STAND behind the mark and shoot eight shots. Score the amount indicated on the board. Each player plays all eight games no matter on which game he starts. FINAL SCORE ———.

TOTAL SCORE — Game 1—2—3—4—5—6—7—8— Total ——.

Repairing Christmas Toys

WHY not give over the party in November and December to the collecting and repairing of Christmas toys to be distributed to poor children at Christmas? Someone who is skilled with the use of tools or in painting could take the lead and the others help. The girls could dress dolls. This will make a pleasant and profitable way to spend the evening and at the same time be doing a great deal of good.

Marionette Construction

A GROUP of boys will get a great deal of enjoyment out of making puppets and putting on a Punch and Judy or Marionette show. Almost any good library will be able to furnish instruction books for the making of puppets and the staging of such a show.

Bird House Construction

THE game room may be profitably turned into a boy's work room occasionally. A group of boys, under a competent instructor, may easily be interested in the making of bird houses. See the *Boy Scout Handbook* for illustrations.

Airplane Modeling

THROUGH the Junior High School in your city, you will probably be able to get an instructor who will assist a group of boys in an airplane modeling project. Almost any boy between the ages of twelve and fourteen years will be interested in this activity.

mental games, problems, and brain twisters

THE FOLLOWING puzzles, problems, and brain twisters are designed as entertainment for small groups in the home, school, or college. The "Now you tell one" plan will usually work. When someone in the group gives a problem, puzzle, or brain twister, someone else is sure to think of one; and many new ones will be introduced.

The writer recalls attending upon one occasion a reception given by a university professor to a class of his graduate students. The affair was held at his home in the afternoon and turned out to be a watermelon cutting. No entertainment had been planned, but someone offered a conundrum, which was soon followed by a brain twister by another, a problem by another, and so on until the whole afternoon was profitably and pleasantly spent. The writer has seen this happen in a number of groups composed of all types of persons.

This section contains one hundred suggested problems and brain twisters.

Cat in the Corner

IF a room with eight corners has a cat in each corner, seven cats before each cat, and a cat on each cat's tail, how many cats in the room?

ANSWER: Eight cats:

The Backbiter

Legs I have but seldom walk;
I backbite all, but never talk.
ANSWER: Flea.

Vowels

WHICH two words in the English language have the five vowels in successive order?

ANSWER: Facetious and abstemious.

Lord Palmerson

REPUNCTUATE the following paragraph so that it will make a true and possible statement:

"Lord Palmerson then entered upon his head, a white hat
upon his feet, large but well-polished boots upon his brow,
a dark cloud in his hand, a faithful walking stick in his eye,
a menacing glare saying nothing."

ANSWER:

"Lord Palmerson then entered, upon his head a white hat,
upon his feet large but well-polished boots, upon his brow
a dark cloud, in his hand a faithful walking stick, in his eye
a menacing glare, saying nothing."

Lady in the Land

REPUNCTUATE the following verse so that it will really be true:

There is a lady in the land,
With twenty nails on each hand,
Five and twenty on hands and feet,
This is true without deceit.

ANSWER:

There is a lady in the land
With twenty nails; on each hand
Five, and twenty on hands and feet.
This is true without deceit.

Read

READ the following so that a clear meaning will be conveyed:

The professor said that that that that that that referred to was the first that.

ANSWER:

After the verb, said, begin indirect quotations as: The professor said that that "that," etc.

Had, Had, Had

PUNCTUATE the following sentence:

Smith altho Jones had had had had had had had had had had had the professor's approval.

ANSWER:

Smith, altho Jones had had "had," had had "had had"; "had had" had had the professor's approval.

Five Ands

IS IT POSSIBLE to make a good sentence with five consecutive "ands" in it? Here's one about the owner of the Pig and Whistle who had a sign painted—and didn't like it when it was finished. He said to the sign painter, "There should be more space between Pig and and and and and Whistle." Punctuate this so that it will make good sense.

ANSWER: There should be more space between "Pig" and "and" and "and" and "Whistle."

Time Flies

PUNCTUATE so that it conveys a clear meaning, the following sentence:

Time flies one cannot they are too fast for us.

ANSWER:

Time flies? One cannot. They are too fast for us.

Punctuate

It was and I said not or.

ANSWER: It was "and," I said, not "or."

What Is Her Name?

HER initials begin with A. She has A at the end of her name. The whole of her name is an A. And it is backward and forward the same. What is her name?

ANSWER: Anna.

What Letter?

WHAT letter is it,

Which is the beginning of eternity,
The end of time and space,
The beginning of every end,
And the end of every race?

ANSWER: The letter E.

What Is the Sentence?

INSERT the same letter eleven times in the following succession of letters and make a sentence.

I E M E F A E D I E I I E I I G S

ANSWER: Nine men fanned in nine innings.

Postal Problem

TO WHOM would you deliver a letter addressed as follows:

Wood
John ?
Mass.

ANSWER: John Underwood, Andover, Mass.

Deaf as a Post

MAKE the following into verse without changing a single word: "Deborah, Deborah, I can see you're deaf as a post."

ANSWER: "Deborah, Deborah, I can see
You're as deaf as a p-o-s-t (Spell post)

Dumber

ASK some one the following question:

Would you rather be dumber than you look, or
would you rather look dumber than you are?

ANSWER: If the answer is, "I would like to be dumber than I look" the questioner says, "Impossible."

On the other hand, if the answer is, "I had rather look dumber than I am," the questioner also says, "Impossible."

Not and Shot

Not and Shot fought a duel.
Not was shot and Shot was not.
Now would you rather be Shot or Not?

ANSWER: Shot—for Not was shot.

Three Ducks

Two fathers and two sons went hunting. They shot three ducks, and divided them equally among themselves without shooting any more ducks, cutting any of the ducks, or without one of their number getting shot. After the division was made each one had a complete duck. How could this be possible?

ANSWER: There were not four hunters but three. A grandfather, a son, and a grandson. Thus we have two fathers in the grandfather and his son and two sons in the son and the grandson.

The Lying Native

THE NATIVES in a certain tribe were similar yet different in one respect. Although they were physically alike, some of them were addicts of a drug which they obtained by chewing the leaves of a jungle plant. This drug made them lie when otherwise they would have told the truth like their neighbors.

A stranger in the district met three of the natives, and, having been told by his companion that only one of the three was an addict, he proceeded to find out which one it was. When the stranger asked the group whether they were addicts or not, the first one mumbled something that was indistinguishable; the second one, pointing to the first one, said, "He says that he is not an addict." The third one pointed to the second one and said, "He is a liar." The stranger was able to deduce from these statements which one of the three was the addict. Can you?

ANSWER: If you start your deduction by assuming that the third native was telling the truth about the second, this would make the second one the addict because he would be lying. But if he was an addict, he would have been lying when he pointed to the first one and said that he was not an addict. We can deduce from this that the second native was not lying because if he had been lying, he would have been an addict, and number one would have been an addict. From this we know that the second native told the truth, and that the third native lied and was the addict.

The Publisher

THE heirs of a wealthy book publisher tried to break his will. He had been found shot at his office, and a note was found saying that a will was to be found between pages 157 and 158 of the book on his desk. Some of the heirs claimed that it was murder instead of suicide, and that the note was forged.

ANSWER: The note was forged. The book publisher would have known that it would not be possible to put a will between pages 157 and 158. He would have known that in a book, all right-hand pages have odd numbers, and all left-hand pages have even numbers. A will could have been placed between pages 158 and 159 but not as the note said, between pages 157 and 158.

Sight Reading

CAN you read the following:

I 8 0 M

day

ANSWER: I ate nothing Monday. (M-on day)

More Sight Reading

CAN you read the following:

X U R, X U B;
X, 2X, U R 2 me.

ANSWER: Cross you are, cross you be,
Cross, too cross, you are to me

Letter Words

CAN you read?

If the B m t put :

ANSWER: If the grate be (great B) empty, put coal on.

More Letter Words

CAN you read the following:

Yy u r yy u b i c u r yy 4 me.

ANSWER: Too wise you are, too wise you be;
I see you are too wise for me.

Backwards

CAN you think of a word that reads the same backwards and forwards?

ANSWER: Reviver.

Backward Sentence

CAN you think of a sentence that reads the same backwards and forwards?

ANSWER: Words that Napoleon is supposed to have spoken, "Able was I ere I saw Elba."

Amoeba

IF THERE are seven amoeba (a tiny or miscroscopic animal) in the bottom of a jar, and we suppose that these multiply so fast that they double in volume every minute, if it takes forty minutes to fill the jar, how long would it take to fill it half full?

ANSWER: Thirty-nine minutes. The next minute the amoeba would double and fill the jar.

Two Cars

IF TWO cars start from Denver to drive to Colorado Springs, a distance of approximately eighty miles, if they are both the same make of car, and if both are being driven at the same rate of speed, and yet, while one of the cars makes the distance in eighty minutes, it takes the other one hour and twenty minutes. Can you explain the reason?

ANSWER: Eighty minutes and one hour and twenty minutes are the same.

Cats and Rats

IF one hundred cats will catch one hundred rats in one hundred minutes, how long will it take six cats to catch six rats?

ANSWER: One hundred minutes.

Descending Numbers

HAVE some person mark down on a piece of paper three descending numbers below ten. (Note that they must be descending, as 972.) Have him then reverse the numbers, write them underneath the descending numbers as,

```
 972
 279  Subtract
 ---
 693
 396  Reverse and add
 ---
1089
```

1089 The result will be 1089 always no matter what the numbers selected. (This may be used as a stunt by writing the number 1089 on your forearm with wet soap, before the guests arrive, burning the answers and rubbing the ashes on the forearm. It could be done also by writing the number on a piece of paper with lemon juice and holding the paper over a lighted candle, which will bring out the number.)

No Negative

WHAT question cannot be answered in the negative?

ANSWER: What does y-e-s spell?

Can't Be Written

WHAT is an example of something that can be spoken but not written?

ANSWER: Only an idea may be obtained from the answer: There are three (twos, tos, toos) in the English language.

Birth Month, Day, and Age Formula

WRITE down the month and day of your birth

May fifth month, 17th Day	517
Multiply by 2	2
Result	1034
Add 5	5
	1039
Multiply by 50	50
	51950
Add your age (30 years)	30
	51980
Add 365	365
Result	52345
Subtract 615	615
	51730

First 5 indicates month, 17 day, 30 age.
This will work for any month, or birthday, or age.

White of an Egg

FIRST, ask the one who is being questioned to spell folk, and next ask him to spell joke, and then ask him to spell the white of an egg. Usually he will spell, y-o-l-k, but this does not spell the white of an egg.

Windows

I WALKED up the street to the top of the hill and counted 50 windows on my right. I turned around and walked back and counted fifty windows on my left. How many windows did I count?

ANSWER: Fifty. The windows on my right going up were on my left coming back.

A Brick

IF A brick weighs seven pounds and a half a brick, what will a brick and a half weigh?

ANSWER: Twenty-one pounds. It is evident that a half brick weighs 7 pounds; therefore, a brick and a half will weight 21 pounds.

What?

IF A person were confined in a room that had in it only a bed and a calendar, what would he eat and drink?

ANSWER: Water from the springs and dates from the calendar.

Baby Duck

PAPA duck, mamma duck, and baby duck went for a swim. Baby duck said, "Aren't we all four having a lot of fun?" Why did baby duck say four instead of three?

ANSWER: Baby duck was too young to count.

Marriage Problem

When first the marriage knot was tied
Betwixt my wife and me,
My age did hers as far exceed
As three times three does three.

But when ten years and half ten years
We man and wife had been,
My age did come as near to hers
As eight does to sixteen.

What were their ages when married and at the expiration of fifteen years?

ANSWER: At marriage, man 45, wife 15; fifteen years later, man 60, wife 30.

Relationship Problem No. 1

WHAT would your relation be to your aunt's mother's father's wife?

ANSWER: She would be your great-grandmother.

Relationship Problem No. 2

WHAT would your relation be to your father's uncle's brother's sister?

ANSWER: She would be your great-aunt.

Relationship Problem No. 3

WHAT would be your relation to your mother's nephew's daughter's son?

ANSWER: He would be your third cousin.

Relationship Problem No. 4

WHAT would your relation be to your brother's son's sister's mother?

ANSWER: She would be your sister-in-law.

Relationship Problem No. 5

WHAT would be your relation to your sister-in-law's father-in-law's grandson?

ANSWER: He would be your nephew.

Relationship Problem No. 6

WHAT would be your relation to your sister's father's stepson's mother?

ANSWER: She would be your step-mother.

Relationship Problem No. 7

WHAT would be your relation to your uncle's father's only granddaughter?

ANSWER: That would be yourself, if of the female sex. (In asking the question to one of the male sex, grandson should be substituted for granddaughter.)

Relationship Problem No. 8

WHAT would be your relation to your brother-in-law's wife's grandmother's husband?

ANSWER: He would be your grandfather.

Relationship Problem No. 9

WHAT would be your relation to your father's father's daughter's daughter?

ANSWER: She would be your first cousin.

Relationship Problem No. 10

WHAT would be your relation to the granddaughter of the only son of your mother's mother-in-law?

ANSWER: She would be either your niece or your daughter.

The Cab Driver

SUPPOSE you are a cab driver. A lady with two suitcases hails you and asks to be driven to the railway station in a hurry. On the way three is an accident which results in a traffic jam. The lady gets impatient, jumps out of the cab, and runs to the depot. She had forgotten the suitcases. She missed the train and now she starts looking for the cab driver. She does not know his name. What was the cab driver's name?

ANSWER: His name is the same as yours, for "You are the cab driver."

The Coin

A MAN claimed he had an old coin with the date on it 2000 B.C. How would you know that the date was faked?

ANSWER: Dates before Christ were not written B.C. They were only written that way after Christ came.

Equal Twenty

PUT down the following numbers:

777 111 999

Erase all but three and make those that are left total 20.

ANSWER: leave the first two 1's and one of the 9's therefore 9 plus 11 equals 20.

Cutting Problem

TAKE a piece of paper 3½ by 8½ inches and cut it so that you can slip it over your head and body.

ANSWER: This may be done by starting at the upper right hand corner and cutting strips back and forth as indicated in the drawing.

Shoe Dealer

A SHOE dealer sold a pair of shoes for eight dollars and received in payment a $20 bill. He could not change the bill, so he went to the grocery store next door and had it changed and gave the customer $12 in change. The grocer, on taking the bill to the bank, discovered that it was counterfeit. The shoe-store man had to make it good. How much did the shoe-store man lose in the transaction?

ANSWER: He lost $20, or rather $12 and a pair of shoes. He kept $8 of the groceryman's money and so only lost the $12 and the shoes.

Change

CHANGE a dollar into fifty coins.

ANSWER: Two solutions:

1—45 pennies, 1 quarter, 2 nickels, 2 dimes.
2—40 pennies, 8 nickels, 2 dimes.

Bank President

ONE morning a bank president came down to the bank early, on his way to catch an early train. He met the night watchman and told him that he was going to catch the train. The night watchman said to the president, "If I were you I would not catch that train. I am a very superstitious person and while it may be a coincidence, I dreamed last night that that train was wrecked and that all the passengers were killed." The bank president said, "Unlike you, I am not superstitious, and so I am going on the train." That president went on the trip and returned safe and sound, but on his return he fired the night watchman. Why?

ANSWER: The night watchman said that he had had a dream at *night*. Evidently, he had been asleep on his post of duty.

Dreaming

HERE is another, so like the one above, that it should not be told with the first one: A man did not want to go to church. His wife insisted that he go. In getting ready he lost his collar button. He looked everywhere for the collar button and could not find it. His wife, getting impatient, came to help him and found the collar button in the cuff of his trousers. The church service was so dry and uninteresting that the man went to sleep. He was thinking how cruel his wife was to make him come to church. He dreamed that a band of Indians was after him and that they were just about to scalp him. At the conclusion of the services his wife punched him to awaken him but he was dead. What is the flaw in the story?

ANSWER: It would not have been possible to know what he dreamed.

Eleven Fingers

TO PROVE that you have eleven fingers count your fingers beginning with the thumb of your right hand and counting through to the thumb of your left hand. Then start and count backwards as follows: Thumb, 10; index finger, 9; second finger, 8; ring finger, 7; little finger, 6; then instead of counting the fingers on the right hand say, "Six and five are eleven."

ANSWER: This works in this way because the little finger is not the sixth finger from the left thumb, but is rather the sixth finger from the right thumb.

Ticket to Heaven

TAKE a piece of paper one-half letter size, that is, about 5½ by 8½ inches. Fold back about 2¾ inches, then double this leaving the fold on the outside. Fold over the outside corner, then either cut or tear off about ¾ of an inch. Cut off another ¾ of an inch strip, and you will find that you have pieces of paper which if laid out properly will spell h-e-l-l. The first strip making the "h" and the middle part of "e" and the second strip making the two ends of the "e" and the two "l's." You will find that by unfolding the other piece of paper you have a perfect cross.

As a joke on two of your friends, this might be done in the following way: Take a piece of paper and start folding it as you say, "Tom and John were on their way to heaven. When they were nearing the celestial city, Tom said to John, 'Haven't you a ticket?' John said, 'No, I do not have a ticket; I did not know that you had to have a ticket.' "

By this time you should have the paper folded as described above, and as you continue the story, cut or tear off a strip of the paper and say, "Tom said to John, 'Since you do not have a ticket, I will give you a piece of mine.' John then said, 'That is such a measly bit of ticket, won't you give me more?' Tom generously tore off another part of the ticket and handed it to John. (The storyteller here tears the folded paper for the second time.)

"When Tom and John reached the gate of heaven, Tom handed his ticket to Peter who unfolded it (storyteller unfolds the paper and shows the cross) and said, 'That is a good ticket; you may enter.' Peter then took John's ticket and looked at it and said, 'What kind of ticket is this?' (The storyteller lays the pieces out so that they spell the word, "hell.") You would not expect to get into heaven on a ticket like this would you? Admission refused."

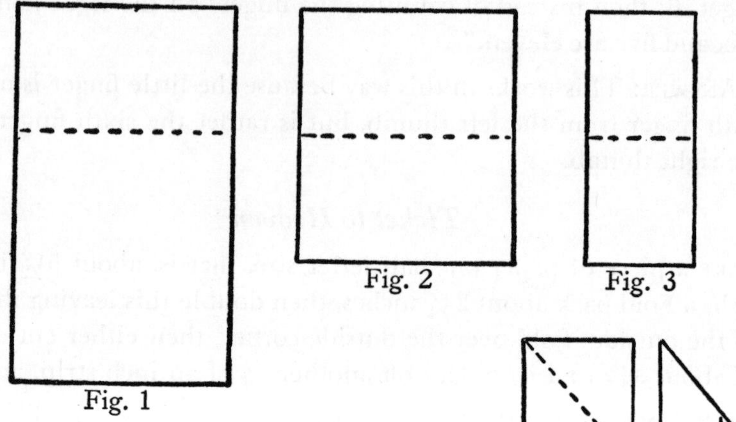

Fig. 1 Fig. 2 Fig. 3

Fold back on dotted line. Figure 2 shows paper folded back. Figure 3 shows the 3rd fold, keep first fold on outside. Figure 4, fold down corner from open edges. Figure 5, cut on dotted lines.

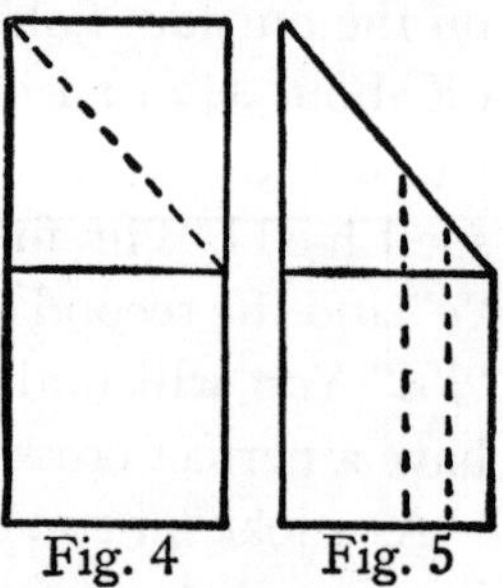

Fig. 4 Fig. 5

Two Trains

A TRAIN left New York for Boston at 9 A.M. and traveled at the rate of 60 miles per hour. At the same time a train left Boston for New York but traveled at the rate of only 40 miles per hour. The distance is 400 miles. When they met, which trains was nearer New York?

ANSWER: They were both the same distance from New York when they met.

Ten Guests

CAN you put ten guests in nine rooms and give each a separate room? When ten guests arrived one evening at a hotel and each demanded a single room, the clerk, who only had nine rooms, said, "Will two of you please wait in room number one?" He then put guest number three in room two, guest number four in room number three, guest number five in room number four, guest number six in room number five, guest number seven in room number six, guest number eight in room number seven, guest number nine in room number eight. He went then to room number one and conducted guest number 10 to the ninth room. Wherein lies the fallacy?

ANSWER: Guest number ten was not in room number one; guests number one and two were in room number one. Guest number ten was, in fact, not accommodated.

Dog in Woods

How far can a dog go into a woods?

ANSWER: Only half way. When he gets halfway in, he starts coming out again.

Widow's Sister

IN the church of which you are a member, is a man allowed to marry his widow's sister?

ANSWER: A man who has a widow is a dead man.

Brother

MR. BROWN was telling Mr. White about his family. He said, "I have six daughters and each of my daughters has a brother." Mr. White said, "I do not see how a man can support twelve children." But Mr. Brown said, "I do not have twelve, I have only seven.

ANSWER: He had only one son and each of his daughters had a brother.

Raise Wanted

A YOUNG clerk was working for a stingy employer. He made up his mind to ask for a raise. Accordingly, he went to the boss and told him he wanted a raise in salary. The boss said, "A raise, why, you only work for me eight hours in each twenty-four, which is only one-third of a day. This is a leap year and has 366 days in it and one-third of that is 122 days. You don't work on Saturdays and Sundays and when you take 104 days from the 122 that leaves only eighteen days. There are four bank holidays that you do not work and that leaves only fourteen days. Each year I give you a two-weeks vacation. In fact, you don't work for me at all. I don't know what I pay you for. And you have enough nerve to ask me for a raise."

ANSWER: On a nonworking day the clerk is off only one-third of a day. The rest has already been subtracted.

How Many Eggs?

IF EGGS are worth twenty-six cents a dozen, how many could you buy for a cent and a quarter?

ANSWER: A dozen. A cent and a quarter are twenty-six cents.

Cutting Up

IF YOU cut 30 yards of material into pieces one yard long, and cut one yard per day, how many days will it require?

ANSWER: Twenty-nine days.

Separate Room

THERE are three mothers, each of whom has two daughters living in a seven-room house. Each woman has a separate room. How is this possible?

ANSWER: Two of the mothers are also daughters, making only seven in all.

Three Eights

ARRANGE three eights so that they will equal 7.

ANSWER: 8–8/8 equals 7.

Buying a Hat

A MAN went into a store to buy a hat. He wanted a $10 hat but he did not have as much as ten dollars. He said to the clerk, "If you will give me as much money as I have, I will give you $10 for the hat. Although a very foolish thing to do, the clerk agreed to do this and the customer bought the hat. He went to a second and a third store and made a similar proposition and bought a $10 hat at each. When he left the third store, he had three hats but no money. How much money did he have when he entered the first store?

Answer: $8.75. The clerk gave him $8.75 which made a total of $17.50. He gave the clerk $10 and had $7.50 left. In the next store, he received $7.50, thus making $15. He gave the clerk $10 and had $5 left. In the third store he received $5 and paid $10 for the hat, thus using up all his money.

The Clock

The clock in the courthouse tower takes seven seconds to strike seven. How long will it take to strike eleven o'clock?

Answer: 11 and 2-3 seconds. Note: We begin counting from the first stroke so that the strokes are really 1 and 1-6 seconds apart (not counting the first stroke) ; therefore, 10 times 1 1-6 will be 11 and 2-3 seconds. The first stroke is not counted in either case because we begin timing from the first stroke.

Six Bills

A man owed $63; he paid it with six bills. He did not use one-dollar bills. What bills did he use?

Answer: One fifty, one five, and four twos.

Sisters and Brothers

In a family where each son has twice as many sisters as he has brothers, and each daughter has the same number of brothers as sisters, how many boys are there and how many girls are there?

Answer: There are four girls and three boys.

Think of a Number

It's possible to determine what number you thought of in the following way: Think of a number, for example, 15, double it which equals 30, add one, equals 31, multiply by five, equals 155, add five, equals 160, multiply by ten, equals 1,600, substract 100, strike off the last two figures and it leaves 15, the number thought of. This will work for any number.

Marbles

A SMALL boy collects and plays with marbles. He places them sometimes in pairs, sometimes in groups of three, sometimes in groups of four, sometimes in groups of five, and sometimes in groups of six. By arranging them in any of the above named groups, he always has one left over. When he arranges them in groups of seven, none remain. How many marbles does the boy have?

ANSWER: 301.

Blue Marbles

THE boy mentioned in the problem above finds that he has a certain number of blue marbles. If he arranges these marbles in groups of three, he has one over; if he arranges them in groups of four, he has two over; if he arranges them in groups of five, he has three left over; and if he arranges them in groups of six, he has four over. How many marbles has he?

ANSWER: Fifty-eight marbles.

Multiply By Eleven

DO YOU know how to multiply a number by eleven quickly? Well, this is the way it may be done. Suppose the number is 36. Add the 3 and the 6, place your nine between the 3 and the 6 and you have 396. Eleven times 36. But suppose the number is 77. Add 7 and 7 which makes 14. Put the 4 between the two sevens but it will be necessary to add one to your first seven, making 847. What you do in this case is to put the units between as with the four and carry the ten. Any number may be multiplied by eleven in this way.

Passenger

A MAN rented an automobile to drive from Palm Beach to Miami, a distance of seventy miles. He paid $8 for the use of the car and the gas. He picked up a passenger at the town of Pompano, halfway between Palm Beach and Miami and carried him to Miami and brought him back to Pompano. How much should this passenger have paid if he paid his proportional part?

ANSWER: Two dollars. He shared equally one-half of the trip.

Storage Garage

A STORAGE garage proprietor wanted to take in twelve more cars. Being already full, he decided to build an addition to his garage and increase the size of it by half. When this addition was finished, he found that he was able, not only to accommodate the twelve cars that he had planned to take in, but twelve others as well. How many cars could he accommodate in his garage?

ANSWER: Seventy-two cars. He was able to accommodate twenty-four in one-third of it, that is, by increasing the original garage 50 per cent.

The Orange Grower

A FLORIDA orange grower gave the following problem to his son. "Plant twenty-one orange trees so that they will be in nine straight rows and so that there will be five trees in each row." How do you suppose he did it?

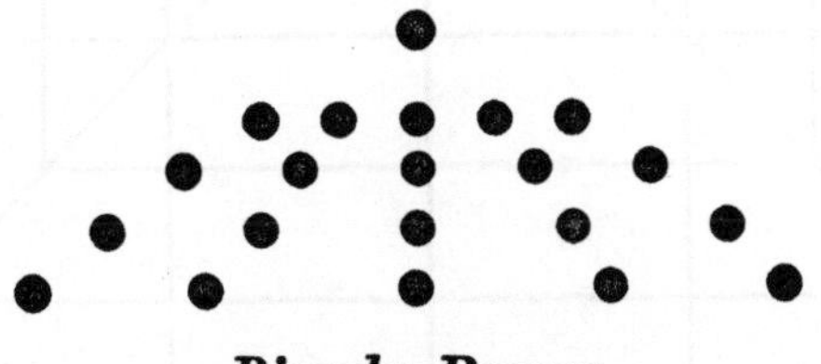

Bicycle Racers

SMITH and Brown were bicycle racers and they raced on a circular track. Smith could complete one circuit in nine minutes, and Brown could do it in six minutes. If they start off from the same mark in a race, how long will it be before they will again be side by side.

ANSWER: It will be eighteen minutes. At the end of eighteen minutes, Smith will have made two circuits and Brown three.

Pronounced Differently

WHAT word in the English language is pronounced differently when captalized?

ANSWER: polish, Polish.

Drawing

HERE is a problem in drawing without removing your pencil from the paper after you once start. You are not, however, restricted from crossing lines. Draw a square about four inches on each side. Divide this into sixteen one-inch squares. Now place a dot in the center of each square. The problem is to join all these points with six straight lines without removing your pencil from the paper until all six are completed.

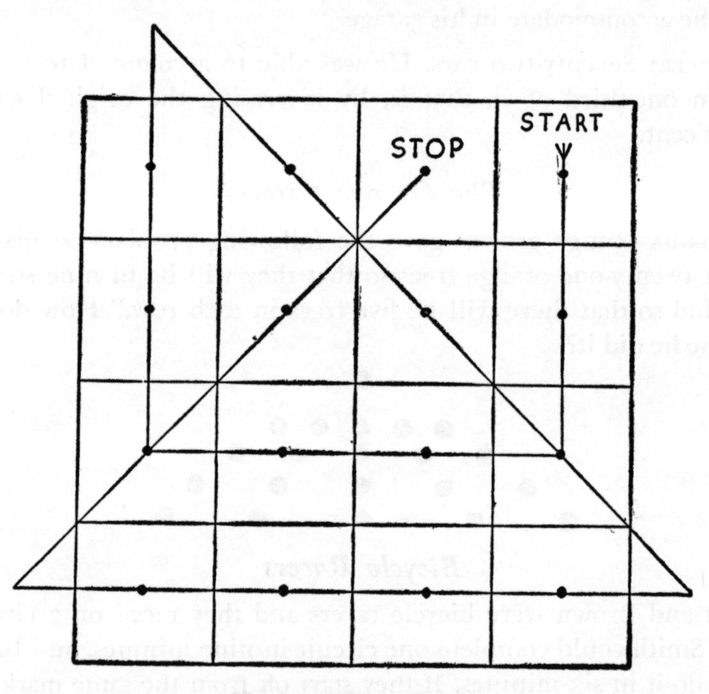

Twenty-One Sacks

A MILLER once submitted the following problem to three boys. He said, "I have twenty-one sacks—seven are full, seven are half full, and seven are empty. Can you divide these twenty-one sacks among yourselves without shifting any grain and so that each one will have the same quantity of grain and the same number of sacks?

ANSWER: First solution:

First boy: 2 full sacks, 2 empty, and 3 half full.

Second boy: 2 full sacks, 2 empty and 3 half full.
Third boy: 3 full sacks, 3 empty and 1 half full.

Second solution:
First boy: 3 full sacks, 3 empty and 1 half full.
Second boy: 3 full sacks, 3 empty and 1 half full.
Third boy: 1 full sack, 1 empty, and 5 half full.

Age of Chivalry

A YOUNG man said, "It certainly is too bad that the age of chivalry has passed. I was riding on the bus the other day when an old lady came in who looked tired. She was loaded down with bundles. I watched a young man two seats in front of me, fully expecting him to give her his seat. The old lady had to stand the whole way. It certainly is lamentable that chivalry is dead." What is the matter with this story?

ANSWER: Why did not this young man give the old lady his own seat?

Ignorance

Is "Ignorance is bliss" a quotation from the Bible?

ANSWER: You will find it in the 17th chapter of Mark, but you will have to look for it.

Problem in Poetry

THE following is a problem in poetry.

> What does man love ev'n more than life,
> Hate more than death or mortal strife?
> That which contented men desire,
> The poorest have and the rich require,
> The miser spends and the spendthrift saves,
> And all men carry to their graves.

ANSWER: Nothing.

Chronology

CAN you arrange the following names in their proper chronological order?

Julius Caesar	Shakespeare
Napoleon	Washington
Abraham	Solomon
Columbus	Paul
Mohammed	Moses

ANSWER: Abraham 2000 B.C., Moses 1500 B.C., Solomon 1000 B.C., Julius Caesar 100 B.C., Paul 1 A.D., Mohammed 570 A.D., Columbus 1445 A.D., Shakespearse 1564 A.D., Washington 1732 A.D., Napoleon 1769 A.D.

Seven Coins

LAY out seven coins as per the arrangement of the dots below. Move two of them in such a way as to leave five coins in a row either vertically or horizontally.

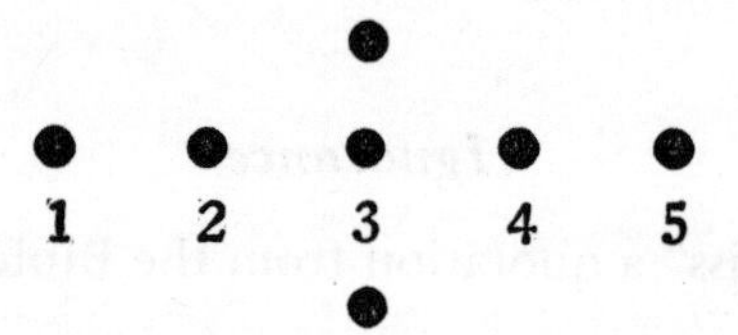

ANSWER: Pick up coins No. 1 and No. 5 and lay them on coin No. 3. This will make five each way.

Long Division

WHAT will be the unusual result if you divide 987654312 by 8?

ANSWER: You will find that your result is 123456789.

Multiplication

WHAT will be the unusual result if you multiply 37 by 3, and again by 6, 9, 12, 15, 18, 21, 24, 27, all multiples of three?

ANSWER: Results will be respectively 111, 222, 333, 444, 555, 666, 777, 888, and 999.

Heirs

A MAN bequeathed $20,000 to his five children and directed that it be divided equally among his three sons and two daughters. The sons agreed among themselves, however, that they would each give half of their shares to be divided equally between the sisters. How much did each sister receive.

ANSWER: $7,000.

Benevolent Man

A BENEVOLENT man, desiring to give coal to some poor families, found that if he gave four tons to each family whom he desired to help, he would need four more tons than he already had. He found that if he would only give three tons to each, he would have twelve tons left over. How many families did he desire to help and how many tons of coal had he?

ANSWER: Sixteen families and sixty tons of coal.

Bicycle Traveler

A MAN starts from town A, on a bicycle, and travels toward town B at the rate of twelve miles per hour. When he is halfway to town B, he punctures his bicycle tire and goes the next two miles on foot in one-half hour. He is then picked up by a truckman who carries him the rest of the journey at the rate of 8 miles per hour. If it takes one hour and a half to make the whole journey, how far is it from town A to town B?

ANSWER: Twelve miles.

Name in One Letter

WRITE your name in one letter.

ANSWER:

Three-Word Phrase

READ the following making a three-word phrase:

ALL 0.

ANSWER: Nothing after all.

Crossing the Moat

THE following diagram represents a fort surrounded by a moat 20 feet wide. How would it be possible for some soldiers, who had been out late, to cross the moat by using two boards, one board 18 feet in length, and one 15 feet? How could they cross the 20-foot moat with these boards?

ANSWER: By placing the boards as shown in the following diagram:

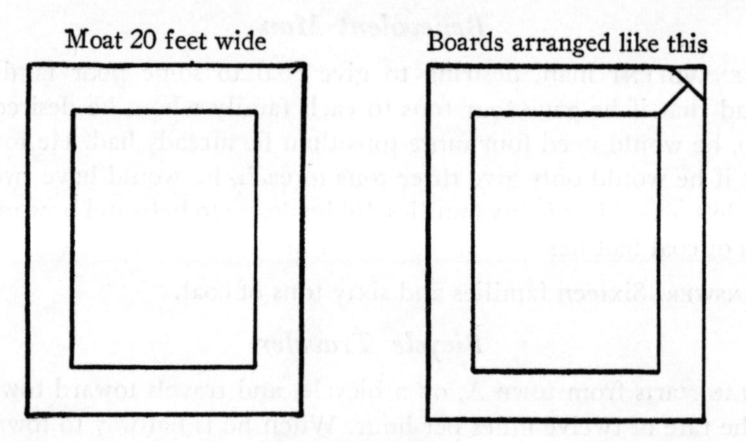

Blind Jailor

A BLIND jailor once had twenty-four prisoners in cells arranged as follows:

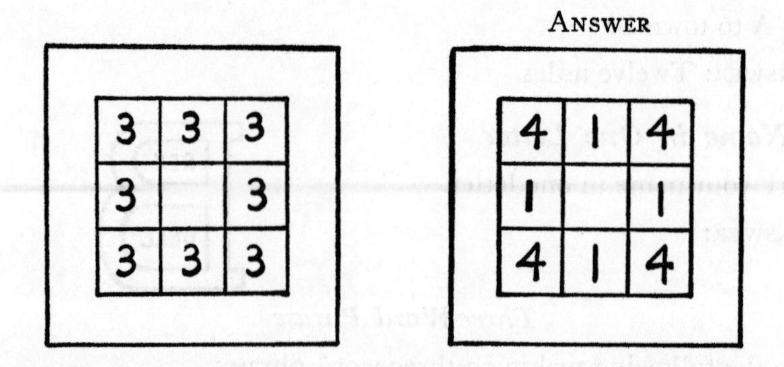

The blind jailor would have the prisoners stick their hand through the bars and count them as he walked along the corridor. Some of the prisoners, desiring to escape, planned a rearrangement of the prisoners so that four of them could escape, and the jailor could still count nine on each side. How could this be done?

One Word

MAKE one word from the letters in the two words *new door.*

ANSWER: One word.

Twenty-Four

THREE times 8 equals 24, but can you add, multiply, subtract, divide, square, or cube any one of the digits so that by using it three times the sum will be 24?

ANSWER: (1) $3^3 - 3 = 24$. (2) $22 + 2 = 24$.

A Plot of Ground

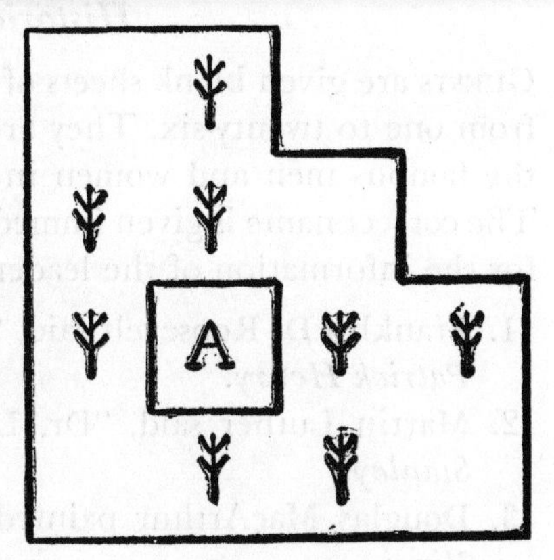

IT IS said that a father left his four sons a piece of ground on which were 8 trees. The will specified that the house was to be shared by all the sons, but that each was to have a piece of ground the same size and shape with two trees on it. He also specified that each son's ground should be so situated that he could step from his land into the yard of the house without setting foot on the land of the other brothers. If the plot of ground was shaped as indicated by the above figure with "A" representing the plot of ground on which the house was built, draw another figure to indicate how the land was divided so that all the sons should have a plot the same size and shape with two trees on each plot.

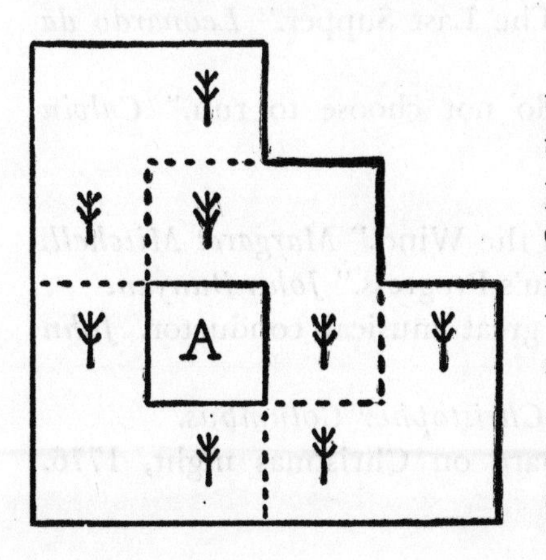

Section 7

cultural games

Historical Crosses

GUESTS are given blank sheets of paper on which they place numbers from one to twenty-six. They are asked to give the correct names of the famous men and women in the following incorrect statements. The correct name is given immediately following each false statement for the information of the leader.

1. Franklin D. Roosevelt said, "Give me liberty or give me death." *Patrick Henry.*
2. Martin Luther said, "Dr. Livingstone, I presume?" *Henry M. Stanley.*
3. Douglas MacArthur painted "The Last Supper." *Leonardo da Vinci.*
4. Madame Eve Curie said, "I do not choose to run." *Calvin Coolidge.*
5. Eli Whitney built the ark. *Noah.*
6. Edward VIII wrote "Gone with the Wind." *Margaret Mitchell.*
7. Abraham Lincoln wrote "Pilgrim's Progress." *John Bunyan.*
8. Harriet Beecher Stowe was a great musical conductor. *John Philip Sousa.*
9. Confucius discovered America. *Christopher Columbus.*
10. Mohammed crossed the Delaware on Christmas night, 1776. *George Washington.*

11. John Hancock was an American humorist and author. *Mark Twain.*
12. Samson said, "I came, I saw, I conquered." *Julius Caesar.*
13. Will Rogers invented motion pictures. *Thomas A. Edison.*
14. Patrick Henry discovered radium. *Madame Eve Curie.*
15. Henry M. Stanley invented the cotton gin. *Eli Whitney.*
16. Leonardo da Vinci abdicated the British throne. *Edward VIII.*
17. Calvin Coolidge was called the "rail splitter." *Abraham Lincoln.*
18. Noah wrote "Uncle Tom's Cabin." *Harriet Beecher Stowe.*
19. Margaret Mitchell was a Chinese philosopher. *Confucius.*
20. John Bunyan founded the Mohammedan religion. *Mohammed.*
21. John Philip Sousa signed the Declaration of Independence. *John Hancock.*
22. Christopher Columbus was a strong man of the Bible. *Samson.*
23. George Washington was a popular Western humorist and actor. *Will Rogers.*
24. Mark Twain was afflicted with polio. *Franklin D. Roosevelt.*
25. Julius Caesar was the leader of the Protestant Reformation. *Martin Luther.*
26. Thomas A. Edison said, "I shall return." *Douglas MacArthur.*

Musical Terms

GIVE the guests sheets of paper on which have been written the following questions to be answered with musical terms.

1. A place of residence. *Flat.*
2. Used to tie up a bundle. *Chord (cord).*
3. A reflection on character. *Slur.*
4. Bottom of a triangle. *Bass (base).*
5. Describes an unaffected person. *Natural.*
6. What makes a check good. *Signature.*
7. Not blunt. *Sharp.*
8. Used in all stores. *Counter.*
9. What we breathe every day. *Air.*
10. What betrays nationality. *Accent.*
11. A note that is a girl's name. *Grace.*
12. Found on a fish. *Scale.*

13. A part of a sentence. *Phrase.*
14. What the lawyers belong to. *Bar.*
15. What boys and girls write in school. *Notes.*
16. Seen and felt on the ocean. *Swell.*
17. Used in climbing. *Staff.*
18. Found on a bicycle. *Pedals.*
19. Used in driving horses. *Lines.*

Last Line Contest

THIS contest may be conducted in any number of ways. One way would be to mimeograph the poems leaving the last line blank, and letting the guests fill in the last line. Another would be for the leader to read the poems and ask guests to write the last line on blank sheets of paper, which have been supplied them. A third way would be for the leader to read the poems, omitting to read the last line, and ask guests who are able to quote the last line to raise their hands. They should then be asked one by one to quote their answer, until finally the correct line is given.

The following are suggested poems:

1

The mind has a thousand eyes
And the heart but one
Yet the light of the whole world dies
When love is done.

FROM "THE NIGHT HAS A THOUSAND EYES" (BOURDILLON)

2

Then why should I sit in the scorner's seat
Or hurl the cynic's ban?
Let me live in my house by the side of the road
And be a friend to man.

FROM "THE HOUSE BY THE SIDE OF THE ROAD (FOSS)

3

In Flander's fields the poppies blow
Between the crosses, row on row.

FROM "IN FLANDER'S FIELDS" (MCCRAE)

4

Build thee more stately mansions, O my soul,
As the swift seasons roll!

FROM "THE CHAMBERED NAUTILUS" (HOLMES)

5 Time was when the little toy dog was new,
And the soldier was passing fair,
And that was the time when our Little Boy Blue,
Kissed them and put them there.

FROM "LITTLE BOY BLUE" (FIELD)

6 No price is set on the lavish summer;
June may be had by the poorest comer.

FROM "THE VISION OF SIR LAUNFAL" (LOWELL)

7 By the shores of Gitche Gumee,
By the shining Big Sea Water,
Stood the wigwam of Nokomis.

FROM "HIAWATHA" (LONGFELLOW)

8 He gained a world; he gave that world
Its grandest lesson; On! Sail on!

FROM "COLUMBUS" (MILLER)

9 Under the sod and the dew
Waiting the judgment day
Under the one, the blue,
Under the other, the gray.

FROM "THE BLUE AND THE GRAY" (FINCH)

10 Lord God of Hosts, be with us yet,
Lest we forget, lest we forget.

FROM "RECESSIONAL" (KIPLING)

11 The quality of mercy is not strained;
It droppeth as the gentle rain from heaven.

FROM "THE MERCHANT OF VENICE" (SHAKESPEARE)

12 The gingham dog and the calico cat,
Side by side on the table sat.

FROM "THE DUEL" (FIELD)

13 And all over upland and lowland,
The charm of the goldenrod,
Some of us call it autumn,
And others call it God.

FROM "EACH IN HIS OWN TONGUE" (CARRUTH)

14 Thou too sail on, O Ship of State,
Sail on, O Union strong and great.

FROM "THE BUILDING OF THE SHIP" (LONGFELLOW)

15 Hear the mellow wedding bells,
Golden bells!
What a world of happiness their harmony foretells!

FROM "THE BELLS" (POE)

16 Breathes there a man with soul so dead
Who never to himself hath said:
"This is my own, my native land"?

FROM "THE LAY OF THE LAST MINSTREL" (SCOTT)

17 Leave my loneliness unbroken—quit the bust above my door!
Take thy beak from out my heart, and take thy form from off my door!
Quoth the raven, "Nevermore."

FROM "THE RAVEN" (POE)

18 Cannon to right of them,
Cannon to left of them,
Cannon in front of them
Volleyed and thundered.

FROM "THE CHARGE OF THE LIGHT BRIGADE" (TENNYSON)

19 Lives of great men all remind us
We can make our lives sublime,
And, departing, leave behind us,
Footprints on the sands of time.

FROM "THE PSALM OF LIFE" (LONGFELLOW)

20 Blessings on thee, little man,
Barefoot boy, with cheeks of tan!

FROM "THE BAREFOOT BOY" (WHITTIER)

21 "Will you walk into my parlor?" said the spider to the fly.
"'Tis the prettiest little parlor that ever you did spy."

FROM "THE SPIDER AND THE FLY" (HOWITT)

22 The stockings were hung by the chimney with care,
In hopes that St. Nicholas soon would be there.

FROM "THE NIGHT BEFORE CHRISTMAS" (MOORE)

23 Gie fools their silks, and knaves their wine—
A man's a man for a' that!

FROM "FOR A' THAT AND A' THAT" (BURNS)

24 Maud Muller, on a summer's day,
Raked the meadow sweet with hay.

FROM "MAUD MULLER" (WHITTIER)

25 The curfew tolls the knell of parting day,
The lowing herd winds slowly o'er the lea,
The plowman homeward winds his weary way,
And leaves the world to darkness and to me.

FROM "ELEGY WRITTEN IN A COUNTRY CHURCH YARD" (GRAY)

Who's Who in Fact and Fiction

1. Who, to give the people warning,
Rode "through the night" until the morning? *Paul Revere.*
2. What maiden, "on a summer's day,
Raked the meadow sweet with hay"? *Maud Muller.*
3. Who paced the floor with martial stride,
Yet sent his friend to win his bride? *Miles Standish.*
4. Who, by recording angel's pen,
Was listed 'loves his fellow men'? *Abou Ben Adhem.*
5. Who served his queen with a muddy cloak,
Then crossed the sea and learned to smoke? *Sir Walter Raleigh.*
6. Who kept the bridge in days of old,
With Larcius and Herminius bold? *Horatius.*
7. Who, in "the time when lilies blow,"
Brought his cousin a lily white doe? *Lord Ronald.*
8. Who sought the east by sailing west,
And found this land, of all, the best? *Columbus.*
9. Who, by the moonbeam's misty light,
Was buried "darkly at dead of night"? *Sir John Moore.*
10. What brave dame in Frederick town,
"Took up the flag the men hauled down"? *Barbara Frietchie.*

11. Who, with the "courage born of Rome,"
    Leaped to his death for friends and home? *Curtius.*
12. Who, with pure heart before all men,
    Had strength that was "the strength of ten"? *Sir Galahad.*
13. Who, with intent to reach the sea,
    Went "Marching through Georgia," his army and he?
    W. T. Sherman.
14. Who lived in a tub (believe if you can)
    And sought with a lantern "an honest man"? *Diogenes.*
15. Who bore the mystic title: "Our lady with the lamp"?
    The soldiers kissed her shadow in hospital and camp?
    Florence Nightingale.
16. Who cheered his soldiers with the cry:
    "Beyond the Alps lies Italy"? *Hannibal.*
17. Who calmly served the nation's call
    "With malice toward none, charity for all"? *Abraham Lincoln.*
18. Who, as he lay in the apple tree's shade,
    By the fall of an apple a discovery made? *Sir Isaac Newton*
19. What soldier bold, on conquest bent,
    The message Veni, vidi, vici sent? *Julius Caesar.*
20. Who, all alone on the wild desert strand,
    Grew pale at the print of a foot in the sand? *Robinson Crusoe.*
21. Who, till time and war shall cease,
    Stands, "First in war and first in peace"? *George Washington.*
22. Who, with hard questions tried, a queen to please,
    Told false flowers from true by a swarm of bees? *King Solomon.*
23. Who ended the toast by his father begun,
    Saying: "God bless us every one"? *Tiny Tim.*
24. Who with a kite, bottle, and key
    Stored a jar of electricity? *Benjamin Franklin*

Who is Who

WHILE one of the group leaves the room, the rest choose a name of a character who may be living or dead, but must have been very well known or known to the group playing the game. The object is to guess the name of the character by asking questions which may only be answered by yes or no. Let us suppose that the name has been chosen? The questions begin this way. Was a man chosen? ANSWER: *Yes.* Is he living? *No.* Did he die as long as one hundred years ago? *Yes.* Was he an American? *Yes.* Was he over fifty? *Yes.* Was he northern born? *No.* Did he live in the South? *Yes.* Was he a statesman? *Yes.* Was he a soldier? *Yes.* Was he a President? *Yes.* Was it President Washington? *Yes.*

The guesser is allowed three guesses.

More Musical Terms

FOUND IN SHEET MUSIC

1. Machine for weighing. *Scales.*
2. I promise to pay. *Note.*
3. Worn around the neck. *Tie.*
4. Slang for money. *Do.*
5. Most important person. *Mi.*
6. The sun. *Sol.*
7. Lawyers are members of it. *Bar.*
8. Another name for cane. *Staff.*
9. What you want when you are tired. *Rest.*

MUSICAL TERMS

10. Made from boiled tar. *Pitch.*
11. What a watch tells you. *Time.*
12. Fits the lock. *Key.*
13. What you need when you are run down physically. *Tonic.*

MUSICAL INSTRUMENTS

14. A girl's name and a device for catching fish. *Clarinet.*
15. Large bone in chicken's leg. *Drum stick.*
16. A corn cob. *Cornet* (*corn et*).
17. Description of a soft apple plus a telephone. *Mellowphone.*

COMPOSERS

18. Business card of a shoe dealer. *Schumann.*
19. Part of a tool or vessel grasped by the hand. *Handel* (*handle*).

Quotation Contest

THE various articles mentioned below are to be numbered and arranged in different parts of the room and are to suggest the accompanying quotations. The guests are given pencils and papers to write the suggestions.

1. Cups of tea (*"Cups that cheer but not inebriate"*).
2. Rose labeled "Tulip" (*"A rose by any other name would smell as sweet"*).
3. Soap and Bible (*"Cleanliness is indeed next to Godliness"*).
4. Candle (*"How far that little candle throws his beams!"*).
5. Toy horse (*"A horse, a horse, my kingdom for a horse!"*).
6. Feathers (*"Fine feathers do not make fine birds"*).
7. Stocking with a hole in it (*"A stitch in time saves nine"*).
8. Washboard (*"There's the rub"*).
9. Slipper soles (*"Two souls with but a single thought"*).
10. Tea pot (*"Tempest in a tea pot"*).
11. Pansies (*"Pansies, that's for thought"*).
12. Music (*"Music hath charm to soothe the savage beast"*).
13. Plasterhead (*"And still the wonder grew
That one small head could carry all he knew"*).
14. Frying-pan (*"Out of the frying-pan into the fire"*).
15. Stone (*"The stone that is rolling can gather no moss"*).
16. Broken glass with rose petals
(*"You may break, you may shatter the vase if you will
But the scent of the roses will hang around it still"*)
17. Empty goblet with pair of spectacles (*"Drink to me only with thine eyes"*)
18. Heart (*"'Tis love that makes the world go round"*).
19. Star (*"Twinkle, twinkle, little star"*)
20. Purse (*"Who steals my purse steals trash"*).
21. Short story (*"And thereby hangs the tale"*).
22. A broken chain (*"A chain is as strong as its weakest link"*).

Answer with Names of Literary Men

1. Breakfast pork—*Bacon.*
2. Untamed—*Wilde.*

3. A polite name for the devil—*Dickens.*
4. What the fire does—*Burns.*
5. A tall fellow—*Longfellow.*
6. A servant in uniform—*Butler.*
7. Two or a pair—*Twain.*
8. What we sing at Christmas—*Caroll.*
9. An adjective meaning fleet—*Swift.*
10. A man who works in gold—*Goldsmith.*
11. A plot of ground—*Field.*
12. A color—*Gray.*
13. What we live in—*Holmes.*
14. A baby sheep—*Lamb.*
15. Head of the Roman Catholic Church—*Pope.*
16. Term used in measuring electricity—*Watts.*
17. It's painful to the foot—*Bunyan.*

Make-believe Rose

THIS game would be suitable for a group interested in literary affairs and might be used as a test of knowledge gained during a period of study.

The leader or hostess should arrange a "Make-believe" rose and have it occupy a prominent place in the decorations of the room. The rose is made in this way: On strips of paper five inches long and about one inch wide, write quotations from various poets; the rose petals might be made from taffeta or crepe paper and the quotations pasted on one end; the petals should be graduated in size so that the larger ones could form the outer rim of the rose, the smaller ones the center. Green ribbon or crepe paper should be wrapped around the paper slips in order to form the stem. In order to make it more realistic, the rose might be perfumed.

The leader takes the flower in one hand and plucking a petal from it reads the quotation aloud to the group. The guest who first identifies the quotation receives the petal. For example, one quotation might read,

> "That which we call a rose
> By any other name would smell as sweet,"

and the guest who first answered Shakespeare's *Juliet* receives the petal.

The guest who has the largest number of petals when the rose is completely shattered is proclaimed the winner.

A rose covering many different fields, such as art, science, music, or history, could be arranged for any group.

Famous Persons

ARRANGE the following objects or pictures of objects around the room and let the guests supply the answers to the following question: "What famous person do these objects suggest?" The player who reads the correct list should be able to tell briefly the incident with which each object is connected.

1. A hatchet—*George Washington.*
2. A spider's web—*Robert Bruce.*
3. A fiddle—*Nero.*
4. A muddy cloak—*Sir Walter Raleigh.*
5. A coat of many colors—*Joseph.*
6. A wooden horse—*Ulysses.*
7. A lonely island—*Robinson Crusoe, Napoleon.*
8. A silver cup—*Benjamin.*
9. A burning bush—*Moses.*
10. A glass slipper—*Cinderella.*
11. A ruff—*Queen Elizabeth.*
12. An apple—*Newton, Eve, William Tell.*
13. Long hair—*Samson, Absalom.*
14. A silver lamp—*Aladdin.*
15. A gray-goose shaft—*Robin Hood.*
16. A dove—*Noah.*
17. A bridge—*Horatius.*
18. A sling shot—*David.*
19. A little lamb—*Mary.*
20. A lantern—*Diogenes.*

Can You Find the Birds?

1. Beth rushed down the steps and got into the sleigh.
2. She said, "Here, Rob, in you go."

3. She lifted her little brother onto the seat. "I will drive awhile, Ole," she said to the coachman. "Or, I, Ole," said little Rob.
4. The mountains in the distance were part ridged with snow although it was midsummer.
5. As they reached the shore, a boat with a single spar rowed silently out to sea.
6. While returning the horse became frightened and Ole wrenched the lines from Beth's hands.
7. This saved the sleigh from running into an old poplar, knotty and tough.
8. "If that were a wobbly spar, rotten and weak, it would not have been so dangerous," said Beth.
9. "Ow, let's hurry home," cried Rob.
10. His golden crown of hair was all covered with mud.

ANSWERS: 1—*Thrush.* 2—*Robin.* 3—*Oriole.* 4—*Partridge.* 5—*Sparrow.* 6—*Wren.* 7—*Lark.* 8—*Parrot.* 9—*Owl.* 10—*Crow.*

Hidden Geography

THE following sentences contain geographic names. See if you can find them.

1. He has my R. N. as a monogram on all his note paper.
2. I am her stupid sister.
3. Kate can't tell a wren cemented, from a wren demented.
4. In adjusting the baby jumpers, I adjusted the baby so that it fell out.
5. The calmest man is sometimes made irate.
6. Away they went and over the race course they spun.
7. The sale must commence at one o'clock.
8. Would you bid a cow or ox bury their dead?
9. Why do you call Mr. Ramey, a horse tamer, I call him a cow boy.
10. They made a hue and cry, but ah, of no avail.
11. Did you ever read in Goldsmith of the curse of ambition?
12. The wounded are borne off the field on litters.
13. In the great Indian wars, a wicked prince oppressed the people.
14. A surveyor looked at the debris, told me the wreck was fearful.
15. Let no woman or man dye their hair.

ANSWER: 1—*Smyrna.* 2—*Amherst.* 3—*Lawrence.* 4—*Persia.* 5—*Madeira.* 6—*Dover.* 7—*Salem.* 8—*Roxbury.* 9—*America.* 10—*Utah.* 11—*Reading.* 12—*Borneo.* .13—*Warsaw.* 14—*Bristol.* 15—*Normandy.*

Hidden Mountains

THE following sentences contain the names of mountains. Can you find them?

1. That woman is washing tons and tons of clothes.
2. Her monotone is irritating.
3. Do you think the name Idaho odd?
4. He was ever establishing something.
5. Look at this shine bought at the barber shop.
6. Did she get her money?
7. A word that begins with C as cadence.
8. The tent had a blue ridge pole.
9. The states Mo., Ky., and Tenn. join each other.
10. If you throw a rock you may hit a child.
11. Do your cats kill mice?
12. Can't one sin airing his neighbor's faults?

ANSWER: 1—*Washington.* 2—*Hermon.* 3—*Hood.* 4—*Everest.* 5—*Nebo.* 6—*Hermon.* 7—*Cascade.* 8—*Blue Ridge.* 9—*Smoky.* 10—*Rocky.* 11—*Catskill.* 12—*Sinai.*

Poetic Mountains

IN the following verses, mountains are to be supplied to complete the verse.

1. He looked at the mountain and tipped his hat.
   It was the biblical mountain ———.
2. He hoped and prayed he might not die
   Till he had seen Mount ———.
3. His wife was buxom, stout, and stocky,
   And liked all mountains, even the ———.
4. When they have reached these, they will seek
   To watch the sunrise from ——— ———.
5. See four states or there about

When you climb Mt. ———.
6. To another place he wished to go,
   To the mountain called ———.
7. He climbed soon after he was born
   The great mountain called ———.
8. He could not climb to his great sorrow
   The African mountain ———.
9. It stands near Atlanta all alone,
   The granite mountain that's called ———.
10. Chiseled faces number four
    On the mountain called ———.
11. John wrote a letter telling his mama
    He'd seen the Japanese mountain ———.
12. He said to his wife, "Goodbye dear,
    I'm going to climb Mt. ———."
13. He climbed the first mountain he ever saw,
    It was the Swiss mountain named ———.
14. We'll climb to the top if you'll go with us,
    This mountain of the gods is called ———.

ANSWERS: 1—*Ararat.* 2—*Sinai.* 3—*Rocky.* 4—*Pike's Peak.* 5—*Lookout.* 6—*Nebo.* 7—*Matterhorn.* 8—*Kilimanjaro.* 9—*Stone.* 10—*Rushmore.* 11—*Fujiyama.* 12—*Ranier.* 13—*Jungfrau.* 14—*Olympus.*

Poets and Authors

GIVE each guest a mimeographed sheet on which the following riddles have been written. Answers are to be supplied by using the names of American poets and authors.

1. A house for fowls and done by a cat.
2. A command to oxen and a briar.
3. A beautiful wild animal.
4. A query and part of a house.
5. A tall man.
6. A small part and a part of a wheel.
7. A strong rope.
8. A river in Europe.
9. A regular grinder.

10. To pack things away.
11. Name of a defeated politician and a beverage.
12. A place for athletic sports.
13. A knight's attendant.
14. A type measure, to do wrong, and a luminary.
15. A nickname for Albert, and a folding bed.

ANSWERS: 1—*Cooper.* 2—*Hawthorne.* 3—*Harte.* 4—*Howell.* 5—*Longfellow.* 6—*Whittier.* 7—*Cable.* 8—*Poe.* 9—*Mills,* 10—*Stowe.* 11—*Bryant.* 12—*Field.* 13—*Page.* 14—*Emerson.* 15—*Alcott.*

Catch Phrases

WHOM do the following phrases suggest?

1. "I have made the crossword puzzle possible."
2. "Monkey beezness! Monkey beezness!"
3. "I lost by a hair."
4. "This part's too hot for me."
5. "Oh, you Brute."
6. "Four out of five are victims."
7. "It isn't the original cost, it's the upkeep."
8. "I may be little, but oh, my."
9. "There's always room for one more."
10. "They go wild, simply wild, over me."
11. "I'm losing my head over you."
12. "I do not like fish."

ANSWERS: 1—*Webster.* 2—*Darwin.* 3—*Samson.* 4—*Joan of Arc.* 5—*Caesar.* 6—*Lucretia Borgia.* 7—*Solomon.* 8—*Napoleon.* 9—*Brigham Young.* 10—*Cleopatra.* 11—*Marie Antoinette.* 12—*Jonah.*

Rhyming

THE following are some old sayings which have been rhymed, and are offered as samples for the game which is to follow.

From the old sayings listed below, ask the guests to use four of them in producing rhymes such as those given as samples.

SAMPLES:

As hard as a flint | As heavy as lead

As soft as a mole
As white as a lily
As black as a coal

As proud as a peacock
As sly as a fox
As mad as a March hare
As strong as an ox

As light as a feather
As steady as time
Uncertain as weather

As round as an apple
As black as your hat
As brown as a berry
As blind as a bat

List of Old Sayings:

As wet as a fish
A hot as an oven
As live as a bird
As thin as a herring
As strong as a horse
As gay as a lark
As slow as a tortoise
As plump as a partridge
As poor as a rat
As false as mankind
As fair as a lily
As poor as a church mouse
As bright as a six-pence
As blithe as a brig
As pure as an angel
As true as the gospel
As weak as a rat
As ugly as sin
As dead as a doornail
As smart as a steel trap
As white as a sheet
As flat as a pancake

As plain as a pikestaff
As sick as a dog
As dry as a bone
As tight as a drum
As swift as the wind
As rough as a bear
As brave as a lion
As dead as a stone
As free as the air
As weak as a cat
As proud as a peacock
As fat as a pig
As spry as a cat
As rough as a gale
As thin as a rail
As cold as a frog
As cross as a bear
As rich as was Croesus
As neat as a pin
As empty as air
As fat as a porpoise
As red as a beet

Familiar Allusions

Ask the guests to state what the following allusions refer to:

1. Abraham's Bosom. *The rest of the blessed dead, Luke XIV: 22.*
2. Ambrosia. *The food of the gods.*

3. Bard of Avon. *Shakespeare, who was born at Stratford-on-Avon.*
4. Babylonish Captivity. *The seventy years' captivity of the Jews at Babylon, 608-538 B.C.*
5. Begging the question. *Assuming as true what is still to be proven.*
6. Crocodile tears. *Hypocritical grief. The crocodile was fabled to weep as it ate its victim.*
7. The eternal city. *Rome.*
8. Eureka. *Greek, I have found it.*
9. The Emerald Isle. *Ireland.*
10. Gordian Knot. *A vexing question; an obstacle to be overcome by bold action.*
11. Year of Jubilee. *Among the Jews, came every fiftieth year. All debts considered paid and land reverted to its original owner.*
12. Venus de Milo. *Considered the most beautiful Greek statue.*
13. War of the Roses. *English Civil War between Lancaster* (*red rose*) *and York* (*white rose*).
14. John Bull. *Nickname for England.*

Identify the Author

1. Veni, vidi, vici — *Julius Caesar*
2. A man's a man for a' that — *Robert Burns*
3. I do not choose to run — *Cal Coolidge*
4. War is hell — *General Sherman*
5. If winter comes can spring be far behind? — *Shelley*
6. The wedding guest sat on a stone — *Coleridge*
7. A little learning is a dangerous thing — *Alexander Pope*
8. If the people can't eat bread, let them eat cake — *Marie Antoinette*
9. A thing of beauty is a joy forever — *John Keats*
10. Poems are made by fools like me — *Joyce Kilmer*
11. We must all hang together; or assuredly we will all hang separately — *Benjamin Franklin*
12. Beyond the Alps lies Italy — *Hannibal*
13. With malice toward none and charity for all — *Abraham Lincoln*

14. Give me liberty or give me death — *Patrick Henry*
15. A rose by any other name would smell as sweet — *Shakespeare*

Shakespeare Blanks

MIMEOGRAPH or typewrite the following story, the blanks to be filled in with the names of Shakespearean plays.

The boy's name was (1) ——— ——— ——— was the name of the girl. They planned to be married on the (2) ——— ——— in June. The bride's mother, one of those who always liked to make (3) ——— ——— ——— ——— wanted to have a large wedding. She took her daughter to the (4) ——— ——— ——— to buy her trousseau. In the meanwhile, the groom met (5) ——— ——— ——— ———, and they all went out to a night club where they met (6) ——— ——— ——— ———. When the bride heard about it, she decided that she would give him (7) ——— ——— ———. There was quiet a (8) ——— until the groom succeeded in (9) ——— ——— ——— ——— ——— with the aid of (10) ——— ——— ——— ———. When peace was finally restored, all agreed that (11) ——— ——— ——— ———.

ANSWERS: 1—*Romeo and Juliet.* 2—*Twelfth Night.* 3—*Much Ado About Nothing.* 4—*Merchant of Venice.* 5—*Two Gentlemen of Verona.* 6—*The Merry Wives of Windsor.* 7—*Measure for Measure.* 8—*Tempest.* 9—*The Taming of the Shrew.* 10—*The Two Noble Kinsmen.* 11—*All's Well that Ends Well.*

Song Identification

WHAT songs do the following places make you think of? Give guests the names of the places and let them supply the name of the song.

The list given below are only suggestions. Many other song titles would of course be permissible answers.

1. New York — *The Sidewalks of New York*
2. Ocean — *Rocked in the Cradle of the Deep*
3. Ireland — *Where the River Shannon Flows*; *When Irish Eyes are Smiling*

4. Scotland	*Annie Laurie*
	Loch Lomond
5. England	*God Save the King*
6. France	*La Marseillaise*
7. Russia	*Song of the Volga Boatmen*
8. Germany	*The Watch on the Rhine*
9. Italy	*Isle of Capri*
10. Spain	*The Spanish Cavalier*
	Juanita
11. Rocky Mountains	*When its Springtime in the Rockies*
12. Indiana	*Back Home Again in Indiana*
13. Kentucky	*My Old Kentucky Home*
14. Florida	*Suwannee River*
15. Virginia	*Carry Me Back to Old Virginia*
16. Maryland	*Maryland, My Maryland*
17. America	*America the Beautiful*

Religious Books

CAN you identify the authors as given at the right of the following well-known books that in some way deal with religion?

1. Pilgrim's Progress	*John Bunyan*
2. Paradise Lost	*John Milton*
3. In His Steps	*Charles Sheldon*
4. The Other Wise Man	*Henry van Dyke*
5. Ben-Hur	*Lew Wallace*
6. The Book Nobody Knows	*Bruce Barton*
7. The Man Nobody Knows	*Bruce Barton*
8. The Christ of the Indian Road	*E. Stanley Jones*
9. The Robe	*Lloyd C. Douglas*
10. The Greatest Thing in the World	*Henry Drummond*
11. The Divine Comedy	*Dante*
12. Christmas Carol	*Charles Dickens*

Religious Art

CAN you give the name of the artist of each of the following well-known paintings? In some cases there will be more than one permissible answer.

1.	The Annunciation to Mary	*H. Hofmann*
2.	Flight into Egypt	*B. Plockhorst*
3.	Christ and the Rich Young Ruler	*H. Hofmann*
4.	Christ Before Pilate	*Munkacsy*
5.	Jesus in Gethsemane	*H. Hofmann*
6.	The Sistine Madonna	*Raphael*
7.	The Last Supper	*Leonardo da Vinci*
8.	The Child Jesus in the Temple	*H. Hofmann*
9.	I Am the Light of the World	*Hunt*
10.	The Angelus	*Millet*
11.	The Crucifixion	*Murillo*
12.	Peter and John Hastening to the Sepulcher	*Burnand*

Definitions

READ the following words and have the guests, one by one give the definition. A guest who is unable to do this must drop out of the game. The object is to see who can remain in the game the longest.

1.	Aborigines	*Original inhabitants of a country*
2.	Barnacles	*Shell fish that fasten on ships*
3.	Camouflage	*Used to make objects inconspicuous*
4.	Coxswain	*The one who steers a boat*
5.	Epaulettes	*Shoulder badges worn by military officers*
6.	Fathom	*Six feet in nautical terms*
7.	Gendarme	*French policeman*
8.	Hieroglyphics	*Writing in pictures*
9.	Ich Dien	*Motto of the Prince of Wales, meaning, I serve*
10.	Jetsam	*Articles thrown overboard to lighten a ship*
11.	Kayak	*Canoe used by Eskimos*
12.	Longitude	*Distance east and west of Greenwich*
13.	Mirage	*An optical illusion*
14.	Yukon	*In Canada and Alaska, gold field*

Famous Characters in Poetry and Prose

SUPPLY guests with paper and pencil on which the following characters are listed. Ask them to identify the characters.

1. Aladdin	*Hero of one of the Arabian Nights tales*
2. Alice	*The child heroine of Lewis Carroll's "Alice's Adventures in Wonderland"*
3. Enoch Arden	*A shipwrecked sailor in Tennyson's poem, "Enoch Arden"*
4. Barkis	*An eccentric character in Dickens' "David Copperfield"*
5. Tom Brown	*The hero of Thomas Hughes' famous story of English school life, "Tom Brown's School-days."*
6. Caliban	*A savage and deformed slave in Shakespeare's "The Tempest"*
7. Christian	*Hero of Bunyan's "Pilgrim's Progress"*
8. Don Quixote	*Eccentric hero of Cervantes' romance "Don Quixote"*
9. Friday	*Crusoe's servant in De Foe's "Robinson Crusoe"*
10. Mr. Hyde	*One phase of the dual personality in Steven-son's "Dr. Jekyll and Mr. Hyde"*
11. Leatherstocking	*Sobriquet given to Natty Bumpo, a hero of Cooper's "The Pathfinder," etc.*
12. Lenore	*Mentioned in Poe's poem, "The Raven"*
13. Evangeline	*Heroine of Longfellow's "Evangeline"*
14. Peter Pan	*Hero of Barrie's fairy play, "Peter Pan"*

musical games and folk songs

RHYTHMIC games deserve a larger place in the social and recreational program, especially that of young people. As "mixers" rhythmic games are unequaled. They serve to break the ice and put everyone at ease. The fun element makes them popular, and the rhythm is a unifying force. During the past generation efforts have been made to collect them from many lands and make them available to all.

Rhythmic folk games grew up and flourished where communities were isolated and dependent upon their own resources. Musical instruments were not necessary, and the rhythm was made by the voice or the clapping of the hands. They have always been popular with those who know how to play them. Moreover, they are easily learned, and little equipment is needed. They can be used almost any time and place.

Rhythmic folk games are wholesome. They provide group sociability. The group may participate 100 per cent, and each individual must contribute something in the way of music or action; this in turn demands alertness and initiative.

Now it is possible to play most all of the popular folk games using recorded music. Lists of available records may be easily found by consulting recording companies' catalogs.

Come, Let Us Be Joyful

FORMATION: Each boy takes two girls as partners, one on his right and the other on his left. It may be necessary in some cases to have one girl take two boys as her partners. Each boy with his two partners lines up facing another boy with his partners, making six in a group. These groups form a large circle around the floor.

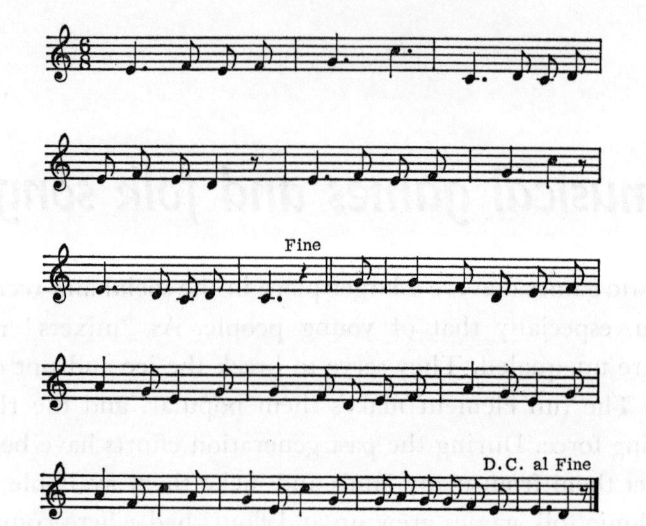

1. Come, let us be joyful
   While life is bright and gay
2. Gather its roses
   'Ere they fade away.
3. We're always making our lives so blue
   We look for thorns and find them too,
   And leave the violets quite unseen
   That grow to cheer our way.
4. (Repeat first four lines.)

DIRECTIONS FOR PLAYING:

1. The boy joins hands with the girls on either side of him, holding hands about shoulder high. Each trio advances three steps and on the fourth count bows. All then return to their original positions.

2. Repeat the action in (1).

3. Each boy links right arms with the girl on his right and skips around her. He then links left arms with the girl on the left and swings her. Each time, the extra girl may skip around to the music until her turn comes.

4. Repeat the actions in (1) and (2). This time, however, when the trio advances for the second time, they drop hands and pass through the opposite trio. Each trio is then facing a new trio, which has passed through from the next group, and the game begins again.

Bingo

FORMATION: Double circle: boys on the inside, girls on the boys' right. All march counterclockwise.

1. There was a farmer had a dog,
   And Bingo is his name, sir.
   That farmer's dog's at our back door,
   Begging for a bone, sir.
2. B with an I and I with an N,
   N with a G and G with an O,
   B—I—N—G—O
   And Bingo is his name, sir.

DIRECTIONS FOR PLAYING:

1. All march around the circle, singing the song. At the word

"sir," after "begging for a bone," all the boys face about while the girls continue in the same direction.

2. While singing the chorus, the lines move in opposite directions with a skipping step. On the word "sir" at the end of the song, each boy takes the girl nearest him for a partner, turns about, and the game is played again as at first.

The Chimes of Dunkirk

FORMATION: A double circle, the boy on the inside and the girl on the outside. The girls, who face the center of the circle, remain in the same place throughout the game, while the boys, who face out, move counterclockwise from partner to partner.

DIRECTIONS FOR PLAYING:

1. All stamp their feet three times and pause. All clap their hands three times and pause.
2. Partners join hands and walk around each other.
3. Balance off. Partners join right hands and step forward on the right foot—putting entire weight on this foot—then back. This is repeated joining left hands and stepping forward on the left foot.
4. With right hands joined, partners walk around each other

once more. When this is completed, the boy moves counterclockwise to the next girl and the game begins again.

Continue to play until each boy has had each one of the girls as a partner, or as long as the group enjoys the game.

The Wheat [1]

FORMATION: Three abreast, a boy between two girls, with arms linked. The sets of three form a circle around the floor.

From the feast there came a farmer,
On his back a bag of bran,
And the bad boys shouted at him,
"Let those pigeons out, old man.
Let those pigeons out, old man,
Let those pigeons out, old man!"
And the bad boys shouted at him,
"Let those pigeons out, old man!"

DIRECTIONS FOR PLAYING:

Beginning with the left foot, these sets of three walk forward heavily sixteen steps (bars 1 to 8). The boy and the girl on his right

[1] From the book *Folk Dances of Bohemia and Moravia,* by permission of the publishers, H. T. FitzSimons Co., Inc., Chicago.

link right arms and turn quickly with eight skipping steps (bars 9 to 12). The boy and the girl on his left then link left arms and turn in the same way (bars 13 to 16).

Gustaf's Toast [2]

FORMATION: Four couples form a square, girls on the boys' right, couples 1 and 3 facing each other and couples 2 and 4 facing each other.

A toast we pledge to Gustaf who is brave and true,
A toast we pledge to Gustaf brave and true.
Tra la la la la la la la la la, Tra la la la la la la la la la,
Tra la la la la la la la la la, Tra la la.

DIRECTIONS FOR PLAYING:

Fig. 1—Couples 1 and 3 walk three steps toward the center, bring the heels together (bars 1 and 2), bow on the first beat of bar 3, and walk backward three steps to place (bars 3 and 4). Couples 2 and 4 repeat (bars 5 to 8), bowing on the first beat of bar 7.

Fig. 1 is then repeated exactly as before (repeat of bars 1 to 8).

[2] From the book *Folk Games of Denmark and Sweden,* by permission of the publishers, H. T. FitzSimons Co., Inc., Chicago.

Fig. 2—Couples 2 and 4 raise their joined hands, making an arch. At the same time, couples 1 and 3 walk to the center and change partners. Boy 1 and girl 3 join hands and turn, going under the arch made by couple 4. Boy 3 and girl 1 do the same, going under the arch made by couple 2. They then release hands, clap on the first beat of bar 13, skip quickly back into place and join both hands with their original partners. They swing around in place, with both hands still joined.

Couples 2 and 4 then repeat Fig. 2—changing partners and going under the arches made by couples 1 and 3.

If an extra boy can get in at the end of Fig. 2 and swing the girl, he may keep her for the repetition of the game. The boy who lost his partner may rob another in the same way.

Oh, Suzannah

FORMATION: Single circle of couples, boys have partners on their right side.

Tune and words "Oh, Suzannah"

1. "I came from Alabama with my banjo on my knee
2. I'm going to Louisiana my true love for to see
3. It rained all night the day I left, the weather was so dry
   The sun so hot I froze to death, Suzannah don't you cry.
4. CHORUS. Oh, Suzannah don't you cry fo' me
   Fo' I'm goin' to Louisiana with my banjo on my knee."

DIRECTIONS FOR PLAYING:

(1) Boys remain in place while the girls take four steps towards the center and return on four steps. The entire circle clap hands to the rhythm of the song.

(2) While the girls remain in their places, the boys take four steps towards the center and four steps back. Clap hands as at first.

(3) Partners face each other; grasp right hands; move in opposite directions giving the left hand to the next player, then the right hand to the next and so alternating around the circle until the word "cry" is reached in the song; at which time those clasping hands at that time promenade as partners around the circle while singing.

(4) Repeat the game from the start; each time all players will probably have a new partner.

Goodnight Ladies

FORMATION: Four couples form a square; one couple on each side.

Tune and words "Goodnight Ladies."

1. "Goodnight ladies
2. Goodnight ladies
3. Goodnight ladies
4. We're going to leave you now
5. Merrily we roll along, roll along, roll along
6. Merrily we roll along, O'er the deep blue sea."

DIRECTIONS FOR PLAYING:

Partners lock right arms: (1) take three steps in clockwise circle, pause; (2) take three more steps in the same direction, pause; (3)—(4) repeat the same directions as for (1)—(2). (5) Partners 1 and 3 turning back to back girls skip around the outside of the circle and exchange places. (6) Boys do the same as the girls in (5); which will bring partners together again.

Repeat the entire game same as at first except partners 2 and 4 exchange instead of 1 and 3.

VARIATION:

(1), (2), (3), and (4) same as in the first game. (5) Boys of partners 1 and 3 exchange but the girls remain in position. (6) boys of partners 2 and 4 exchange. This causes every one to have a new partner. Repeat the game and this time the girls exchange partners instead of the boys. Original partners should be back together again.

My Ole Man

FORMATION: Partners in single circle, boys having their partners on the right.

Tune "Captain Jinks."

1. My ole man came home last night
2. Pass your neighbor on the right

3. Swing this lassie so polite
4. And all join in on the chorus
5. All promenade around the hall, around the hall, around the hall;
6. All promenade around the hall
7. And take a breath for another.

Directions for Playing:

(1) All players take two steps towards center of the circle; then return to their places on two more steps; clap hands on the accented beat.

(2) Girls remain in their original places. The boys change partners by moving to their right behind their former partner.

(3), (4) Catching both hands of their new partner the boys swing the girls around twice, in time to the music.

(5), (6), (7) Partners join hands and promenade clockwise around the circle.

Repeat lines (1), (2), (3), and (4) with the same directions as the first.

Auld Lang Syne

Formation: Couples in a single circle.

Tune and words "Auld Lang Syne."

1. "Should auld acquaintance be forgot and never brought to mind
2. Should auld acquaintance be forgot and days of auld lang syne
3. For auld lang syne my dear
   For auld lang syne
   We'll take a cup of kindness yet
   For auld lang syne."

Directions for Playing:

(1) Link right arms; swing your partner all the way around a complete circle.

(2) Change, link left arms, then swing your partners around again.

(3) The game continues as a "grand right and left"; use a waltz step (i.e., 1-2-3; 1-2-3); do not grasp hands as you move around the circle in the "grand right and left"; instead, when passing a partner place the outside hand on the hip and slightly raise the inside shoul-

der. Thus you alternate "hands on hips." On the last "syne" take the new partner at hand and begin the game again.

Polly Wolly Doodle

FORMATION: Partners facing each other in double circle.

Tune and words "Polly Wolly Doodle."

1. "Oh, I'm going down south for to see my gal
2. Singing Polly Wolly Doodle all the day;
3. Oh, my gal she am a spunky gal
4. Singing Polly Wolly Doodle all the day.
5. Fare thee well, fare thee well
   Fare thee well my fairie fae
   For I'm going to Louisiana for to see my Suzanna
   Singing Polly Wolly Doodle all the day."

DIRECTIONS FOR PLAYING:

(1) While facing each other the partners sing.

(2) With quick steps the boys leave their partners for new ones, moving to the left to the next girl.

(3) Sing this line while facing each other.

(4) The same as in (2) the boys move up to the left with quick running steps.

(5) With the last partner, the boys promenade around the circle in a skating position.

Repeat the game with the girls following the directions given for the boys.

Shoo Fly

FORMATION: Single circle; all join hands; one player designated as leader.

1. Shoo fly, don't bother me
2. Shoo fly, don't bother me
3. Shoo fly, don't bother me
4. Cause I belong to somebody
5. I do, I do, I do,
   I ain't going to tell you who
   But I belong to somebody
   Yes, indeed, I do.

(1) Without breaking hands the girls take steps towards the center, as if the boys were "shooing" them away. Then take the steps back in position.

(2) The boys take the step towards the center, as if the girls were "shooing" the boys; return in position.

(3) The girls repeat the same as in (1).

(4) The boys repeat as in (2).

(5) The leader leads the entire circle under the arms of a couple on the opposite of the circle, turning the entire circle "wrong side out." (All players follow the leader under the same arms.) Do not "break" the circle. Repeat the entire game turned outwards and return to original places.

Pop Goes the Weasel

FORMATION: In circle in groups of three. The groups of three form a "horse and chariot"; i.e., one player stands in front. With his right hand he grasps the right hand of the player behind him on his right. With his left hand he grasps the left hand of the other player. The two players who form the chariot join their other hands behind the front player.

Tune and words "Pop Goes the Weasel."

"All around the chicken coop
The monkey chased the weasel,
That's the way the money goes
Pop goes the weasel.

CHORUS: I've no time to wait or sigh
I've no time to wheedle
Only time to say good bye
Pop goes the weasel.

A penny for a spool of thread
A penny for a needle
That's the way the money goes
Pop goes the weasel.

DIRECTIONS FOR PLAYING:

While singing the song all groups skip around the circle to the left until the word, "pop." At this word the back two players raise their joined hands and the front player "pops" under them and meets the next two players which were behind his group at the beginning. Continue as above. Change the "horse" (the player which "pops") quite often, as this player will become tired quite readily.

Weasel's Nest

THIS game is played to the tune of "Pop Goes the Weasel." The guests are divided into groups of four, consisting of two couples if possible. They form a number of small circles about the room. There is one weasel, and if the group is large, there may be a number of weasels. The weasel or weasels are not attached to any small circle. During the singing of the first verse, "All around the chicken coop" (see above), all circle and sing. At the conclusion of the first verse and on "pop goes the weasel," one of the girls in the small circle "pops" into the center of the circle and the other three march around her and sing the chorus.

At the completion of the chorus and on "pop goes the weasel," the ones in the nests run out, join hands with the others who have been in the nests and circle around the weasel, as all sing, "I've no time to wait or sigh," etc. When this verse is concluded and on the word "weasel," all break from the center circle and try to get back to their nests. The weasel or weasels try also to get into a nest. Those who do not find a nest become the weasels and the game starts again.

Sandy Land

FORMATION: Partners in single circle.

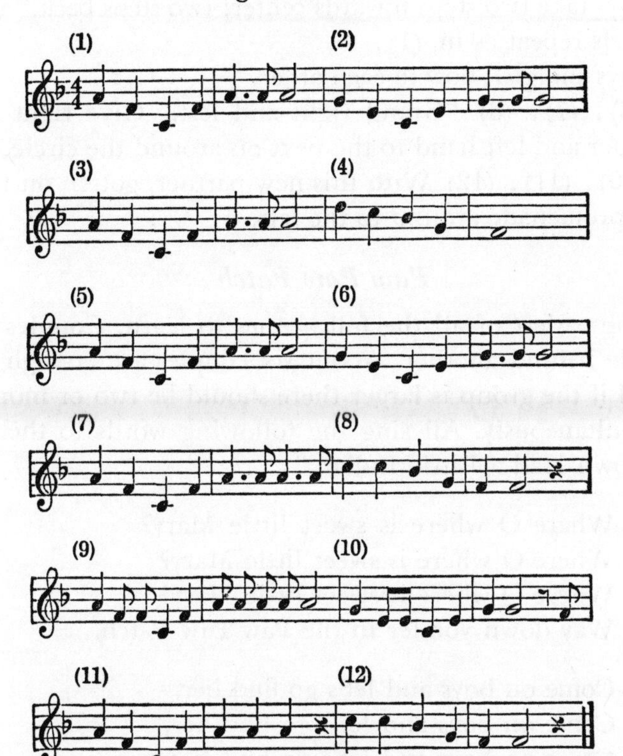

(1) Make my living on sandy land
(2) Make my living on sandy land
(3) Make my living on sandy land
(4) Ladies fare thee well
(5) One more river I'm bound to cross
(6) One more river I'm bound to cross
(7) One more river I'm bound to cross
(8) Before I meet my Honey.
(9) How old are you my pretty little miss
(10) How old are you my honey
(11) She answered me with a ha, ha, ha
(12) I'll be sixteen Sunday.

Directions for Playing:

(1) Girls take two steps toward center; two steps back.

(2) Boys take two steps towards center; two steps back.

(3) Girls repeat as in (1).

(4) Boys and girls bow to each other.

(5), (6), (7), (8) "Grand right and left." Give right hand to your partner and left hand to the next on around the circle.

(9), (10), (11). (12) With this new partner, gotten on the word "honey," promenade around to the left.

Paw Paw Patch

This is the easiest of all the folk games to learn. Couples line up one couple behind another. About six couples are enough for one game, and if the group is larger there should be two or more games going simultaneously. All sing the following words to the tune of "John Brown Had a Little Indian."

1—Where O where is sweet little Mary?
Where O where is sweet little Mary?
Where O where is sweet little Mary?
Way down yonder in the Paw Paw Patch.

2—Come on boys and let's go find her,
Come on boys and let's go find her,
Come on boys and let's go find her,
Way down yonder in the Paw Paw Patch.

3—Pickin' up paw paws, puttin' them in her pocket,
Pickin' up paw paws, puttin' them in her pocket.
Pickin' up paw paws, puttin' them in her pocket.
Way down yonder in the Paw Paw Patch.

The action is as follows: During the singing of (1) the girl at the head of the line starts going counterclockwise and runs around the whole group of couples and back to her place. The proper rhythm for the music is a step and a short hop with each foot.

When she is back in place, which she should be by the time the first verse is finished, the boy at the head of the line leads all the boys around the girls counterclockwise (that is to the left) while the (2) is being sung. When the boys are back in place, all are ready for (3).

On (3) each boy takes the hand of his partner, skating fashion, and they skip all the way around a circle to the third verse. In addition, when they come to the words, "pickin' up paw paws" they dip as if picking up something. All should dip at the same time and in order to do this, the leader should tell all to dip on the word, "pickin'." This will make three dips.

When all are around, the couple at the front takes a new position at the back of the line, and the game continues.

Instead of singing, "Where O where is sweet little Mary," substitute always the name of the girl at the head of the line.

After playing this game for awhile change the boys to the right of the girls and let them chase around the circle while all sing, "Where O where is sweet little Jimmie," and so on.

Little Red Caboose

Little red caboose, little red caboose,
Little red caboose behind the train,
Smoke stack on it's back, back, back, back.
Coming down the track, track, track, track,
Little red caboose behind the train.

(Sing this over three times; each time getting softer. At the end of the third time make the sound of a train in the distance; such as "whoo-who-o.")

Sourwood Mountain

1 Chicken crowin' on Sourwood Mountain,
Hey deing dang diddle ally day,
So many pretty girls I can't count 'em,
Hey deing dang diddle ally day,
My true love she lives in Let-cher,
Hey deing dang diddle ally day,
She won't come and I won't fetch her,
Hey deing dang diddle ally day.

2 My true love's a blue-eyed daisy,
Hey deing dang diddle ally day,
If I don't get her I'll go crazy,
Hey deing dang diddle ally day,
Big dog'll bark and little one'll bite you
Hey deing dang diddle ally day,
Big girl'll court and little one'll slight you
Hey deing dang diddle ally day.

3 My true love lives up the river,
Hey deing dang diddle ally day,
A few more jumps and I'll be with her,

Hey deing dang diddle ally day,
My true love lives in the hollow,
Hey deing dang diddle ally day,
She won't come and I won't follow,
Hey deing dang diddle ally day.

Three Little Pigeons

Three little pigeons sitting on a fence
Three little pigeons sitting on a fence
(*speak*) "One flew away." (*leader*)
(*speak*) "Ah!" (*group*)

Two little pigeons sitting on a fence (*repeat*)
"One flew away." (*leader*)
"Ah!" (*group*)

One little pigeon sitting on the fence. (*repeat*)
"It flew away." (*leader*)
"Ah!" (*group*)

No little pigeons sitting on the fence (*repeat*)
"One flew back." (*leader*)
"Whoopee!" (*group*)

Continue the song singing "One little pigeon," "two little pigeons," and "three little pigeons," after each repeat "another flew back," and give the group an opportunity to say "whoopee!"

London Bridge

London Bridge is a good outdoor game. It is a favorite to play on the beach in the moonlight. The simplest form of the game starts with a couple forming an arch. They agree in advance that they are to represent certain objects, for example, a lion and a tiger, or a diamond ring or a pearl necklace. Players are asked by one of the couple whether they would rather be a lion or a tiger. When they make their choice, they take their place behind the one of the couple who represents that animal.

After the arch is formed all players march through singing the words to London Bridge:

London Bridge is falling down,
Falling down, falling down;
London Bridge is falling down,
My fair lady.

On the words, "My fair lady," the couple forming the arch drop their hands and inclose the one who at that time happens to be in the arch, between their arms. One of them says, "Would you rather be a lion or a tiger?" If in this case the girl represents the lion, the players who choose lion take their places behind her. If they choose tiger, they take their place behind the boy. The game continues until all have been caught. When only a few remain, they may be divided equally between the sides. All players now place their arms around the waist of the one in front of them. A tug of war then takes place, each side trying to pull the entire group on the other side across a line that has been drawn between the two who formed the arch.

The Spider

1. An eency weency spider
2. Went up the water spout
3. Out came the rain
4. And washed the spider out
5. Out came the sun
6. And dried up all the rain
7. And the eency weency spider
8. Went up the spout again.

Directions for actions: Touch the forefinger of the right hand to the thumb of the left hand; then touch the forefinger of the left hand to the thumb of the right hand; now bring the thumb and forefinger that is on the bottom to the top, repeat again and so on while singing lines 1 and 2.

On line 3 raise the hands high in front and wiggle the fingers to represent falling rain.

On line 4, bring both hands down together in front of you as if to "wash the spider out."

On lines 5 and 6 raise the hands high in front as if to form a sun.

On lines 7 and 8, repeat the same direction as for lines 1 and 2.

Sing Your Way Home

Sing your way home at the close of the day
Sing your way home, drive the shadows away
Smile every mile for wherever you roam

It will lighten your load
It will brighten your road,
If you sing your way home.

Musical Treasure Hunt

HAVE peanuts or other objects hidden about the room. Divide the guests into groups of seven and appoint a leader for each group. Each group constitutes an orchestra with a director and players for the following instruments: Piano, saxophone, violin, cornet, drum, and banjo.

Anyone may find an object but no one but a director may pick it up, and he may do so only for members of his orchestra. When anyone finds a hidden object, he must stand beside it and go through the motions of playing his instrument; and at the same time, try to imitate with his voice the sound of the instrument until his director comes and picks up the object.

Farmer in the Dell

SOME games are so old that they are new to many people who live today. "Farmer in the Dell" is still a favorite with children and young people. It is best played out of doors, at a picnic or on the beach.

The players stand in a circle with one of the players in the center to represent the "farmer." All sing the words to the familiar tune, "Farmer in the Dell"; as they march around the farmer.

1—The farmer in the dell,
The farmer in the dell,
Heigh-o, the merry-o,
The farmer in the dell.
2—The farmer takes a wife (repeat as in No. 1)
3—The wife takes a child.
4—The child takes a nurse.
5—The nurse takes a cat.
6—The cat takes a rat.
7—The rat takes a cheese.
8—The cheese stands alone.

The players act out the song as all sing. The farmer takes one from the circle for his wife, she takes one for a child, and so on.

When the rat takes a cheese, this means that there is going to be a chase. The rat must chase the cheese. On the verse the "The cheese stands alone," the cheese takes his place just outside the circle and when the verse is finished, the rat chases the cheese. If the cheese can make a circuit and get back of the group before being caught, he is safe, and the game proceeds with the rat taking the place of the farmer. If, however, the rat catches the cheese, the cheese must then become the farmer and continue the game.

Musical Tune Test

A READER and a versatile pianist work together in this game. Each has been supplied, in advance, with the following poem in which are found very familiar song titles, most of them of American origin, all of which should be familiar to most persons.

The guests are supplied with pencils and papers. It is explained that the tunes are mentioned in the poem and that the reader will stop every time he comes to the title of a song and, instead of reading the title, the pianist will play a few measures on the piano. The reading will continue until the poem is finished. The object of the game is for the players to try to guess all of the tunes. The player that guesses the largest number will be declared the winner.

Now here is a game that may puzzle you,
To play it, this is what you must do:

When the poem mentions a song by name,
The pianist will play to help with the game.

You guess the name of the tune that is played,
Quickly too—the game must not be delayed.

The boy wore uniform—on his breast were wings,
He sang THE HALLS OF MONTEZUMA among other things.

The girl was JEANIE WITH THE LIGHT BROWN HAIR,
He met her at the CAMPTOWN RACES at the fair.

It was near the SUWANEE RIVER that they met,
She's never seen the MOONLIGHT ON THE WABASH yet.

He said, LET ME CALL YOU SWEETHEART, dear,
She said, You're not from DIXIE, what you doin' here?

He said, I'm back from the war, a YANKEE DOODLE DANDY,
I've heard Southern girls were sweeter far than candy.

I see AMERICA THE BEAUTIFUL in your form and face,
With you and me HOME SWEET HOME could be any place.

He said, THERE'S A LONG, LONG TRAIL A WINDING,
But my SWEETHEART OF SIGMA CHI I'm just finding.

It was a night of MOONLIGHT AND ROSES—perpetual spring
And one could LISTEN TO THE MOCKING BIRD sing.

She played and they sang LOVE'S OLD SWEET SONG,
And he said to her, O PROMISE ME before very long.

She said, THERE'LL BE A HOT TIME IN THE OLD TOWN TONIGHT,
And we'll dance to the tune of OH, SUSANNA until daylight.

The years have brought SILVER THREADS AMONG THE GOLD
Now they sing AULD LANG SYNE, and think of growing old.

How Green

THE guests are taught to sing to the tune, "Auld Lang Syne," the following words:

How green you are, how green you are
How green you are, how green
How green you are, how green you are
How green you are, how green.

One player is sent out of the room while the others decide on some object which he is to hunt upon his return. When this player returns to the room, all start singing. When he comes near to the object, the singing grows very low, and if he touches the object the singing stops. As he gets farther away from the object, the singing grows louder and when he is entirely at the opposite end of the room, the guests sing at the top of their voices. When the object is finally located, another player is sent out and the game continues.

Couple Scramble

THIS and the following game are very interesting variations of the old familiar game, "Going to Jerusalem." In this game the group is divided into couples. Chairs are placed around the room by twos. There are two fewer chairs than persons playing, so that when the music stops, and all scramble for chairs, one couple will be without chairs and will consequently be eliminated. While the music continues, all march around the room. As soon as the music ceases, all try to take chairs. The rules are that partners must remain together, and if either one of the partners can seat himself in a chair before one partner of another group is seated in either chair, the couple that occupied one of the chairs first is entitled to both of them. The game continues each time taking away two chairs and eliminating a couple, until finally only two are left. The couple last to get chairs should be given a prize.

Hats

"HATS" is another variation of "Going to Jerusalem" which could be made quite funny by securing a number of out-of-fashion hats, particularly those discarded by the ladies. It would not be out of place to have a few sunbonnets or even a few bathing caps.

The guests are seated in a circle and enough hats are supplied to take care of all except one. This individual must remain hatless when the game starts. When the music starts, the players start passing the hats to the right. The rule is that each player must first put the hat on his head and then pass it on to the next. Whoever is hatless when the music stops must drop out of the game. The leader then takes away a hat and continues to do so each time the music stops in order that there may always be one hatless person.

Elimination

PLAYERS form a circle, and each one is given a book. This book must be balanced on the head of the player as he marches. When the music stops, each player must kneel on the floor and remain in this position until the music is resumed, whereupon all continue to march. If the book should fall to the floor or be touched by the hand of the player, that player is disqualified and must withdraw. The game continues until only one player is left. This one should receive an appropriate prize. This game can very well be played two or three times.

Calling Numbers

THE players form a circle and march around the room to music. The leader should know in advance the number of players in the group. When the music stops, the leader calls a number, for example, seven. This means that players must form themselves in new circles with seven in each circle. If there are twenty-four players, and the number seven is called, this would mean that three circles would be formed and three players would be eliminated. The players again form themselves into a large circle and the leader calls another number. There being twenty-one players left, the leader may call the number, five, thus eliminating only one. The game continues until only three remain.

Leap Frog

TUNE: "John Brown's Body."

One grasshopper jumped right over the other grasshopper's back,
One grasshopper jumped right over the other grasshopper's back,
One grasshopper jumped right over the other grasshopper's back,
And the other grasshopper jumped right over the other grasshopper's back.
They were only playing leap frog,
They were only playing leap frog,
They were only playing leap frog,
And the other grasshopper jumped right over the other grasshopper's back.

Musical Spell Down

DIVIDE the guests into two groups and have them stand facing each other. The leader acts as "pronouncer" for the spell down. Have someone at the piano who is familiar with a lot of tunes, or have several songbooks available for use. When the game starts, the first player on one team tries to guess the first tune played by the pianist. If he fails, he is eliminated. The first player on the next side then has a turn. The object is to see which side can eliminate the other.

Old Woman

(Boys) Old woman, old woman will you do my carding?
Old woman, old woman will you do my carding?
(Girls) Speak a little louder sir, I'm very hard of hearing.
Speak a little louder sir, I'm very hard of hearing.

(Boys) Old woman, old woman, will you do my weaving?
Old woman, old woman, will you do my weaving?
(Girls) Speak a little louder sir, I'm very hard of hearing.
Speak a little louder sir, I'm very hard of hearing.

(Boys) Old woman, old woman, will you let me court you?
Old woman, old woman, will you let me court you?
(Girls) Speak a little louder sir, I've just begun to hear you.
Speak a little louder sir, I've just begun to hear you.

(Boys) Old woman, old woman, will you let me marry you?
Old woman, old woman, will you let me marry you?
(Girls) Law have mercy on my soul, I believe that now I hear you.
Law have mercy on my soul, I believe that now I hear you.

(This song may be made more effective if on every verse the boys sing more softly and the girls louder.)

Down in the Valley

Down in the valley, the valley so low,
Bend your head over, hear the wind blow;
Hear the wind blow dear, hear the wind blow,
Bend your head over, hear the wind blow.

Roses love sunshine, violets love dew
God in his heaven knows I love you;
Knows I love you dear, knows I love you,
God in his heaven knows I love you.

If you don't love me, love whom you please,
Throw your arms round me, give my heart ease;
Give my heart ease dear, give my heart ease,
Throw your arms round me, give my heart ease.

Build me a tower forty feet high,
So I may see him as he goes by,
As he goes by dear, as he goes by;
So I may see him as he goes by.

Good Fellowship

TUNE: "Yankee Doodle."

Folks from cities and from towns
Meeting here together,
Let's all be happy, blithe, and free,
No matter what the weather.

You'll greet Mary, she'll greet Kate,
Kate will greet Suzannah,
She in turn will smile at me;
Will I be glum—how can I?

Yankee Doodle

A DOUBLE circle marches with girls on the inside as "Yankee Doodle" is played and the following words sung to the tune.

Yankee Doodle came to town, ridin' on a pony,
Stuck a feather in his cap, and called it macaroni.
Yankee Doodle, step right up. Yankee Doodle dandy,
Yankee Doodle skip three girls and catch a partner's hand-y.

One player is in the center of the circle and has no partner. On the words, "skip three girl and catch a partner's hand-y," all boys move up to the girl three places in front of them, while the boy in the center tries to catch a partner. After playing with the girls on the inside and a boy in the center for awhile, change and put a girl in the center and the boys on the inside circle.

Haste Away to the Wedding

Haste away to the wedding, haste away to the wedding
Haste away to the wedding, Jennie my own true love.

When will us be married, when will us be married?
When will us be married, Johnnie my own true love?

When taters are ripe on vine, when taters are ripe on vine,
When taters are ripe on vine, Jennie my own true love.

The Lady and the Pig

Once a lady loved a pig,
"Honey," said she,
"Darling swine will you be mine?"
"Oink," said he.

"You shall have a silver sty,
Honey," said she;
"And a piece of pumpkin pie."
"Oink," said he.

Divide the group into three small groups. Let one be the story-teller, one the lady, and one the pig.

Aunt Jemima

Aunt Jemima, look at uncle Jim.
He's in the duck pond learning how to swim.
First he does the back stroke, then he does the side,
Now he's under the water, swimming against the tide.

Rounds

For these rounds the group is divided into two, three, or four parts, as indicated by the music or the lines of the song.

White Coral Bells

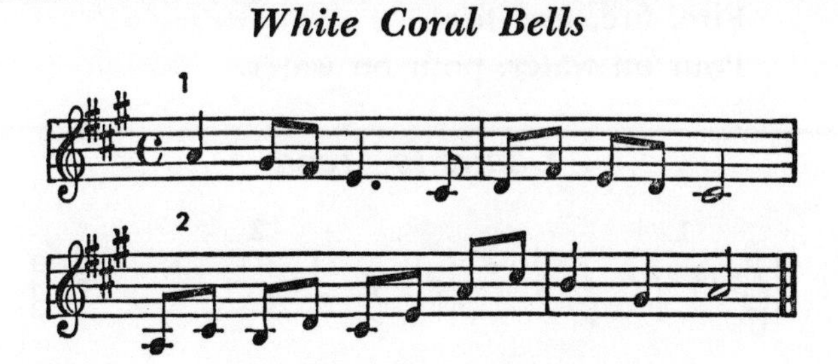

White coral bells upon a slender stalk,
Lilies-of-the-valley deck our garden walk,
Oh, don't you wish that you could hear them ring?
That would happen only when the fairies sing.

Merrily, Merrily

Merrily, merrily, greet the morn,
Cheerily, cheerily, sound the horn;
Hark to the echoes, hear them play
O'er hill and dale far, far away.

Scotland's Burning

Scotland's burning, Scotland's burning,
Look out, look out!

Fire, fire, fire, fire!
Pour on water, pour on water.

Chairs to Mend

Chairs to mend, old chairs to mend,
Mackerel, fresh mackerel,
Any old rags, any old rags.

List to the Bells

List to the bells, silver-y bells,
Rhyming and chiming their melody swells,
O the beautiful chiming of bells,
Bells, bells, chiming of bells.

Fare Thee Well

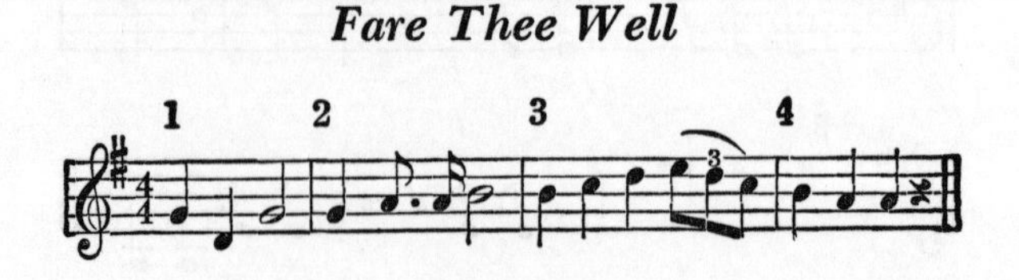

Fare thee well, luck go with thee,
When I'm far remember me.

Rose Red

Rose, rose, rose, rose, shall I ever see thee red?
I marry that thou wilt, if thou but stay.

Section 9

games for special occasions

JANUARY

January Burlesque Horoscope

It is in January that we begin the new year. Because January stands at the beginning of the year, it was so named by the Romans after their God, Janus, the God of Beginnings, whose festival fell within this month. He was represented as a double-headed deity with one face looking backward and one looking forward. This is symbolic of the month of January. It is the month when we review the accomplishments of the past year as well as the month in which we make resolutions and plans for the new year. The special flower of this month is the snowdrop and the garnet is the stone of the month. January was not one of the original months of the year, the year according to the earliest Roman calendar having begun with March. Numa Pompulius, tradition says, added January but gave it only thirty days. The calendar formed under Julius Caesar gave January thirty-one days.

Famous Persons and Events of January

Below is a list of famous persons born in January.

Paul Revere, 1735	Famous ride, Boston to Lexington

Joan of Arc, 1412	French Martyr
Alexander Hamilton, 1757	American statesman, first Secretary of Treasury
Edmund Burke, 1729	British statesman and orator
Moliere, 1622	French dramatist
Benjamin Franklin, 1706	American writer, statesman, and financier
Daniel Webster, 1782	American statesman and orator
James Watt, 1736	Scotchman and inventor of steam engine
Robert E. Lee, 1807	Great Southern General
Edgar Allan Poe, 1809	Famous American poet
"Stonewall" Jackson, 1824	Great Southern General
Robert Burns, 1759	Scottish poet
Mozart, 1756	German composer
William McKinley, 1843	Twenty-fifth President of the United States
Franz Schubert, 1797	Austrian composer
Franklin Delano Roosevelt, 1882	President of the United States

A very interesting game may be made from the list of famous birthdays. The leader might copy this list and put an incorrect description of the person and ask the guest to correct the list, as for example. Paul Revere, German composer; James Watt, French martyr. In many instances the correction will not be so obvious.

The following are some famous January events:

First Presidential election in the United States, 1789
Napoleon divorced Josephine, 1810
Lincoln issued Emancipation Proclamation, 1863
Discovery of gold in California, 1848
Edward VII became king of England, 1901
Paris surrendered to the Germans, 1871
Alaskan boundary dispute between Great Britain and United States settled, 1897
Ireland became a part of the United Kingdom of Great Britain, 1801

These important events may be used as a contest as well. The statement might be rewritten leaving part of it blank; for example,

First presidential election, ——, 1789, the guests will then fill in the words, in United States. While this would probably be over the heads of most of the guests, these events of January would prove to be interesting topics of conversation.

Wheel of Time

DRAW on paper, so that there will be one for each guest, a wheel with twelve spokes in it. Use the pattern in the diagram below, numbering the spokes from one to twelve. Each guest is given such a wheel and upon a signal from the leader, each guest must fill in his wheel with the name of a person of the opposite sex, with his or her consent, of course. When all have filled their wheel of time, the leader announces topics of conversation for each spoke. The following may be used, or other topics of greater interest to the group may be substituted by the leader:

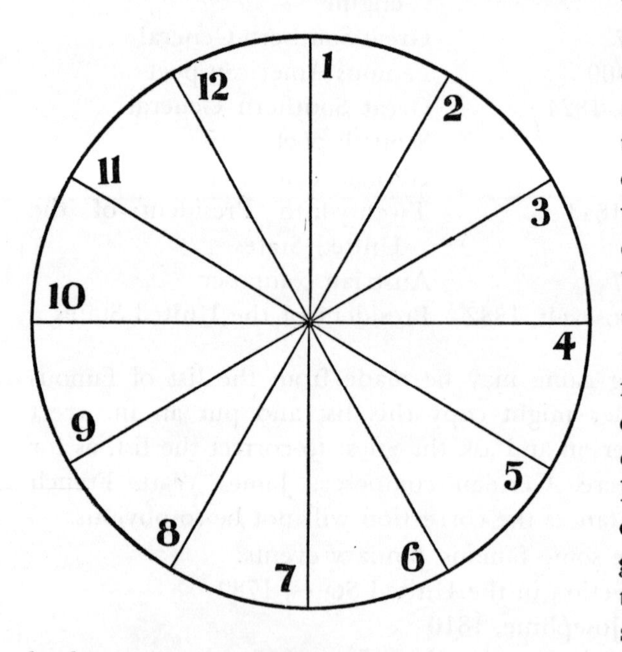

(1) My most embarrassing moment, (2) School days, (3) Athletics, (4) An accident, (5) An interesting trip I took, (6) A movie I enjoyed, (7) Where I spent the Fourth of July, (8) What I want my husband (or wife) to be like, (9) Friend, (10) My hobby, (11) Reading, (12) My favorite music.

Allow time for partners to contact each other between spokes. About two or three minutes should be allowed each couple for conversation.

New Year's Candle Magic

PREPARE slips of paper on which fortunes have been written with invisible ink or lemon juice. These slips are distributed among the guests and each guest is asked to write his name on the slip of paper and hand it back to the leader. Assemble the guests in a dark corner and by the light of a candle heat the slips carefully above the flame. After the slips have been heated, light the room so that guests may read their messages which seemingly have come by magic.

Future for the New Year

GIVE each guest a half of an English walnut shell and a small birthday candle. Tubs of water have been provided in which to float these English walnut shells when used as small boats. Guests should mark their walnut shell or candle in some way so that it can always be identified, and then set it adrift on top of the water. If it clings to the side, it indicates that the year will be quiet for them. If two boats belonging to persons of opposite sex float together, it may mean that a love affair is in the brewing. If ships collide and shipwreck, it means trouble for the year. The candle that burns the longest will indicate that its owner will marry first.

New Year's Prophecies

PLACE three cups on a table. One should be half full of milk, the second half full of water, and the third half full of vinegar. The guests are blindfolded and asked to touch one of the cups. The guest must dip his finger into the first cup touched, and if it contains milk, it will indicate that his life will be happy and that he will be married. If it contains water, it will mean that single blessedness will last another year, and if it contains vinegar, it will mean that the future wife or husband will cause much trouble.

Month Scramble

WRITE the names of the twelve months of the year on cards, making two sets, or if the group is large, make three or four sets. The leader, without telling the guests what he plans to do, divides the guests into groups of twelve and passes out to that group the cards with the names of the month on them. He tells all to keep their places until final instructions are given and then he tells them that they must arrange themselves, as soon as the signal is given, in the order that the months come with January at the leader's left. There will be a mad scramble as soon as the signal is given, and in case there are more than two groups, judges will have to be appointed to determine the winning group.

Watch Game

CAN YOU find on your watch the following things: 1. Standard equipment even for new babies. 2. Something used when you want to look into the future. 3. Also found on a flower. 4. Always found under the mattress. 5. The relation of a noun, pronoun, or adjective to another word. 6. The kind of mate a widow or widower yearns for. 7. In football language it is sometimes full, sometimes half, sometimes quarter. 8. Read by the secretary at the beginning of a meeting. 9. Sometimes found on a dog. 10. Characters used in mathematics.

ANSWERS: 1. *Hands and face.* 2. *Crystal.* 3. *Stem.* 4. *Springs.* 5. *Case.* 6. *Second.* 7. *Back.* 8. *Minutes.* 9. *Tick.* 10. *Figures.*

Rug Scooter

FOR THIS contest, which is really a relay, it will be necessary to have a smooth, slippery floor. If the room is large enough, have two groups of equal number participating at the same time; otherwise, it will be necessary to time each group to determine the winner. In either case, provide a group with a small rug to be used as the scooter which the first player must propel to the opposite end of the room and around some object placed on the floor and back to the starting point, keeping one foot on the rug and the other on the floor in the manner that a small boy propels a scooter. The next person on the team is then given the rug, and so on until all members of each group have participated.

Progressive Up-Jenkins

A MINIMUM of twenty-four guests is needed to play Progressive Up-Jenkins. Thirty-two or more players would make the game more exciting. The guests are divided into groups of four, each four constituting a team. Each of the teams selects a Captain. Tables that will seat eight, with four on a side, should be provided. Two teams of four sit at a table, one team facing the other across the table.

The leader supplies each table with a coin. This is given to one of the teams at the table. The players on this team put their hands under the table and pass the coin back and forth until the Captain of the opposite team calls out, "Up-Jenkins." Whereupon the members of the team having the coin place their elbows on the table. Then the leader of the opposing team calls out, "Down-Jenkins." All players on the side having the coin slap their hands on the table, palms down.

The object of the game is for the opposing Captain to call for the removal of the hands from the table in such a manner that the hand under which he thinks the coin is to be found is removed last. If he succeeds in doing this, the score of the side which was holding the coin would be zero. On the other hand, if the Captain of the opposing team should happen to remove first the hand under which the coin is held, this would leave seven hands on the table, and the side holding the coin would score seven. Each team gets a score equal to the number of hands left on the table when the coin is discovered. Only the Captain of the team may give orders to remove hands from the table although other players may make suggestions.

After one team has had the coin, it is passed to the opposing team and the same process is repeated. When both sides at all tables have had a turn, the score is added up. The team at each table having the highest score progresses. The losers at the head table must go to the foot table, while the winners at the head table remain there as long as they win.

Balloon Tournament

HERE is a boisterous and exciting game that will create a lot of ridiculous and funny situations. Divide the group into couples, one being designated as the horse and the other the rider, although, of course, they do not ride the horses. Place an equal number of couples at each end of the room and fasten an inflated toy balloon on the back of each horse. The object of the game is to have this couple, upon a signal given by the leader, charge another couple on the opposite side of the room and try to burst the toy balloon on the back of the opposing horse. The horse should go on all fours and should not be allowed to have any part in the bursting of the balloon except to go where his rider leads him or commands him. The rider, on the other hand, is to try to protect the balloon on his horse from being burst by the opposing rider. This game may continue as an elimination contest, the winners being paired against others who win in the first heat, and so on until only two couples remain for the finals.

News

THE guests are divided into two groups, and they form lines on each side of the room facing each other. Two judges are stationed at the foot of the lines. The leader has prepared a number of news items from some of the important events of the past year, making two copies. When the signal is given, the person at the head of the line is given a slip of paper with the news item on it. He reads it over and repeats it to the next one in line. The rule is that it may be repeated only one time. This one repeats it to the next, and so on down the line. The last one must write it on a slip of paper and give it to the judges. Allow two points for the line that finishes first and four points to the line that gets the news the least garbled. This game could continue until as many as ten items had been passed down the lines and the judges could then announce the winners.

FEBRUARY

February Burlesque Horoscope

THE stars say that those born in February will be of a festive disposition, although of serious thought on spiritual things. Women born in February will be meticulous about their housekeeping and never neglect their spring cleaning. It might well be expected that all born in this month would have the characteristics of the famous folk born in it. They will be truthful like Washington, honest like Lincoln, and be ardent lovers, catching the spirit of St. Valentine. People born in February will delight in much feasting, as February was the month of feasting and overeating by the Romans. February is the month of romance as it not only has in it St. Valentine's Day, but one year in every four, it is the leap-year month.

Famous February Folk

THE following is a list of famous persons born in February together with the things for which they were famous:

Birthdays	*Things for which famous*
Henry W. Longfellow, 1807	American poet
Elihu Root, 1845	American statesman
Dwight L. Moody, 1837	Noted evangelist
Charles Dickens, 1812	Famous British novelist
Thomas A. Edison, 1847	American inventor
Abraham Lincoln, 1809	Civil War President
George Washington, 1732	First President of United States
Felix Mendelssohn, 1809	German musical composer
Susan B. Anthony, 1820	Founder of woman suffrage movement
James Russell Lowell, 1819	American poet
Galileo, 1564	Astronomer and natural philosopher
Horace Greeley, 1811	American journalist and politician
Sidney Lanier, 1842	American poet
Handel, 1685	German Composer

A very interesting game may be made by writing on slips of paper the names of the famous folk born in February and asking the guests to write the reason they were famous. Give a prize to the one that has the most nearly correct list.

February Guessing Contest

1. What ship was blown up in Havana harbor in February, 1898? *Maine*
2. When is ground-hog day? *February 2*

3. What famous person escaped from Elba in February, 1815? *Napoleon*
4. What is the February birthstone? *Amethyst*
5. What President was elected in February, 1825? *John Quincy Adams*
6. What great American inventor was born February 11, 1847? *Edison*
7. What famous war ended in February, 1783? *Revolutionary War*
8. What effect does leap year have on February? *Adds one day to the length of the month*
9. What famous American person cried first on February 22? *George Washington*
10. What two Presidents were born in February? *Washington and Lincoln*
11. What is the origin of the Valentine legend? *St. Valentine, a benevolent early Christian bishop, was killed in Rome on February 14, A.D. 270.*
12. What famous American poet was born February 27? *Longfellow*

These questions may be given out with the answers left blank, and guests may be asked to fill in the answers. If a list of these questions has not been prepared in advance for each guest, the leader may give to each a blank piece of paper and ask him to write numbers from one to twelve in the lefthand margin. The leader then may read the questions and have the guests write the answer by number. Have guests exchange papers and grade them. Give an appropriate prize to the one which is most nearly correct.

Lincoln Party Games

For a Lincoln party, February 12, decorate with flags, stick candy, log cabins, kitchen chairs, old-time furnishings, etc. A costume house-party with guests dressed in clothing of that period would be a novel idea. Serve refreshments of gingerbread and coffee. The following are listed for Lincoln party games:

1—Have guests make as many words as possible from the letters in Abraham Lincoln.

2—Procure an old blue-back speller and have an old-time spelling match.

3—Provide guests with blank paper and colored crayons and give a prize to the one who can draw the best face of Lincoln.

4—Lincoln penny contest. Give each guest a penny and this list of objects that are to be found on it. Either the old Lincoln penny or the new series may be used for this game. They are to list after each descriptive phrase an object found on the penny described by the phrase. In some cases this may be a letter, a word, a part of the body, and so on.

A book of the Bible	Numbers
A policeman	Copper
A hotel	Inn (in)
A deity	God
A small animal	Hare (hair)
Worn by a work horse	Collar
A layer of paint	Coat
An Indian weapon	Bow
A messenger	One cent (one sent)
The doors have them	Locks
A part of a hill	Brow
The end of the river	Mouth
What Patrick Henry wanted	Liberty
What lovers write	Letters
One end of a nail	Head
The state of a couple after the wedding ceremony	United

Valentine Song Fest

A GOOD way to begin a Valentine party is to start with a song fest. While the guests are assembling, have those who have already arrived join in the singing of love songs, old and new. Some suggestions would be: "Love's Old Sweet Song," "Believe Me if All Those Endearing Young Charms," "Let Me Call You Sweetheart," "O Promise Me," "My Bonnie Lies Over the Ocean," "Annie Laurie,"

"Spanish Cavalier," "Juanita," and perhaps some of the popular new ones.

Cobweb Hunt

PROCURE in advance balls of twine in number to equal half of your guests. As the men arrive, each one is given a ball of twine. When no one is looking, they are to tie one end of the twine to some object, and as they move about the room "Up stairs and down stairs, and in my lady's chamber" they carry with them the ball of twine, letting it out as they move along. With a dozen people doing this it is easy to imaigne that even some persons will get tangled in the web. As soon as each person has unwound his entire ball of twine, he hands the loose end to the leader. When the leader has in hand all the loose ends, she calls the ladies to her and distributes them. Each lady is then asked to reroll the ball of twine while each gentleman is asked to go to his starting point, untie the other end, and start rolling the twine until he meets his partner. These can work together on other games during the evening.

Lover's Examination

WHEN Valentine's Day rolls around, each one is supposed to have thoughts of love in his mind and heart. He should therefore be ready to pass the lover's examination. The guests are given sheets of paper and the leader reads the following:

1—Describe briefly your ideal man (or woman)
2—Enumerate ten symptoms of love
3—Write fifty words of advice to those who are lovelorn
4—Who is the best friend of Cupid?
5—Who is Cupid's worst enemy?
6—Write a ten-word telegram of proposal to your lover
7—What do you consider the most admirable trait in a husband (or wife)?
8—Write a four-line jingle about St. Valentine

After the papers have been read, take a vote and award the prize to the one giving the most humorous answers.

Winged Hearts

USING tissue paper, cut hearts and write the name of a girl present on each. To distribute the hearts, drop them one or two at a time before an electric fan. When a heart comes to a stop, the boy nearest it picks it up and finds on it the name of his partner for the next game.

When it is desirable to change partners again, do the same with the boys' names written on the hearts. The girls then pick up the names of their next partners.

Valentine Relay

DIVIDE the guests into two groups of equal number and have the groups stand on opposite sides of the room. The leader at the head of each line is given an envelope which has in it three valentines, on each of which must be written a valentine verse or other valentine sentiment in prose. The leader should take care that the readings on the different sides should be approximately the same length. When the signal is given for the game to start, the leader at the head of the line takes the valentines out of the envelope one by one, reads them aloud, and places them back in the envelope and hands the envelope to the next player. This will make quite a hilarious noise when both sides are reading valentines at the same time. The first line to get the valentines all the way down is declared the winner.

Candy Heart Sentences

IT is always possible in February to buy at the five- and ten-cent stores candy hearts on which are found some sentimental and some slang expressions. Procure some of these hearts and divide them out among the guests, offering a prize to the one who will make the most complete sentence from the words on the hearts.

Washington Compliments

PREPARE as many slips of paper as there are guests and write one guest's name on each. These are then shuffled and passed around, in every case the guest being given the name of a person of the opposite sex. The guests are then asked to write something complimentary about this person, whose name is on the paper, using the letters in Washington's name in the order in which they appear to begin the words. For example, a boy might describe a girl as follows: "Winsome, Awfully sly. Has intriguing natural grace. Takes only nourishment." Or another example, "Was always successful husband. Is never glum, tiresome, or niggardly." Each person writes on the back of his finished compliment the name of the person described and his own name. A vote should be taken and a prize given to the one writing the best compliment, and the one who most properly described the person intended.

Cherry Race

DIVIDE the guests into two groups of equal number and have them assemble in different corners of one end of the room. The leader of each group is given three or four large cherries (either real or imitation), and when the signal is given, one contestant from each group must place the cherries on the back of his left hand and race with them in this position to the goal at the other end of the room and back. If a cherry rolls off or if all of them roll off, the runner must pick them up unassisted and continue. When the first player returns, the second player goes, and so on until all have had a try.

MARCH

March Burlesque Horoscope

MARS (for whom March was named) was the ancient Roman god of war. He was also associated in the minds of the ancient peoples with thunder and lightning. Mars was a god who was believed to be able to do almost anything because he was so strong. The ancient people prayed to him for rain and consulted him about their private affairs. Thus, the person born in this month will be of strong character, inviting confidence and counsel; temperamental in nature, yet heeding the advice of friends. This individual will also possess inventive genius as that of Alexander Graham Bell, inventor of the telephone;

love for nature, as that of Burbank; love of horses, as that of Rosa Bonheur; the deep love, as that of Elizabeth Barrett Browning.

Using the names of the famous persons born in March, have a costumed "crystal gazer" give a prophecy that people born in this month will possess the characteristics of these and other famous people of the month.

Famous Folk of March

THE following is a list of famous persons born in March, together with the things for which they were famous.

William Dean Howell, 1837	American novelist
James Madison, 1751	Fourth President of the United States
John C. Calhoun, 1782	American statesman
Grover Cleveland, 1837	Twenty-second President of the United States
Alexander Graham Bell, 1847	Inventor of the telephone, American inventor
David Livingstone, 1813	Missionary to Africa (Scottish)
William Jennings Bryan, 1860	American political leader
Elizabeth Barrett Browning, 1806	English poet
Michelangelo, 1475	Italian artist
Johann Bach, 1685	German composer
Rosa Bonheur, 1822	French painter
Americus Vespucius, 1451	Explorer for whom America is named
Andrew Jackson, 1767	Seventh President of the United States
Franz Joseph Haydn, 1732	Austrian composer

The names of the famous persons may be jumbled and the players required to write them correctly, or the players may be required to write after each name the reason why it is famous.

The guests may also be given the list of famous persons and asked to draw a picture representative of the fame attached to the name.

Famous Events of March

1—Florida became a state of the Union, 1845
2—William Penn given grant of Pennsylvania, 1681
3—United States Constitution went into effect, 1789
4—Washington became first President in 1789
5—The massacre at the Alamo in Texas, 1836
6—Discovery of South Pole announced by Amundsen, 1912
7—Grant made commander of all Federal armies, 1864
8—Whitney's cotton gin patented, 1794
9—West Point Military Academy founded, 1802
10—British evacuated Boston, 1776
11—Robert P. Scott and companions died on return from South Pole, 1912
12—Patrick Henry's famous oration delivered, 1775
13—First meeting of Congress under new Constitution, 1789
14—Last American troops left Cuba, 1909

Write these statements on numbered slips of paper and pin them at various places around the room. Give each guest a slip of paper with numbers on it from one to fourteen, instructing the guests to find the statement corresponding to the number and write it on their slip of paper.

Shamrock

THE answers to these are to be words made from the letters in shamrock.

1—An Irish city	Cork
2—A month of the year	March
3—Member of the human body	Arm
4—Article of man's apparel	Sock
5—A common article of food	Ham
6—A bright planet	Mars
7—A detested pest	Roach
8—Used in making towels	Crash
9—Replaced by the auto	Hack
10—An instrument of torture	Rack

11—What we lacked when the banks closed	Cash
12—Common means of transportation	Car
13—An article used in disguise	Mask
14—Swampy land	Marsh
15—Something very solid	Rock
16—Something not real	Sham
17—A well known uncle	Sam
18—A gospel writer	Mark
19—Noah's boat	Ark
20—To mimic	Mock

Irish Tests

1—STICK a knife into wall or window frame, about shoulder high and put a piece of candy on the handle of the knife. Guests, one at a time, start eight feet from the knife, holding one eye closed, extending the other hand toward the knife and walking briskly, attempt to push the candy off the knife. Only one push is allowed.

2—Cut out three green or yellow or red (all of one color) discs, about the size of a half dollar; paste them on a large triangular piece of white paper, near the base. Pin this sheet of paper to the wall and ask the guest to stare at the colored discs steadily for two minutes. Then ask the guest to lift his eyes quickly to the blank part of the paper and tell what he sees. He will see three more spots, but of different colors, which astonishes him.

3—Telling ages. Guests think of their age. This number is then doubled and then that result is multiplied by five. The last digit is then taken off and the result is the age of the guests.

4—Blarney burning. Soak a thread about a foot in length in 50 per cent salt water solution, straighten it out and let it dry for several hours. Tie a lightweight, small ring on one end and tie the other end so as to suspend the ring. Light the string with a candle and it will burn to an ash which will still support the ring.

5—Snake tag. One person is "It." The others form a line with hands on each other's shoulders. "It" must tag the *last* person in the line. The line winds in and out to keep "It" from being able to tag the last person of the "snake's tail." When the last person is tagged, he becomes "It," or if anyone breaks the line, that player becomes "It."

6—Irishman's relay. Place potatoes in a line, each potato bearing a number. Guests roll golf balls to hit them by numbers. There should be a numbered list of stunts corresponding to the number of the potatoes and when a potato is hit, the player is required to perform the corresponding numbered stunt.

Mad March

THIS is a mad relay race as you will see when you try to do the stunt. The guests are divided into two groups of equal number. The first one in each group is given a cane; and when the signal for starting is given, he is asked to put this forehead on the top of the cane and keep it there without moving the cane until he sidesteps six times around in a circle, counting each time he makes a circuit, one, two, three, and so on. When he has finished the sixth round, he is to walk to the opposite end of the room, touch a designated spot on the wall or floor, and then go back to the starting point, giving the cane to the next contestant. The game continues until all have had a try. The group whose members all finish first wins the contest.

Irish Clans

DIVIDE the guests into groups according to the seasons of the year, those born in the spring would make up one Irish Clan, those in the summer another, etc. These clans assemble in groups and plan a big story about a fishing or hunting trip or an adventure. Allow about five or ten minutes for the clan to secretly plan their yarn. When they reassemble, have a clan in each corner of the room seated on chairs or on the floor. When the competition starts, one member of the spring group begins his yarn. The next person may add to it, and so on until it is finished or an allotted portion of time consumed. This may be decided on in advance and may be from three to ten minutes. When the judges have decided which yarn was the best, the cleverest, or the most ridiculous, a bag of candy should be awarded to the group as a prize.

Basket of Corks

HAVE a large green wicker basket filled with corks of all sizes. These corks have been counted in advance and the guests are asked to guess the number of corks in the basket. An appropriate prize should be given to the one whose guess is most nearly correct.

Cork Toss

DISTRIBUTE among the guests the corks used in the guessing contest. The leader will know the number of corks and the number of guests and will be able to determine how many each guest shall receive. Place the basket at one end of the room for a target and have guests stand ten or twelve feet away and attempt to toss the corks in the basket. This will be more difficult than it might seem as the corks are light and of different sizes and it will also be difficult to keep them from bouncing out of the basket. An individual prize may be given to the one getting the largest number in, or the group may be divided into two sides and a prize may be given the side making the highest score.

Hull-Gull

AFTER the cork toss described above, each player gets back his corks and keeps them for a game of Hull-Gull. The first player holds his hands closed, full of corks, trying to make it appear that he has a large number, and says to another player, "Hull-gull." This player answers, "Hands full." The first player says, "How many?" The second player must name a number. If he says, "nine" and the first player holds only six corks in his hand, the first player then says, "Give me three to make it nine," and the second player must give away three of his corks. If the second player, however, guesses the exact number of corks which the first player holds, this player must forfeit all the corks in his hand. If the second player guesses too low a number, as for example, if there are five corks in the first player's hand, and the second player guesses three, he must give the first player two corks. The object of the game is to pick out the most successful player, that is the one who in ten minutes' time is able to acquire the largest number of corks. This one should be given an appropriate prize.

Round Cork in Square Hole

MORE fun with the corks will result from having the guests try to fit a round cork in a square hole. Where are we going to get square holes? Any lumber mill will fix a number of blocks with square holes at a small cost for this game, as machines for making square holes are used for making windows and doors. Each guest must be provided with a pocket or paring knife. It will look easy but prove very difficult to fit the cork into the square hole. Cork is not easily cut. The unexpected difficulty will make the game more amusing.

Scrambled Shamrocks

PREPARE in advance a large number of shamrocks, cutting them in large sizes, about three or four inches across. Cut each one in two parts, making an irregular cut and cutting others in a similar fashion. Place one part of the shamrock on a table at one end of the room and the other part on a table at the other end of the room. When the leader explains the game, guests are to go to the table in the end of the room designated as the starting table and take up a part of a shamrock, going then to the table in the other end of the room and attempt to find the other part. As soon as a guest has completed one shamrock, he may give it to the leader and get another. No guest may take more than one part from the table at a time. The guest who turns in the largest number of completed shamrocks should receive a prize.

APRIL

April Burlesque Horoscope

APRIL has been called the Angel of Spring—gracious, exquisite, tender, and kind. It is the month of beauty and the time of new birth when the earth wakes from its winter of sleep. Persons born in April will be easily aroused to tears because April is a rainy month; but as April showers pass quickly and the skies clear, so will these moody dispositions pass away quickly for those born in April. Those born in April will be lovers of poetry because this is the month of Wordsworth and of the immortal Shakespeare. They will likewise have the patriotic fervor of Henry Clay and Thomas Jefferson. Of course, withal, they will be a bit foolish, as this is the month of All Fools' Day. Some stories they tell will sound a bit fishy, as in some way the fish has come to be associated with All Fools' Day. People born in April ought to be good eggs because this is the month of Easter eggs.

Famous Folk of April

Thomas Jefferson, 1743	Third President of the United States
William Shakespeare, 1564	English poet
Henry Clay, 1777	American statesman
Hans Christian Andersen, 1805	Danish author of fairy tales
William Wordsworth, 1770	English poet
Washington Irvin 1783,	American author
Oliver Cromwell, 1599	Puritan English ruler
U. S. Grant, 1822	American general and President
James Monroe, 1758	Fifth President of the United States

It would be interesting and instructive to guests to plan a literary program around some of the April characters. For example, ask guests to give a quotation from Shakespeare; others might be asked to tell one of the fairy tales as told by Hans Christian Andersen. Ask guests to repeat the first sentence of the Declaration of Independence written by Thomas Jefferson. Have someone read a poem from Wordsworth. Ask someone to give a talk on the Monroe Doctrine. Of course, this would be much better if arranged for in advance.

April Fool Frolic

HAVE guests come in costume. Some suggestions are: represent funny-paper characters, movie actors, or Mother Goose characters. Decorate with fresh vegetables instead of flowers. Make guests enter through the back door and jump over a rope in the doorway, jump over chairs, boxes, and other obstacles, into the living room. The reception committee keeps backs turned to guests on arrival and shakes hands only over their shoulders. Have judging for costumes and give prizes.

Sardines

SARDINES is a game of hide and seek played in a very different way. Choose one person to hide. Several rooms should be left open so that the hiding may take place, and the lights should be turned out, or turned very low. When the hider has had sufficient time to get himself securely hidden, the others go looking for him in the dark. When anyone finds him, he must keep perfectly quiet and not reveal his hiding place but on the other hand, must join him and hide with him. Each other one who finds the hiding place must himself hide there also. Give a booby prize to the one who last finds the hiding place or make him the victim in other games.

Partners

PLAYERS choose partners and stand in parallel lines facing each other. The rule is that one's partner must always answer for him. One must not answer for himself. Two people walk up and down the lines asking questions of either party. One of these might say to a young man, "Who was that blonde I saw you with last might?" No matter how much he is tempted to respond, his partner must answer the question. Of course, it is so natural for one to answer a question that is asked one, that many will find it difficult to resist. In that case, this one must take the place of the questioner.

Opposites

PLAYERS are seated in a circle with the leader in the center of the circle. The leader explains the game, telling the group that when one is engaged in conversation, he must do just exactly the opposite of what the leader does. If the leader pretends to sit, the player must stand. If the leader rubs his left ear, the player must rub his right ear. If the leader opens his mouth, the other must close his and mumble his reply. When a player makes a slip, he must take the center and try to catch someone else. The ingenuity of some of the players in the center of the circle will add zest to the game.

How Do You Feel?

PREPARE for this game some twenty-five articles and put them in cloth bags. They must be recognized by the players by touch and shape. The bags should be numbered and players should be given sheets of paper with corresponding numbers in the left-hand margin. Players are to write down by number their guess as to what the bag contains. Some suggestions for articles to be placed in the bag follow: scissors, golf ball, pipe, pot cleaners, carrot, banana, shoe horn, cuff link, purse, coin (the exact denomination to be given), measuring spoons, rubber bands, sugar scoop, thimble, and so forth.

Tasty

PREPARE glasses containing several liquids of distinctive tastes and place a number somewhere on the glass. Have the guests identify the different liquids by taste. This will probably have to be done with the guests blindfolded as the appearance of many of the liquids would enable them to identify them. Some of the following would be suitable liquids: tea, milk, cocoa, coffee, water, lemonade, soft drinks, cider, orange juice, grapefruit juice, grape juice, and root beer.

Test of Hearing

FOR this test, the leader must stand behind a screen and drop the articles on the floor or table, while the guests must identify the object from the sound. The leader will have to call the number of each object before he drops it. Some suggestions for objects for this test are: a lemon, a golf ball, a pencil, a pack of cards, a string of beads, a cushion, tennis ball, a magazine, a coin, a spoon, a book, a newspaper, and a wet cloth.

Fish Race

THE guests are divided into two groups of equal number and assembled in opposite corners at one end of the room. The leader has cut from paper two fish and placed them on the floor about eight feet apart. When the signal is given, the first player in each group must use a fan to blow his fish to the goal, which is at the opposite end of the room, and back. Each player then has a turn, the side finishing first being declared the winner.

Bird in the Cage Relay

FOR this relay you will need two paper fans, two paper plates, and two birds cut out of tissue paper, preferably colored. Divide the guests into two groups and choose four to six players from each group to engage in this relay. The other players should watch and root for their side.

The object of the game is for each player to fan the bird into the cage, which is a paper plate, using only the fan. The bird is placed about two feet in front of the cage, and during the game may not be touched with the hand. When a player on one team has succeeded in getting the bird into the cage, the leader removes the bird and again places it about two feet from the plate, and the next player on the team has his turn. The side which has all of its players cage the bird first is the winner.

Egg Relay

Two eggs, either hard boiled or toy eggs, are used for this relay. Guests are divided into two equal groups and stand against opposite walls facing each other. The one at the head of each line is told that he cannot pass the egg until he has sung up and down the scale three times; he can then pass it to the next one who must do likewise, and so on until it has gone down and back. This will appear easier than it is but one will get so amused at the sour notes of another that he will not be able to sing for laughing.

Egg Rolling Contest

For this game prepare two hard-boiled eggs. If the guests have been divided into groups, select one man from each group for this stunt and let the other members of his team cheer for him while he rolls. A straight line has been drawn with chalk on the floor which each contestant must follow. He must roll the egg on the line, getting down on his hands and knees, using his nose to propel it. Prizes of candy eggs should be given to the winner or to all members of his group.

MAY

May Burlesque Horoscope

In the Roman world the Goddess Maia was one of the daughters of Atlas who bore all the weight of the world upon his shoulders. Maia was his most famous daughter because of her son Mercury who ran swiftly from heaven to earth on errands for the gods and goddesses. The cluster of six stars, called The Pleiades, are supposed to be Maia and her five sisters (the seventh star is invisible). However, Maia is the most brilliant of the stars; thus the individual born in May will possess brilliance; love such as that of Robert Browning; the gifts of Florence Nightingale; the wisdom of Queen Victoria; the adventuresome spirit of Robert Peary; the patriotic fervor of Patrick Henry. Using the name of famous folk of the month (and any others you choose), have a costumed "crystal gazer" give briefly a paper or talk on the prophecies concerning the individuals born in this month.

Famous Folk of May

Joseph Addison, 1672	English author
Horace Mann, 1796	American educator
Hubert Howe Bancroft, 1832	American historian
Robert E. Peary, 1856	American arctic explorer
Robert Browning, 1812	English Poet
William Howe, 1803	British general
Gabriel Fahrenheit, 1686	German physicist
Florence Nightingale, 1820	English nurse
John Stuart Mill, 1806	English philosopher
Richard Wagner, 1813	German composer
Thomas Hood, 1799	English humorist and poet
Queen Victoria, 1819	English queen
Ralph Waldo Emerson, 1803	American poet and essayist
George Bulwer-Lytton, 1803	English novelist
Julia Ward Howe, 1819	American author
William Pitt, 1759	English statesman
Patrick Henry, 1736	American statesman and orator
Walt Whitman, 1819	American poet

In using the names above, write them on slips of paper, placing the given names with the wrong surnames and require the guests to assemble them correctly.

If the group is composed of literary folk, see who can write the correct profession after each of the names.

A third suggestion for the use of the names is to have the guests make charades pertaining to the names most familiar.

The following is a jumbled list of the famous folk of May:

Patrick Addison	Thomas Nightingale
Walt Mann	George Wagner
Gabriel Bancroft	Hubert Howe Hood
Joseph Peary	William Victoria
Horace Browning	Julia Ward Emerson
Florence Howe	Robert E. Bulwer-Lytton
Queen Fahrenheit	John Stuart Howe
Ralph Waldo Mill	William Henry

Robert Whitman

May Events

IN PLANNING entertainment for May, the following events will suggest themselves: First, of course, is May Day, with the May Queen and dancing around the May pole. May is usually the time also for such events as class banquets, such as the Junior-Senior banquet, and other events in connection with the closing of school. Why should not Mother's Day come in for a place on the program? It would be a good idea for a group of young people to give a party honoring their mothers, or have a mother and daughter or mother and son banquet. It would not be out of place to express some sentiment growing out of Memorial Day.

Dressing the May Queen

THE LEADER has provided in advance a table filled with scarfs, hats, furs, ribbon, unbrellas, gloves, flowers, coats, and other articles. The boys select partners, either by choice or in some other manner designated by the leader. The leader gives the signal and all boys rush to the table to secure adornment for their queens. All the dressing of the May Queen must be done by the boy without any assistance whatever from his partner. When the decorations have been completed, have the queens promenade by the judges who will select the winning costume and give an appropriate prize, or crown, to the winner.

Dime on the Forehead

A GOOD stunt will always liven up a party. Choose someone to be the victim and tell him that you are going to place a dime on his forehead, offering him a handsome prize if he can shake it off in two minutes. Tell him that you will use no kind of sticky substance but that the dime will stick there nevertheless. The leader then presses a dime to the forehead of the victim for a few seconds and takes the dime off. It will feel as if the dime is still there, and the victim will try to shake it off. After he has shaken his head a few times, drop the dime on the floor to make it appear that it has fallen off. Tell the victim then that you want to try it again, and this time double the prize and give him three minutes. The stunt will grow funnier if the victim tries again.

Donkey Bite

GET the picture of a donkey, such as those used for the game, "Pinning on the donkey's tail." If such a one cannot be procured, have someone draw a picture of a donkey with long ears, etc. Choose several victims and put them in an adjoining room, bringing them out one at a time. Tell them that you are going to show them a donkey, after which they are to be blindfolded. After the blindfold is adjusted, they must then poke their finger in the donkey's ear. After the players have been blindfolded and have been brought up to the donkey and extend their fingers to poke the donkey's ear, someone gives the finger a sharp bite. This may be done with toy animal teeth, with a spring clothes pin, or with a large clip which is used to hold paper together. The first victim, of course, will have the fun of watching the others brought in.

Pass Ball

HERE is a good active game that any group will enjoy. Divide the guests into two groups of equal number and call them "ones" and "twos." The players stand in a circle with the numbers alternating. The leader gives a ball to one of the players, a number one, and on the opposite side of the circle another ball to a player, a number two. He tells them that they are to pass the ball to the right, that is, of course, the number ones pass them to other number ones; the number two players to number twos. It should be decided in advance whether the ball is to be handed to the next player or tossed to him. The game works better in handing the ball. The object is for number one to pass its ball so quickly that it catches up with number two's ball, or vice versa.

Different Ways

HERE is another novel active game. The guests are divided into two groups of equal number, and they stand facing each other along opposite walls. The first player on team number one must proceed down the room and back and he may do this in any manner he chooses. The first player on team number two must also go up and down the room but he must proceed in a different way. Player number two on team number one then goes, and he must go in some new way not used by the others. Some suggestions for proceeding up and down the room are: Walking, running, side stepping, hopping, walking backwards, running backwards, goose stepping, walking zigzag, crawling head first, crawling feet first, jumping with both feet together, and rolling.

Tossing the Cap

DIVIDE the guests into two groups, seating one group on one side of the room and the other group on the opposite side. The leader stands in the center with a cap in her hand. She tells the group that if she throws the cap up and it comes down right side up, players in group number one are to laugh heartily while players in group number two are to keep perfectly quiet and not even smile. On the other hand, if the cap falls wrong side up, players on side number two must laugh heartily while players on side number one are to remain glum. If a player on side number one is caught laughing or even smiling a wide smile when he is supposed to be glum, he must go over to side number two and vice versa. This game usually ends in everybody laughing and with no one being able to restrain them.

Rigmarole

THE PLAYERS are seated in a circle and the leader stands in the center. The leader gives each player in turn a phrase, such as those given below, and the player must repeat not only his phrase but everything that has been said by the players preceding him. For example, the leader gives the first player the phrase "one old oyster," which the player repeats. He gives the next player the phrase "two tiny tots telling tales." This second player must then say, "one old oyster and two tiny tots telling tales." This continues around the circle. Failure to repeat the entire rigmarole causes a player to drop out. When a player drops out, the next one on his right is given a chance to continue. The following are some possible phrases for the rigmarole.

1—One old oyster
2—Two tiny tots telling tales
3—Three thrifty tinkers talking
4—Four fat fathers fishing
5—Five flies fanning flickering flames
6—Six slick, slim, slender saplings sighing
7—Seven sailors sailing sloops
8—Eight apes aimlessly aping angels
9—Nine noble nymphs nibbling nubbins
10—Ten tiny toads trying to trot

My Big Toe

FOR this game, like the one above, the players sit in a circle, while the leader stands in the circle. The leader points to one part of his body and at the same time names another part of his body. Thus he may point to his big toe and say, "This is my nose." He then points to one of the players and starts counting ten. Before he finishes counting ten, this player must touch his big toe and say, "This is my nose." If he fails to do this before the leader counts ten, he must take the leader's place. This might be done as well with articles of clothing used in the sentences, instead of parts of the body.

What Am I Thinking of?

THE PLAYERS are seated in a circle and the leaders says to one player, "I am thinking about something, I will not tell you what it is, but I want each one of you to tell me what my thought is like." Each one repeats what he thinks the leader's thought is like. One may say, "I think it is like apple sauce." Another may say, "I think it is like Bill's necktie." When this question has gone around the circle, the leader then says, "I was thinking of Professor Jones (use the name of someone known to the group). Why is he like apple sauce?" And the one who answered "apple sauce" must answer. He might say, "Because what he says sounds like apple sauce," or "He's sour like apple sauce." So the question goes around the room, asking why Professor Jones is like whatever answer has been given.

JUNE

June Burlesque Horoscope

JUNE, the sixth month of the year, according to many legends was named after Juno, the wife of Jupiter. It is said that she presided over the marriages of women, and this may be the reason that we associate June with weddings. Juno was said to have been very lovely but of a jealous disposition. Others contend that the sixth month was named for Junius, a proud and haughty god but one possessing many good qualities. As both Juno and Junius are associated with the month, we can therefore conclude that persons born in this month, whether male or female, will be proud and haughty, yet possessing many good qualities. The women will be lovely and the men handsome and both will be jealous. Of course, persons born in June will possess many of the qualities of the great characters born in this month. For example: the fickleness of King Henry VIII of England, the military genius of Winfield Scott, and the literary genius of Charles Kingsley.

June is traditionally the month of brides and, of course, bridegrooms. It would be expected that a person born in June, the month that is so replete with love and marriage, could not possibly be an old maid or bachelor.

June Famous Folk and Events

1—What famous Confederate was born on June 3? Answer. *Jefferson Davis*

2—Who was born June 9 who wrote "Home, Sweet Home"? Ans. *John Howard Payne*

3—What famous English King who had many wives was born in June? Ans. *Henry VIII*
4—What great American battle took place on June 17, 1776? Ans. *Battle of Bunker Hill*
5—What famous American general was born June 13? Ans. *Winfield Scott*
6—What famous English poet and novelist was born on June 12, and wrote *Westward Ho?* Ans. *Charles Kingsley*
7—What important event is celebrated on June 14? Ans. *The making of the United States flag*
8—In what poem is the following line found: "And what is so rare as a day in June"? Ans. *The Vision of Sir Launfal*
9—What are the June birthstones? Ans. *Pearl and agate*
10—What is the June flower? Ans. *Rose or honeysuckle*
11—Who made a famous treaty with the Indians on June 23, 1683? Ans. *William Penn*
12—What poem contains the following line: "In the leafy month of June"? Ans. *The Ancient Mariner,* by Coleridge

The leader may have these questions mimeographed or written on slips of paper and have the guests work singly or in couples in answering them. If such arrangements have not been made in advance, the leader might read the questions, schoolteacher fashion, and have those who know the answer raise their hands. She may then call on them for the answer.

Flower of the Month

WHILE each month is supposed to have a special flower, the flowers of nearly all the months bloom in June. Give guests a list of the months and the flower for the month jumbled as follows: See if they can arrange them correctly. The following is a scrambled list.

January	Chrysanthemum
February	Aster, morning glory
March	Poppy, gladiolus
April	Larkspur, water lily
May	Rose, honeysuckle
June	Narcissus, holly

July	Lily of the valley, hawthorn
August	Sweet pea, daisy
September	Jonquil, daffodil
October	Violet, primrose
November	Calendula, cosmos
December	Carnation, snowdrop

The following is correct: January, *carnation, snowdrop;* February, *violet, primrose;* March, *jonquil, daffodil;* April, *sweet pea, daisy;* May, *lily of the valley, hawthorn;* June, *rose, honeysuckle;* July, *lark-spur, water lily;* August, *poppy, gladiolus;* September, *aster, morning glory;* October, *calendula, cosmos;* November, *chrysanthemum;* December, *narcissus, holly.*

Matrimonial Quiz

SOMETIMES a question for discussion will break the ice quite as well as anything else. Let the leader ask the following questions of different guests at the party, perhaps supplemented by others that she may wish to add.

1—Can love's young dream become a reality?
2—What method would you use to encourage a timid man to propose?
3—Should men be required to study home economics?
4—Should wives buy their husbands' clothes?
5—Should men assist women in selecting their hats?
6—Do you think there is such a thing as an ideal man?
7—How can you break a man from reading the newspaper at breakfast?
8—What do you do with a man who talks about his mother's cooking?
9—Does it pay to darn socks?
10—Is it better to be a young man's slave, or an old man's pet?
11—State some advantages of being an unmarried woman.
12—Give three reasons why bachelors should be taxed.
13—Why do gentlemen prefer blondes?
14—Give a description of an ideal wife.

Flower Jumble

ON STRIPS of cardboard about one inch wide print the names of flowers. Cut the letters apart so they will be about one inch square and turn them upside down on a table. The players sit on either side of the table in two teams of equal number. In turn they draw letters from the pile until the pile is exhausted. Each group uses the letters it has for spelling names of flowers, laying them out on the table one at a time. There should be a judge to mark one point each time a flower is completed. Continue the game for about ten minutes and award a prize to the group having the highest score. If the number at the party is large, it will be necessary to arrange more than one table.

Looking for a Man

AT THIS season of the year nearly everyone of the female sex is looking for a man. Have all try the following contest. Papers are prepared with the following questions which are to be answered with the words given at the right below:

1—The handcuffed man	*Manacle*
2—The man over the fireplace	*Mantle*
3—The man who directs	*Manager*
4—The man who is a court order to perform	*Mandamus*
5—The man who is a musical instrument	*Mandolin*
6—The man who is a native of Manchuria	*Manchu*
7—The man who cares for his nails	*Manicure*
8—The brave man	*Manly*
9—The May apple man	*Mandrake*
10—The man that is a Bay	*Manila*
11—The man used to feed cattle	*Manger*
12—The long-haired man	*Mane*
13—A lot of men	*Many*
14—The written man	*Manuscript*
15—The house man	*Mansion*
16—The skin disease man	*Mange*
17—The preacher's man	*Manse*
18—A crazy man	*Maniac*

19—The fruit man *Mango*
20—The man who is a killer *Manslaughter*
21—The man who is a ship *Man-of-war*
22—The man who is a food *Manna*
23—Man made by hand *Manual*

Bawl Game

EVERYBODY likes to go to the old ball game in the month of June, so why not have a "bawl" game. The leader announces that there will be a ball game and chooses nine players for each side, if enough guests are available. She then pairs players of different size for a bawling contest. The one who can bawl the loudest and best is declared the winner. The team that has the largest number of wins is declared the winner of the Bawl Game.

Handkerchief Throw

WHEN you have the teams made up for the above game, have them compete in pairs in a handkerchief throw. Have a tape measure to measure the distance each one throws the handkerchief. It may be crumpled up in the hand but the rule that it must not be tied into knots must not be violated. The team that has the longest aggregate distance is declared the winner.

Feather Blow

HAVE a feather blowing contest and have someone keep time for the contestants. The object is to keep the feather in the air the longest possible time by blowing it. A player starts the game by holding the feather in his hand and blowing it up into the air. It must not be touched again by the hand, and this player's time is up when the feather touches the floor.

Fox and Squirrel

SELECT two players— one to be the fox and one to be a squirrel. Divide the rest of the guests into groups of four by having them count off as they stand in a circle around the room. It is important for each player to remember his number, as the sequence of the play depends on it. When the guests have been thus divided, they form circles around the room—numbers 2, 3, and 4 joining hands to make the circle with number 1 inside. All players inside the circles are also squirrels.

As the play starts, the fox tries to catch the squirrel who is not in one of the circles. The squirrel may keep from being caught by darting into a circle. As there must not be two squirrels in one circle, the player who has been occupying the circle must leave. He then becomes the homeless squirrel and the fox chases him. When any squirrel is caught, he must become the fox and chase others until he catches a squirrel, thus becoming a squirrel again.

At the end of a few moments of play, the players who are number 2 in each circle become the squirrels and numbers 1, 3, and 4 form the circle. Continue until each player has had an opportunity to be a squirrel. If the group is very large, circles may be enlarged to five, six, or seven players each instead of four.

Iced Tea

OF COURSE, we will want our tea iced for June; but what kind of tea should people drink?

What tea should glum people drink?	*Jolli T*
What tea should auto racers drink?	*Veloci T*
What tea should clergymen drink?	*Divini T*
What tea should farmers drink?	*Fertili T*
What tea should people who are late drink?	*Punctuali T*
What tea should lovers drink?	*Affini T*
What tea should jugglers drink?	*Dexteri T*
What tea should married people drink?	*Fideli T*
What tea should misers drink?	*Chari T*
What tea should dishonest people drink?	*Hones T*
What tea should educators drink?	*Universi T*
What tea should poor people drink?	*Prosperi T*
What tea should criminals drink?	*Penal T*
What tea do Americans love?	*Liber T*
What tea should all be prepared for?	*Eterni T*

Refrigerator

THE GUESTS sit around in a circle and one guest starts the game by saying, "Grandmother keeps in the refrigerator, apples." The next player must repeat this and add something that begins with B, such as beets or any other ridiculous things, such as bears or bats. As the game goes around the circle, each one in turn must repeat everything that has been named before and add a word beginning with the next letter of the alphabet. Finally it will sound something like this: "My grandmother keeps in the refrigerator, apples, bugs, cats, dumplings, eggplant, flies, goats, and so on. When anyone fails to repeat the entire list, he must drop out of the circle and let the next one have a try.

JULY

Burlesque Horoscope of July

JULY, the month of Julius, according to the modern calendar, is the seventh month of the year. The earliest Roman calendar made it the fifth month, and gave it the name of Quintilis, which means fifth. However, this month had the honor to be the birth month of the great Julius Caesar; and when his calendar reform went into effect, it was rechristened for him. Previous to Caesar's time it had but thirty days, but he added an extra day in order to make it the same as the longest months. The special flowers of July are the water lily and larkspur and its gem is the ruby.

A few of the famous folk born in this month are as follows: Nathaniel Hawthorne, 1804; John Paul Jones, 1747; John D. Rockefeller, 1839; Sir William Blackstone, 1733; John Quincy Adams, 1767; Julius Caesar, 100 B.C.; Rembrandt, 1607; Mary Baker Eddy, 1821. Taking the names of these famous folk prepare a brief paper or talk on these great names or any others born in this month. Individuals who are present and who were also born in this month might have prophecies given concerning themselves, including the characteristics of the famous people born in this month. If those who are present are well known to the one making the prophecies, this feature might be very witty.

Famous Folk of July

Nathaniel Hawthorne, 1804	*American novelist*
John Paul Jones, 1747	*American naval commander*
John D. Rockefeller, 1839	*Capitalist and philanthropist*
Elias Howe, 1819	*Inventor of sewing machine*
John Calvin, 1509	*Protestant reformer*
John Quincy Adams, 1767	*Sixth President of United States*
Julius Caesar, 100 B.C.	*Roman statesman and general*
Henry Thoreau, 1819	*American naturalist and essayist*
Rijn van Rembrandt, 1607	*Dutch painter*
Isaac Watts, 1674	*English hymn writer*
William Thackeray, 1811	*English novelist*
Samuel Colt, 1814	*American inventor of firearms*
Giuseppe Garibaldi, 1807	*Italian patriot*
Calvin Coolidge, 1872	*Thirtieth President of United States*

Give to each guest a list of the above names but not a list of the things for which they are famous. Write the things for which they are famous on separate slips of paper and pin these slips about the room. Guests are to study the slips of paper and write the correct vocation for the correct name. The contest might be varied by having the names written in mixed form, requiring the guests to write them correctly.

Famous Events of July

1—Debate on Declaration of ——, 1776.
2—Beginning of Battle of ——, 1863.
3—President Garfield ——, 1881.
4—Declaration of Independence ——, 1776.
5—William Booth founded ——, 1865.
6—Alexander Hamilton wounded by —— ——, 1804.
7—Surrender of Southern city beginning with a V——, 1863.
8—San Juan Hill occupied by ——, 1898.
9—United States acquires —— Islands in Pacific, 1898.
10—France declared war on ——, 1870.
11—District of —— established, 1790.
12—French —— Day, 1789.

Give to each guest a sheet of paper on which is written the above unfinished statements and ask them to fill in the blanks. On slips of paper pinned about the room are these words which are the correct ones for the blanks on the papers: 1—*Independence,* 2—*Gettysburg,* 3—*shot,* 4—*signed,* 5—*Salvation Army,* 6—*Aaron Burr,* 7—*Vicksburg,* 8—*Americans,* 9—*Hawaiian,* 10—*Germany,* 11—*Columbia,* 12—*Bastille.*

Identify the States

To test the knowledge of the guests during this patriotic month, see how many states will be recognized by the shape with no lettering on them. To prepare these nameless maps, make a number of copies by the use of carbon paper. Paste these copies on cardboard, then cut out the states and pin them about the room. Allow fifteen or twenty minutes for the guests to make the trial, writing down the names they think correct opposite the number on their slip of paper which corresponds with the number on the state. A flag might be given the one identifying the largest number.

Yankee Doodle, the King of Hunky-Bunky

This game, which sounds simple, will nevertheless create a great deal of amusement. Select two persons, place them at opposite sides of the room, or as far apart as possible. Give each one a lighted candle and explain that the rules of the game strictly forbid them to laugh or even to smile. These two contestants must then advance very slowly toward each other, looking each other directly in the eye. When they meet in the middle of the room, with hand uplifted, in great sorrow, one of them says, "Yankee Doodle, the king of Hunky-Bunky, is defunct and dead." The other responds, "Alas, alas, how died he?" Then the first speaker with increased grief answers, "Just so, just so, just so." Then the other responds, "How sad, how sad, how sad." It will be difficult for any couple to get through the announcement without breaking down in laughter. A prize should be given the couple successfully completing the message.

Find the Flag

This game is a variation of the game called, *The Organ Grinder Man.* Two people, a man and a girl, are asked to leave the room; and while they are out, they are blindfolded. A small flag is placed somewhere among the guests who are seated about the room. Take care to place the flag in the open so that the two who are searching for it may find it by touching it. When the two blindfolded persons are brought back into the room, they are told that they must find the flag. The other guests will guide them in their search by musical methods; that is, that loud singing will indicate when they are "warm" and that softer music will indicate when they are "cold." The guests sing "Yankee Doodle" and under the direction of the leader, change the volume of the singing according to the success of those who are trying to find the flag. If the blindfolded persons are not allowed to search together, the game will be made more interesting for one of them may be near the flag, and the other far away from it and the changes in the music will make it hard for them to determine whether they are "warm" or "cold."

Signers of the Declaration of Independence

THE FOLLOWING is a list of some of the signers of the Declaration of Independence. These names are arranged in jumbled form in order to test our knowledge of the men who gave us this historic day. At the right there is a key giving the name in correct form:

1—Nnjiebma Rlifknna	*Benjamin Franklin*
2—Msuale Hceas	*Samuel Chase*
3—Saarec Yroend	*Caesar Rodney*
4—Hcarsel Crlorla	*Charles Carroll*
5—Gorer Msanerh	*Roger Sherman*
6—Trebor Rismor	*Robert Morris*
7—Onhj Knachco	*John Hancock*
8—Homtsa Fosrejenf	*Thomas Jefferson*
9—Nhoj Daams	*John Adams*
10—Cranifs Ootfghtil Eel	*Francis Lightfoot Lee*
11—Icharrd Rnyeh Ele	*Richard Henry Lee*

A Study of the Flag

1—What is the official name of the flag?
2—When is Flag Day?

3—What virtues do the colors of the flag represent?
4—How many white stripes in the flag?
5—Repeat the first line of the second stanza of the national anthem, "The Star-Spangled Banner."
6—Give the pledge of allegiance to the flag.
7—What is the nickname of the flag?
8—What is the significance of the flag at half-staff?
9—How should civilians pay respect to the flag when it is passing on parade or review?
10—What should be done with worn-out flags?

ANSWERS:

1—The flag of the United States of America.
2—Flag Day is June 14.
3—Blue is for justice, white is for purity, and red is for the life-blood of those ready to die or live worthily for their country.
4—There are six white stripes in the flag.
5—"On the shore, dimly seen through the mist of the deep."
6—"I pledge allegiance to the flag of the United States of America, and to the Republic for which it stands; one Nation, under God, indivisible, with liberty and justice for all."
7—The nickname of the flag is "Old Glory."
8—The flag at half-staff indicates a period of mourning for the death of a high government official, or in honor of the military dead, as on Memorial Day.
9—Men, standing at attention, should place their hats at their left shoulder until the flag has passed; women should salute by placing the right hand over the heart.
10—Flags should be destroyed as a whole, privately, preferably by burning or some other method lacking in any suggestion of irreverence or disrespect.

In order to test knowledge concerning the flag, the above game is suggested. The questions should be written on slips of paper and given to those present. Those who can successfully answer the questions should be given a flag. At the conclusion of this contest, the guests should all be asked to stand and give the pledge of allegiance to the flag. This might be followed by the singing of the national anthem.

Battle of Bunker Hill

THE GUESTS should be divided into two teams, one team representing the Minutemen and the other British. Draw two lines from ten to fifteen feet apart and stand the contestants on these lines, facing each other. Give each team four beanbags. When the signal is given to "fire," the teams "shoot" at each other by tossing the bags at the opposing line. If a player is hit by a beanbag, he is a "casualty" and must drop out of the game. However, if a player sees a bag coming toward him, he may catch the bag and continue the game. The game should continue until either the Minutemen or the British are vanquished.

America's Most Popular Piece of Silver

SEE that each person is supplied with a United States dime and a lead pencil, also a sheet of paper on which the list below has been either written or printed, with numbered blank spaces for the answers. When these have been distributed, announce that a stated length of time will be given in which to find these articles on the coin. The person who first completes the list, or the one who has the most correct list, might be allowed to retain his dime as a prize.

1—Fruit of a tropical tree	*Date*
2—What the Siamese twins were	*United*
3—What a lazy man seldom gets	*Ahead*
4—The division of a country	*States*
5—The cradle of liberty	*America*
6—Another name for an isthmus	*Neck*
7—Something a schoolboy makes	*Figures*
8—What we love to sing	*America*
9—What a conceited man does	*Knows* (*nose*)
10—Part of a river where the fourth letter of the Greek alphabet is sometimes found	*Mouth* (*Greek word, Delta*)

11—An instrument to catch sound *Ear*
12—What a rejected suitor always does *Leaves*

The Thirteen Colonies

SINCE July is the month in which the Colonies declared their independence, ask the guests to make a list of the thirteen original colonies. Since this should be fairly easy, provide each one with a paper and pencil and declare the winner to be the one who makes the list in the shortest length of time. Below is a list of the thirteen colonies:

New Hampshire	New York	Maryland
Connecticut	Pennsylvania	Virginia
Massachusettes	New Jersey	North Carolina
Rhode Island	Delaware	South Carolina
	Georgia	

The State Nicknames

Connecticut	*"The Nutmeg State"*
Georgia	*"The Cracker State"*
Indiana	*"The Hoosier State"*
Kansas	*"The Sunflower State"*
Kentucky	*"The Bluegrass State"*
Louisiana	*"The Creole State"*
Massachusetts	*"The Old Bay State"*
New Hampshire	*"The Granite State"*
North Carolina	*"The Tarheel State"*
Ohio	*"The Buckeye State"*
Pennsylvania	*"The Keystone State"*
Tennessee	*"The Volunteer State*
Texas	*"The Lone Star State"*
Virginia	*"The Old Dominion State"*

Write the names of the states on a slip of paper and give them to the contestants asking them to supply the nicknames of the states.

This game might also be used to match partners by giving the girls the names of the states, and the boys the nicknames and allowing them to get together.

In order to vary this game, the nicknames of the states might be represented by objects. Crackers might be used to represent Georgia, a key and a stone to represent Pennsylvania, and the guests required to determine the states from these symbols.

AUGUST

August Burlesque Horoscope

THIS MONTH was named for the greatest Roman ruler, Augustus. He desired the honor of having a month named for him and also wished to keep his name in the minds of people forever and ever. Augustus considered August his lucky month. During it, he was elected consul, three times celebrated a victory, and completed the conquest of Egypt.

August is a month of gold and purple and its sun throws a "golden glory" on the yellowing fields. Everywhere there are purple flowers and luscious grapes ripening on the vines. It is one of the warmest months of the year.

The child born in this month, like Napoleon and Augustus, will be possessed of leadership, ambition, power of will and mind. He will have "Lady Luck" at his side, but will not be inclined toward chance-taking. This child will have a love for beauty and very likely will express this love in poetry as did Shelley, Tennyson, Holmes, and Francis Scott Key.

The month's flowers are the poppy and gladiolus, and its gem is the sardonyx, an emblem of spiritual strength.

Famous Folk of August

GIVE each guest a list of the famous folk born in August as listed below. Pin about the room on the walls, curtains, and other places, the list of things for which they are famous. Have the guests attempt to write after each person the thing for which he was famous. Allow about ten minutes for this and give a prize to the one who has the most correct list.

Famous August Birthdays	Things for Which Famous
Alfred Lord Tennyson, 1809	English poet
Isaac Walton, 1593	English writer on outdoor life
Francis Scott Key, 1780	Composer of "Star-Spangled Banner"
Napoleon Bonaparte, 1769	French emperor
Sir Walter Scott, 1771	Scotch novelist and poet
David Crockett, 1786	Texas pioneer
Benjamin Harrison, 1833	Twenty-third President of United States
Bret Harte, 1839	Much loved American writer
John Locke, 1632	English philosopher
Oliver Wendell Holmes, 1809	American physician, poet, author
Percy Shelley, 1792	English poet

Scavenger Hunt

Some events for August will want to be planned for out of doors. Have a scavenger hunt. Designate some home at which the guests are to get their instructions and then send them out in couples, or in groups, to find a list of designated objects. A home should be designated at which they are to meet at the end of the hunt, and a handsome prize should be provided to the couple or individual who most nearly completes the list of objects to be found. The following is a suggested list of things to be brought back: 1—A menu from a local restaurant; 2—A wild flower that is to be found in the locality, as for example, a daisy, dandelion, or sunflower; 3—A hair from the head of a red-headed girl; 4—An apple; 5—An old shoe; 6—Professor Brown's signature (in this case it will be necessary to find a good-natured professor); 7—A package of seed, flower seed, or vegetable seed; 8—Copy of *Huckleberry Finn;* 9—A brick; 10—A copy of a late popular magazine. Others will suggest themselves to those planning the party.

Ice Cube Relay

Players line up in two or more equal lines, standing one behind the other and facing a goal at the other end of the room. Goals may be chairs placed on the floor so that the players may run around them. When the game is ready to start, the leader gives the first player in each line a table knife and an ice cube. When the signal is given, the player must race to the goal and back while balancing the ice cube on the knife. If the cube falls off, which it undoubtedly will, he is to stop until he can pick it up with his hand and replace it. When each player finishes his run, he gives the knife and ice cube to the next player in his line. The group that first gets all of its players around the goal and back is the winner.

Lawn Party

An outdoor party for August would be quite apropos. The lawn might be lighted with Japanese lanterns in which are hung electric light bulbs. A punch bowl in an arbor could supply a part of the refreshments. A great deal of enjoyment could be derived even by older young people by playing such games as Drop the Handkerchief, Three Deep, and London Bridge.

Divide in two groups and have a flower relay. Each group forms a circle, joining hands. One player in each circle is given a flower or bouquet of flowers; holding these in his hand, he starts running around the circle clockwise, weaving in and out of the line. When he has finished, the next one goes. The first group to have all its players complete the run, wins the relay.

Nine Magazines

Nine magazines are laid out on the floor, with three rows of three each. There must be two persons who know the game—the magician and his accomplice. When the game is ready to start, the accomplice leaves the room and the group selects one of the magazines to be identified by the accomplice when he returns.

After the accomplice has returned, the magician touches the magazines one by one with a long stick, saying "Is this it?" The accomplice—as if by magic—identifies the magazine the group has selected.

Here is the way it works: By placing his stick at a certain place on the first magazine he points to, the magician informs his accomplice which one has been selected. If he touches the first magazine in the middle, for example, he means that the middle magazine is the right one. If he touches the first magazine on its lower righthand corner, the magazine in the lower right hand corner is correct. If he touches the first magazine on the right side, about in the middle, the magazine in the middle row on the right is the one to be identified.

When any player thinks he has caught on to the method of identification, let him leave the room and have a try. As many players will think that the words spoken give away the clue, it is advisable to change the question by asking "How about this one?" or "Do you think this is right?"

Chinese Proverbs

As no special days fall in August, it is permissible to use a variety of ideas for entertainment. Why not try some Chinese ideas and games? Write these proverbs on slips of paper and pin them about the room in places that are not too conspicuous. Allow guests about five minutes to copy as many as possible and have these read. Those who have the greatest number should be asked to read their lists.

PROVERBS:

1—Deal with the faults of others as gently as with your own.
2—A man thinks he knows, but a woman knows better.
3—Words whispered on earth sound like thunder in heaven.
4—It is easier to catch a tiger than to ask a favor.
5—With money you can move the gods; without it, you can't move a man.
6—Don't put two saddles on one horse.
7—Long visits bring short compliments.
8—One kind word will keep you warm for three winters.
9—The highest towers begin from the ground.
10—Free sitters at the play always grumble most.
11—Everyone gives a shove to the tumbling wall.
12—He who rides a tiger cannot dismount.
13—One dog barks at something, and the rest bark at him.
14—Without error, there could be no such a thing as truth.

GILES, *History of Chinese Literature.*

Backward Chinese Relay

DIVIDE the guests into two groups of equal number for a backward Chinese relay. Get about two dozen rolled-up newspapers and lay them on the floor in two rows. The rows should be about eight feet apart and the newspapers should be laid at intervals of about two feet. Contestants must hop backward over the newspapers to the goal and return. When the first contestant on each side returns, he touches off the next one. The side which finishes first wins the relay.

Chinese Staff of Life

BOWLS of uncooked rice and chopsticks are needed for this game. If chopsticks are not available, they may be improvised. Allow two or three minutes for this stunt and give a prize for the one who takes the largest number of grains of rice from the bowl with the chopsticks. If large bowls are used, more than one may be able to use the same bowl. A piece of "China" would make a good prize.

Chopsticks are about ten inches long and the size of a pencil. To be exactly proper, they should be slightly tapered, and the end held in the hand may be square. They may be improvised from small flagstaffs, or any pieces of wood about the same diameter as a pencil. The ends that pick up the food are perfectly round.

Bottle and Yardstick Relay

FOR this game get two or more yardsticks (some are likely to be broken) and two soft drink bottles. Line up players in two lines of equal number facing a goal about twenty-five feet away and give the first player in each line a bottle and a yardstick. When the signal is given, he must roll the bottle to the goal and back, using the yardstick. This will not be as easy as it appears, as the bottle will want to go in all directions. When the first player has returned and given the yardstick and bottle to the next player in his line, he takes his place at the back of the line. Each player in each group must roll the bottle to the goal and back. The group that finishes first is the winner.

Fun and Frolic Railway

GUESTS are given a mimeographed timetable of the Fun and Frolic Railway. A description of the station is given, and the passenger must supply the name of the railway station from the description.

The train will stop at the following stations:

1—A necessary part of a watch and a farm	*Springfield*
2—An encore for a singer	*Sing Sing*
3—A place for loafers	*Tarrytown*
4—An accident which results in a ducking	*Falls River*
5—Where all have "bean"	*Boston*
6—The greatest engineering feat	*Wheeling, W. Va.*
7—A girl's name, and a Roman garment	*Saratoga*
8—A small stone	*Little Rock*
9—A city whose end and aim is go	*Chicago*
10—Large rushing waters	*Grand Rapids*
11—Named for one of the Apostles	*St. Paul*
12—A new model of Noah's ship	*Newark*
13—Two thousand pounds of blossoms	*Bloomington*
14—The greatest surgical operation	*Lansing, Michigan*

Name Six

THE guests are seated around the room in chairs, forming a circle. A rubber ball is passed around the circle as music is played from an instrument or record. When the music stops, the person who has the ball must "name six" before the ball can go around the circle again. This may be six boy's names, six girl's names—or it may be cities, rivers, mountains, baseball players, colleges, or any other category the leader announces. While the player is naming his "six" the ball is passed without music. A player who fails to "name six" before the ball can circle the group must drop out of the game. If the group is not large, the number of objects to be named may be reduced to four or five.

SEPTEMBER

September Burlesque Horoscope

SEPTEMBER, the transition month, between summer and autumn, projects something of the character of both seasons. It is the month when the leaves begin to turn from green to gold, and the sky becomes hazy. It is often spoken of as "soft September." Many months have undergone changes in their number of days. It is not so with September. "Thirty days has September" has always been true of this month. It does not, however, retain its original place in the calendar. Formerly, it was the seventh month and is so named from the Latin word, Septem, meaning seven. September was shifted when the calendar was revised by Julius Caesar and it became the ninth month without the name having been changed.

Persons born in September will be of a festive disposition, and at the same time they will be reverent and spiritual. Great people born in this month exemplify the characteristics which are innate in all persons born in September. They will have leadership ability like Alexander the Great, born in September, 356 B.C., and will try to conquer the world. Women, like Queen Elizabeth, 1533, will be feminine but firm. People born in September are sometimes backward in social activities, but will have plenty of true friends. They will be ready to join in funmaking and sports and will be likely to accumulate a fortune. The birthstone for September is the sapphire, and the flower is the morning glory.

Go-Away-to-College Party

SEPTEMBER is the month when young people are getting ready to go away to college. It is a nice gesture to give them a "go-away-to-college" party before they leave. Some games suggested are College Bingo, described on page 14, the two tests given below on the Constitution of the United States, and some items taken from the section on Cultural Games. Also have a college entrance examination, described later on in this chapter. Present a small gift to each one who is going away to college, as for example, a handkerchief.

College Entrance Examination

COLLEGE entrance examination may be conducted orally, or papers may be prepared in advance. The leader is referred to the section on Mental Games, Problems, and Brain Twisters where it will be easy to find ten questions that may be written or mimeographed for such an examination. Such problems as that of punctuation are suggested. Some of the following are suggested as an oral examination.

1—If you were naming the states alphabetically which one would come last and which next to last (allow only about thirty seconds for this answer)? Answer. *Wyoming last; Wisconsin next to last.*

2—How Long is a Chinese scholar (?) Answer. *Most any way it is said it sounds like a question. It is not a question, however, but a statement. How Long is a Chinaman's name.*

3—On a hill there is a house.
In the house there is a door.
In the door there is a bell.
A happy pair lived there of yore.
Their names I've told you.
Now can you tell?
Answer. *Isadore and Isabell.*

September's Most Famous Event

THE most important event of September, as far as the people of the United States are concerned, was the signing of the Constitution of the United States. The following are some questions on the Constitution. They may be mimeographed or written out and given to the guests, or the leader may ask the group the questions and let anyone who can answer. In either case give a prize for the one answering the largest number.

1—When and where was the Constitutional Convention held? Answer. *Philadelphia, beginning May 25, 1787.*

2—On what day of the month is Constitution Day? Answer. *September 17, the day on which the Constitution was signed.*

3—Who was president of the Constitutional Convention? Answer. *George Washington.*

4—Name four of the best known persons who attended. Answer. *George Washington, Benjamin Franklin, James Madison, James Wilson, Robert Morris, Alexander Hamilton, Gouverneur Morris. These are among the best known.*

5—How many men attended the convention? Answer. *Fifty-five.*

6—How many signed the Constitution? Answer. *Thirty-eight.*

7—What was the great compromise of the Constitution? Answer. *The election of representatives in Congress according to population, while each state was to have two Senators.*

8—What was the Bill of Rights? Answer. *The first ten amendments of the Constitution.*

9—What was the purpose of the twelfth amendment? Answer. *To change the method of electing the president, taking political parties into account.*

10—What was the purpose of the seventeenth amendment? Answer. *It changed the method of the election of Senators, so that now they are elected by popular vote.*

11—What was the purpose of the nineteenth amendment? Answer. *The granting of suffrage to women.*

12—What was the purpose of the twentieth amendment? Answer. *It abolished the Lame Duck session of Congress.*

13—Quote the first ten words of the Constitution. Answer. *"We the people of the United States in order to form a more perfect Union."*

14—With what does Article I of the Constitution deal? Answer. *With the legislative department of the government.*

15—With what does Article II of the Constitution deal? Answer. *With the executive department of the government.*

16—With what does Article III of the Constitution deal? Answer. *With the judicial department of the government.*

17—Where is the original manuscript of the Constitution at the present time? Answer. *The Library of Congress, Washington, D. C.*

Poetry

IN THIS poetry test guests may be given the first line of the poem given below and then asked to supply the next line and to give the name of the poem and the poet. If they cannot do this in at least 50 per cent of those given below, they had better spend some time in college studying poetry.

1—The night hath a thousand eyes

2—There are hermit souls that live withdrawn.
3—I have a rendezvous with death
4—In Flanders fields the poppies blow
5—The little toy dog was covered with dust
6—God of our fathers, known of old
7—The quality of mercy is not strained
8—The gingham dog and the calico cat
9—Laugh and the world laughs with you
10—Listen, my children, and you shall hear
11—The curfew tolls the knell of parting day
12—If you can keep your head when all about you
13—Breathes there a man with soul so dead
14—What is so rare as a day in June
15—Under the spreading chestnut tree
16—To be, or not to be: That is the question
17—Tell me not in mournful numbers
18—Friends, Romans, countrymen, lend me your ears.

ANSWERS:

1—"And the day but one," Bourdillion, *The Night Hath a Thousand Eyes.*

2—"In the place of their self-content," Sam W. Foss, *The House by the Side of the Road.*

3—"At some disputed barricade," Allen Seeger, *I Have a Rendezvous with Death.*

4—"Between the crosses row on row," Lieutenant Colonel John McCrae, *In Flanders' Fields.*

5—"But sturdy and staunch he stands," Eugene Field, *Little Boy Blue.*

6—"Lord of our far-flung battle line," Kipling, *Recessional.*

7—"It droppeth as the gentle rain from heaven," Shakespeare, *The Merchant of Venice.*

8—"Side by side on the table sat," Eugene Field, *The Duel.*

9—"Weep and you weep alone," Ella Wheeler Wilcox, *Solitude.*

10—"Of the midnight ride of Paul Revere," Longfellow, *Paul Revere's Ride.*

11—"The lowing herd winds slowly o'er the lea," Thomas Gray, *Elegy Written in a Country Churchyard.*

12—"Are losing theirs and blaming it on you," Kipling, *If.*

13—"Who never to himself hath said," Sir Walter Scott, *The Lay of the Last Minstrel.*

14—"Then if ever come perfect days," Lowell, *The Vision of Sir Launfal.*

15—"The village smithy stands," Longfellow, *The Village Blacksmith.*

16—"Whether 'tis nobler in the mind to suffer," Shakespeare, *Hamlet.*

17—"Life is but an empty dream," Longfellow, *A Psalm of Life.*

18—"I come to bury Caesar, not to praise him," Shakespeare, *Julius Caesar.*

Chest Spelling

For this game as well as the next two, it will be necessary to have lettered cards prepared. It is easy to secure blank cards at almost any job-printing office, and for a small cost have them cut into any convenient size. Cards five inches square are the best size. These cards are shuffled and placed with the letters face downward on a table. Each guest as he enters must choose a letter and pin it on his chest. When the leader gives the signal, all guests must form themselves into four-letter words. They retain their positions until they are inspected by the leader. Those who have not been able to join any group and be a part of any word are made the victims in some later game. The leader may ask all those in each word to become acquainted, and then they may be asked to form other words until the whole group is mixed up and all have become acquainted.

Spelling Relay

The guests are divided into two groups of equal number and are lined up facing each other. A table has been placed at one end of the room on which are two piles of lettered cards with the letters downward. These letters have been shuffled. The leader pronounces a word, preferably a long word, easily spelled, whereupon the two persons at the head of the opposing groups, on the opposite end of the room from the lettered cards, must run down to the table, look through the pack until they find the first letter in the word. This is then laid out on the table. This one takes his place at the foot of the line and the next player looks for the next letter. The side which first completes its word wins the contest. No player must start down until the player just preceding him has taken his place at the foot of the line.

Hopping to Spell

PLAYERS are lined up for a relay as described above and each group has been given a pack of lettered cards which are divided among the players. The leader pronounces a word and whoever has the letter that begins that word must pass it up to the player at the head of the line. The player at the head of the line must then hop to the other end of the room, place the card on the floor in such a position as to begin a word, and hop over to the foot of the line. This same procedure is followed for each letter in the word. The first group that finishes the word is declared the winner.

Upset Tool Chest

AS LABOR DAY comes in September, we will be thinking of the tools used by the tradesmen. However, the tool chest has been upset, and we must get it back in order. The following is a group of tools with the letters pied. Can you straighten them out?

1—Urel	*Rule*
2—Aws	*Saw*
3—Lnai ets	*Nail set*
4—Memhar	*Hammer*
5—Elrwot	*Trowel*
6—Alnep	*Plane*
7—Careb	*Brace*
8—Itb	*Bit*
9—Rcsew Virder	*Screw driver*
10—Velel	*Level*
11—Cenhrw	*Wrench*

12—Placm *Clamp*
13—Rusqae *Square*
14—Life *File*
15—Shicle *Chisel*

H Is for Harvard

CARRYING out the college idea, play "H" is for Harvard. A judge or two will have to be appointed, and the guests divided into two groups of equal number. The leader calls out "H is for Harvard" or "Y is for Yale" and each group must arrange its players to form the letter. The group that can do this in the shortest time is declared the winner by the judges. A variation of this would be to have the players lie on the floor to form the letter.

Uncle Ezra

THE GAME is played following out the action of the following poem:

"My uncle Ezra died last night."
"That's too bad; how did he die?"
"With one eye shut, and his mouth awry,
One foot held high, and waving goodbye."

The players sit in a circle. The leader says to the player on his right, "My Uncle Ezra died last night." This player says, "That's too bad; how did he die?" The leader replies, "With one eye shut." The second player then repeats the action until it has gone entirely around the circle and all have one eye shut. On the second round the leader adds, "and his mouth awry," and all most have one eye shut and mouth awry. On the third round, "one foot held high," and on the fourth round "and waving goodbye," are added.

Stiff Upper Lip

THIS IS a relay race in which a card is used, and it must be passed up and down the line. There are, of course, two groups of equal number in these lines and they should stand facing each other. The player at the head of the line starts the game by holding a card between his upper lip and his nose without the use of his hands. He must pass it on down the line. The hands must not be used unless the card is dropped, in which case it may be picked up with the hand. The side that passes the card up and down the line in the shortest time is declared the winner.

OCTOBER

October Burlesque Horoscope

October, which is the tenth month of the year, in temperate climates is one of the most beautiful of all the months. Its name is from the Latin word, "Might." In the early Roman times, October was the eighth month and only with the revision of the calendar by Julius Caesar did it receive its present place. Many times the Roman senate tried to rechristen the month, as it had rechristened other months, but the names did not become popular, and the month continued to be called October. From the time of Julius Caesar it has had thirty-one days.

Among the notables born in October are, Jennie Lind, 1820; William Penn, 1644; Virgil, 70 B.C., Noah Webster, 1768; Theodore Roosevelt, 1858.

In the north the first frosts are likely to come in October, but this does not mean that cold weather has come to stay, and persons compelled or privileged to spend much time outdoors are fortunate.

Children born in October are especially fortunate because great things are in store for them. They are destined to have many of the fine characteristics of other noble folk born in this month. They will have even tempers; be blessed with pleasing personality; coveted by the opposite sex; have strong feelings of love for their parents; and will be obedient and be guided by the parents' wishes.

The gem for October is the opal, and the flowers are the calendula and cosmos.

Pumpkin Partner

At a Halloween party it is often desired that guests be formed into partnerships. The following is a suggestion whereby this may be done. Cut a number of small pumpkins out of stiff yellow cardboard, and then by the use of a razor blade, cut each of these pumpkins in two pieces. The cut edges should be in various shapes. Give a half pumpkin to each guest and instruct them to compare pumpkin halves. Those whose halves match properly are partners.

Ghost Croquet

ON A table or long board lay out a miniature croquet ground, using wire hoops (which may be made out of wire coat hangers wrapped in orange paper). Each hoop is labeled "good luck," "bad luck," etc. The guests roll small balls or marbles through the hoops and thus find fortunes which have been attached to them. The umpire of the game in some cases holds a list of forfeits written on a piece of paper and these forfeits apply to certain hoops. Those whose ball or marble rolls through these hoops must fulfill certain forfeits.

Ghost Race

FOUR PERSONS take part in this ghost race, two on either side. Each couple is given a suitcase in which there are two sheets and two masks. The object of the game is for these couples to race to a given line, open the suitcase, don the costumes, race to the home line, take off the costumes and replace them in the suitcase. The couple which accomplishes this in the shortest length of time wins.

Serpent of the Nile

FOR THE "Serpent of the Nile" march, the lights in the room should be very dim. All in the room are requested to take a place in a long line, one behind another, arms raised, palms out. To the accompaniment of weird slow music they march about the room, winding tortuously like the snake dances of victorious college boys.

Ghost Stones

CUT A number of "stones" four by four from gray cardboard. The alphabet should be written on the stones with each letter having a number beside it, for example: A would be 1, B would be 2; C would be 3; and so on. These stones are to be given to the boys. A stone in corresponding shape should be given to the girls and on these stones short sentences should be written using the number of the letter instead of the letters to form the words. The guests should then form partners, which might be done by the method suggested above, and work out their sentences with the aid of the code. Give a prize to the two who first decode their sentence.

Find the Amulet

SECRETLY distribute five small, odd-shaped stones among the guests, and tell them to keep mum about it. Then announce to the crowd that five amulets are in possession of five different persons, each of whom will give his amulet to the thirteenth person who shakes his hand. The amulets may be kept by the lucky ones as a protection against witchcraft, bad luck, disease, accidents, and further, to give the possessors an occult power during the remainder of the year.

Melting Lead

EACH PERSON melts some lead and pours it through a wedding ring or key into a dish of ice water. The lead will cool in various shapes supposed to be prophetic. Any ingenious persons will interpret the shapes, and furnish much amusement for the listeners; thus, a bell-shaped drop indicates a wedding within the year; a horn of plenty suggests wealth.

Pumpkin Alphabet

CARVE ALL the letters of the alphabet on a medium size pumpkin. Put it on a dish and set it on a stand or table. Each guest in turn is blindfolded and given a hatpin, then led to the pumpkin, where he or she is expected to stick the pin into one of the letters on the pumpkin, thus indicating the initial of the future life partner.

A Halloween Hike

A HALLOWEEN hike is fun but should be carefully planned in advance. The leaders chart two or three different routes from the starting place to the goal of the hike. The crowd is divided in two or three groups and given directions to the place where the next directions will be found. Directions must be previously hidden at several places along the route. The several groups finally arrive, by different routes, at the same place, where refreshments are served, and a prize awarded to the group first to arrive.

Mysterious Dough Test

TAKE WATER and meal and make dough. Write on slips of paper the names of several friends of the opposite sex, roll papers into balls of dough and drop them into water. The first name to appear will be the future husband or wife.

Stealing Treasures

PLACE A collection of "treasures," such as nuts or stick candy within a small circle in the center of the field. Divide the players in equal groups and assign each group a home base at equal distance from the treasure circle. Within this home circle the players are safe. Each group is designated by a different color of crepe paper. The members of each group have a strip of paper of their group color slipped through the belt at the back.

At the signal to start the game, all the players run out to get the treasure. Only one piece of treasure may be stolen at a time by a player, and a player may be "killed" by any player of opposite group pulling out the slip of paper from the belt. A player thus losing his strip of paper must cease playing.

Ring and Goblet

TIE A wedding ring or key to silken thread or horsehair, and hold it suspended within a glass; then say the alphabet slowly; whenever the ring strikes the glass, begin over again, and in this way spell the name of your future mate. This game should be presided over by one of the fortune tellers or witches.

The Bat Cave

SELECT ONE contestant from each of two sides. Each contestant is given a fan and black paper bat. At the signal to start, each player must blow the bat from the fan and then keep it fanned in the air until the goal line is reached, which is the bat cave. If convenient to provide, a paper bat cave may be suspended in one corner of the room, or from a tree if an outdoor party, and contestants be required to fan the bat into the cave.

"Nuts" Shoot the Nuts

A GIRL AND boy stretch, head high, a "clothesline" of cord on which nuts are suspended by a thread. Each guest is to shoot at the nuts on the line, with a bow and arrow. Each nut on the line has pasted to it a stunt to be done by the "nut" who is lucky enough to hit it. The arrows used in this game should be rubber suction arrows—never arrows with a sharp point.

Key to Bluebeard's Den

A KEY IS placed on a string that is held in the hands of all guests as they are seated in a circle. One player is selected to be It and takes a place in the center. Players pass the key from hand to hand, trying to keep it concealed. When It thinks he has located the key, he stops the play and designates the hand that he thinks holds it. If he is correct, the player who has the key must take the place of It, and the game continues. It must continue in the center until he has located the key.

Apple Peel Fortunes

NUMBERS from 1 to 16 are marked off on the floor with chalk, or the numbers may be written on pieces of cardboard and laid on the floor. Each guest is given an apple to peel. He should keep the peel in one long spiral if possible. The players must then, one at a time, stand with their back to the numbers and throw the peeling over their shoulders. The number nearest which the apple peeling falls indicates the player's fortune according to the following verse:

One, I love; two, I love; three, I love I say;
Four, I love with all my heart; five, I cast away;
Six, he loves; seven, she loves; eight they both love;
Nine, he comes; ten, he tarries; eleven, he courts; twelve,
he marries;

Thirteen, they quarrel; fourteen they part; fifteen, they die
with a broken heart;
Sixteen, riches; all the rest are little witches.

Mind Reading

FOR THIS stunt give each player a slip of paper and ask each one to write a short sentence on it. The slips are then folded, collected, and the mind reader proceeds to perform the task of reading the sentences without opening the papers.

It is done as follows: The mind reader makes an identifying mark on his own paper and places it in the box when the slips are collected. When the reading starts, he picks one of the slips from the box, rubs it on his forehead without opening it, and repeats what he had written on his own paper. It will hardly be noticed that no one identifies the sentence if the mind reader fills the gap with clever patter. Then he opens the paper he has rubbed against his forehead and reads it. When the next paper is placed on his forehead, he repeats the sentence he has read on the previous paper and asks whoever wrote it to identify it. Then he unfolds this paper and gets his next sentence. The important things is to keep one slip ahead. When he comes to his own slip, which has been held until the last, he repeats the sentence on the previous slip.

If this is cleverly done it will greatly mystify the group. The mind reader may conclude by saying that he is able to do this stunt only on Halloween, when he can have the assistance of the witches.

NOVEMBER

November Burlesque Horoscope

NOVEMBER was one of the months to which the Romans never troubled themselves to give a specific name. "The ninth month" it was called, for that was its original place in the year; and from the Latin word, "Novem," meaning nine. November became the eleventh month, but its name was never changed.

The number of days has not been as constant. Originally there were thirty, then twenty-nine, and again thirty-one; but from the time of Augustus, it has had thirty days as at present.

As nature seems to be holding its breath, so many of the outdoor activities are at a standstill. The harvesting season is over; the crops are secure in the barns, and thus there comes each year a repetition of that experience of the Pilgrims which resulted in the proclamation of the first Thanksgiving. In the United States this is the outstanding festival of the month, but in Canada, where crops are gathered somewhat earlier, Thanksgiving Day falls in October.

Persons born in November are destined to have many of the fine characteristics of notable people born in this month, such as: Marie Antoinette, 1755; James K. Polk, 1795; William III of England, 1605; Martin Luther, 1483; James A. Garfield, 1831; Andrew Carnegie, 1837; Ella Wheeler Wilcox, 1855.

Persons born in November have many wonderful things in store for them. First, the cooler weather tends to make them less irritable and less inclined to suffer from the many ailments suffered during the summer months, and on the whole, to enjoy life better on that account.

Persons born in this month are destined to have even tempers and to be blessed with much intellect and foresight, to be lucky in games of chance, and to be strongly attracted by the opposite sex.

The gem for November is the topaz.

Famous Folk of November

To use the famous folk of November for a game, the leader should prepare a paper on which have been written the names of the famous persons with the things for which they were famous, jumbled, as for example James K. Polk, British Satirist; Ella Wheeler Wilcox, Russian Composer.

1—James K. Polk, 1795	*Eleventh President of the United States*
2—William Cullen Bryant, 1794	*Poet, journalist*
3—Ella W. Wilcox, 1855	*American poetess, writer*
4—John Philip Sousa, 1856	*Bandmaster and composer*
5—Martin Luther, 1483	*German religion reformer*
6—Oliver Goldsmith, 1728	*British poet and novelist*

7—Joaquin Miller, 1841	*American poet*
8—Henry van Dyke, 1850	*American poet, writer, and educator*
9—Robert Louis Stevenson, 1850	*British novelist, essayist*
10—William Pitt, 1708	*Famous English statesman*
11—James A. Garfield, 1831	*Twentieth President of the United States*
12—George Eliot, 1820	*English novelist*
13—Andrew Carnegie, 1837	*Born in Scotland, lived in United States; capitalist*
14—Louisa M. Alcott, 1832	*American authoress*
15—Samuel L. Clemens, 1835	*American author, pen name, Mark Twain*
16—Anton Rubenstein, 1829	*Russian composer, pianist*
17—Jonathan Swift, 1667	*British satirist*

Thanksgiving Dinner

GIVE GUESTS the following questionnaire which is supposed to be answered with dishes for the Thanksgiving dinner.

1—A country	*Turkey*
2—A dull-colored V passed with the turkey	*Gray-V (gravy)*
3—A cursed son of Noah	*Ham*
4—What Eve was made from	*Spare-rib*
5—A billy goat	*Butter*
6—A miraculous gift of the spirit	*Tongue*
7—To leave behind	*Dessert (desert)*
8—What one gambles for	*Steak (stake)*
9—Two persons of opposite sex	*Pear (pair)*
10—Used on the golf course	*Tea (tee)*
11—Metrical divisions of music	*Beets (beats)*
12—The name of an old-fashioned dress sleeve	*Leg-o-mutton*
13—When traffic is heavy	*Jam*
14—A letter of the alphabet	*Tea (T)*
15—What I do to be heard	*Ice Cream (I scream)*

16—Considered very dumb *Oyster*
17—A well-known emblem of innocence *Lamb*
18—A fruit tree of the tropics *Bread*
19—Ground hog *Sausage*
20—A low male voice *Bass*
21—Adam's temptation *Apples*

Pumpkin Vine Fortunes

DRAW a pumpkin vine on a large sheet of wrapping paper. Thumbtack it to the wall about shoulder high to the guests. Cut pumpkin leaves out of yellow paper, write Thanksgiving fortunes on these, and pin them along the vine. Guests are blindfolded and must walk to the paper and touch a fortune. The blindfold is then taken off, and they must read their fortune. The following are suggestions:

Be thankful that you're frail and thin,
It's the skinny ones nowadays that win.

Be thankful for your accomplishments,
You are one that has shown good sense.

Be thankful for your eyes of blue,
You'll soon find a mate brave and true.

Be thankful that you are so dumb,
You'll never know when hard times come.

Be thankful that you know your heart,
The one who wins you must do his part.

Be thankful that you can have your pick,
And when you get him he's sure to stick.

Be thankful that your eyes are all right,
For soon you'll see a wonderful sight.

Be thankful for your gift of gab,
You'll soon have the chance to meet the right lad.

Be sure that your lover is true,
For you have rivals quite a few.

Be thankful that you are so sweet,
Prince Charming you are soon to meet.

Be thankful that you are full of wit,
If there ever was a wise-cracker, you are it.

Be thankful that you are very well fixed,
Mates and money must always be mixed.

Be thankful for your beauty and grace,
For you are lithe of body and fair of face.

Be thankful that you're strong and big,
Many an old maid's looking for just such a pig.

Dissecting a Turkey

WRITE OR mimeograph on slips of paper the following questions to be answered with the names of the parts of a turkey.

1—What do the angels have? *Wings*
2—What do eight quarts make? *Peck*
3—Something to use on the hair *Comb*
4—A slang word which means to defraud *Skin*
5—Take off the first two letters of cold wind, substitute a letter used for an exclamation, and get a part preferred by some *Gizzard*
6—What do we say that an egotistical person has? *Gall*
7—Take off the last letter of what a baby does before it learns to walk, and you have a certain part *Craw*
8—Something used by the member of a band *Drum sticks*
9—The most important pronoun of most of us *I (eye)*
10—What the teacher calls her children in the classroom *Pupils*

11—Add a letter to what a refrigerator makes, and get a pest sometimes found on a turkey *Lice*
12—What do twenty-four inches make? *Two feet*
13—A part of a kite *Tail*
14—What a young man offers to the girl he loves *Heart*
15—What cowboys wear *Spurs*
16—The way a greedy person eats *Gobbles*
17—A part of France *Breast (Brest)*

Scrambled Pies

GIVE THE guests this list of scrambled pies and have them decipher it.

1—Kipupmn	*Pumpkin*
2—Cocatoun Drautsc	*Cocoanut Custard*
3—Paelp	*Apple*
4—Heacp	*Peach*
5—Bewyrartrs	*Strawberry*
6—Krecehuylbr	*Huckleberry*
7—Prybarers	*Raspberry*
8—Lmup	*Plum*
9—Ananab mecra	*Banana Cream*
10—Truncra	*Currant*
11—Cienm	*Mince*
12—Neurp	*Prune*
13—Trubet Tocsch	*Butter Scotch*
14—Nemol Greneumi	*Lemon Meringue*
15—Nairsi	*Raisin*
16—Harubrb	*Rhubarb*
17—Triopac	*Apricot*
18—Releubybr	*Blueberry*
19—Perag	*Grape*
20—Yelkabcrbr	*Blackberry*
21—Taem	*Meat*
22—Cyranerbr	*Cranberry*
23—Tholoceac Tucdras	*Chocolate Custard*
24—Ewest Ptoato	*Sweet Potato*

Familiar Pies

HAVE GUESTS answer the questions with a word that begins with Pi.

1—A small, short gun	*Pistol*
2—A heavy ribbed or figured cotton cloth	*Pique*
3—A popular pie in summer	*Piazza*
4—A musical pie	*Piano*
5—A tropical fruit pie	*Pineapple*
6—A desperate pie	*Pirate*
7—A virtuous pie	*Pious*
8—A printed pie	*Pica*
9—A variegated pie	*Pied*
10—A sharp pie	*Pin*
11—A whole baking of pies	*Pile*
12—A pie that will settle	*Pioneer*
13—A guiding pie	*Pilot*
14—A man's favorite pie	*Pipe*
15—Square column or pillar	*Pilaster*
16—Roman governor when Christ was crucified	*Pilate*
17—To steal	*Pilfer*

Toothpick and Raisin Relay

DIVIDE the guests into two groups of equal number and line them up facing each other. Provide each group with a saucer of large raisins, enough for four for each guest. The captain holds the saucer in his hand and passes it down the line. Each player has been provided with a toothpick with which he must spear four raisins and eat them. The captain feeds himself last. The group that finishes first wins.

Water and Straw Relay

DIVIDE THE guests into two groups of equal number for a relay race and have them stand at opposite corners of the room. A pitcher of water for each group and glasses are placed on a table at the opposite end of the room. When the contest starts, one player from each group runs to the table, pours out a glassful of water and drinks it through a straw. He then turns the glass upside down and runs back, touching off the second player. The group that finishes first is declared the winner.

Can You Tell the Time?

A LEADER and an accomplice who know the game tell the guests that the accomplice will leave the room, the guests will then decide on an hour of the day, and when the accomplice returns, he can tell the time selected by the group.

The second word of the leader's sentence after the accomplice returns is to begin with the letter of the alphabet that corresponds to the number of that letter. For example, A represents one o'clock, B, two o'clock, C, three o'clock, and so on.

Suppose the group has decided that the hour is two o'clock. When the accomplice returns, the leader may say, "Now be careful, what time is it?" The accomplice immediately replies "two o'clock." He knows this because the second word used by the leader began with a B, which stands for two o'clock. If the group decides on seven o'clock, the leader may say, "No guesswork, what time is it?" The accomplice knows by the second word beginning with G that the hour is seven o'clock.

As soon as any player feels that he has caught on, he may retire and have a try at guessing the time. If he fails, the leader goes back to his original accomplice until someone really learns. If the players do not learn after a brief time, the game should be explained to them.

Bombs

DIVIDE THE guests into two groups of equal number and have them stand with their backs to opposite walls. Give each a toy balloon and when the game starts, the player at the head of each line must inflate his balloon until it bursts; the next one then starts inflating his balloon and so on down the line. No balloon must be inflated until the proper time. The group that first bursts all its balloons is the winner.

DECEMBER

December Burlesques Horoscope

DECEMBER, the twelfth and last month of the year, is often represented pictorially by a very old and feeble Father Time, leaning on a staff. The "Decem" of its name, so familiar to even the beginning Latin student, seems strange as applied to this month for it means ten; but in the old Roman days, before the reform of the calendar, December was the tenth month. By the time the change was made, the numerical significance of its name had been somewhat lost sight of; at any rate, no learned Roman thought it of enough importance to call for correction. One alteration occurred, however; for centuries December had but twenty-nine days, but Caesar added two, making it one of the longest months. The holly is the special flower of this month, and its gem is the turquoise.

December is generally considered the beginning of the winter season, but in reality, winter does not commence until December 22, the day on which the sun reaches the solstice and turns back for its northward journey. In the southern hemisphere, it is the longest day of the year, and in the northern, the shortest, though for a month thereafter, there is little perceptible change in the length of the days.

Persons born in December are destined to possess characteristics similar to some very fine characters born in this month, such as: Thomas Carlyle, 1795; Martin Van Buren, 1782; Mary, Queen of Scots, 1542; John Milton, 1608; and many others.

Partners With Famous Folk and Events

WRITE on slips of paper the names of famous folk born in December and the things for which they were famous. Cut these apart and give to the male guests the name of the person, and to the ladies the statement of the thing for which he was famous. Have them match these to become partners. If the guest list is large, use some of the famous events of December as well.

Thomas Carlyle, 1795	*English historian*
Martin Van Buren, 1782	*Eighth President of the United States*

George A. Custer, 1839	*Great Indian fighter and soldier*
Eli Whitney, 1765	*American inventor of cotton gin*
Joel Chandler Harris, 1848	*American author of Southern stories*
John Milton, 1608	*English poet*
Phillips Brooks, 1835	*American preacher and author*
Jane Austen, 1775	*English novelist*
Beethoven, 1770	*Great German composer*
John Greenleaf Whittier, 1807	*American poet*
James E. Oglethorpe, 1696	*English general; colonized Georgia*
Kit Carson, 1809	*Kentucky frontiersman*
Clara Barton, 1821	*Founder of the Red Cross*
Woodrow Wilson, 1856	*Twenty-eighth President of the United States*
Sir Isaac Newton, 1642	*English philosopher*

Boston tea party, 1773
Pilgrims landed at Plymouth, Massachusetts, 1620
Washington and his men crossed the Delaware, 1776
Texas admitted to the Union, 1845
Sherman's army completed its march to the sea, 1864
Napoleon crowned emperor of France, 1804
Methodist Church first organized in America, 1784

Christmas Toy Exchange

GUESTS have been told in advance to bring some toy to the party. This should be carefully wrapped so that no one can tell what is in the package. Have guests exchange and trade around without opening the packages. At the leader's command each person must open his toy and play with it. There will be a medley of horns blowing and mechanical toys operating. Toys may be collected and given to poor children.

Eight-line Jingle Contest

THE leader is to read the following eight-line jingles as samples and have the guests write advertising jingles for Christmas ads, the best one to receive a prize.

BANK Be prepared for another Christmas,
Start a bank account;
Get your dollars all together,
Though but small the first amount,
You will thus have formed a nucleus
Round which others will collect;
And next year you'll have a surplus
That today you'd scarce expect.

BAKERY Do you have a real sweet tooth?
Listen to a word of truth.
You can feed it something rare
And save a lot of work and care.
Buy a cake at Johnson's shop.
It's the family's one-place stop,
For cakes and cookies, breads and more,
And a great variety of goodies galore.

Other subjects about which to write are, clothing, watches, fur coats, razors, books, and so on.

The Postman

THE PLAYERS stand around the room in a circle. One player acts as postman and carries a rolled newspaper in his hand. Near each corner of the room are mail boxes represented by circles marked on the floor. Each player is given the name of a town. The postman begins the game by saying, "I have a Christmas card from New York." The player representing New York must chase the postman and tag him. The postman, however, runs to a letter box and places his newspaper in it. The one chasing him must first get the newspaper from the letter box to use in tagging the postman. If the postman gets back to the position occupied by New York before he is tagged, the next one becomes postman. This game may be varied by the postman saying, "I have a package from Boston." When the word package is used, both the player and the postman must hop on one leg while the postman is being chased.

Stocking Stuffing Relay

THE GUESTS are divided into two groups of equal number and stand in opposite corners of the room. On the opposite end of the room two baskets of wrapped parcels have been placed. To make the game fair, the parcels in one basket should duplicate in size and shape those in the other basket, and it should be possible to put all of them in a stocking. A large cotton, nylon, or wool stocking should be used. There must, of course, be one for each team. When the race starts, the first player in each group runs to the basket and must put all the packages in the stocking. He then takes them out, puts them back in the basket and returns the stocking to the second player on his team. The group whose last player finishes first wins the contest.

Christmas Treasure Hunt

EACH GUEST is provided with a small red Christmas stocking and is given a list of objects hidden about the room which he is to find. No guest is allowed to pick up more than one each of the objects hidden, such as those listed below. Give a prize to the one that brings back the largest number of treasures. Some of the things that may be on the list are: Rubber doll, unsharpened lead pencil, eraser, peanuts, lollipops, animal cracker, chocolate candy, mints, small toys, and tennis ball.

Santa Claus Jig-saw Puzzle

FIND a large picture of Santa Claus, such as would be used for advertising purposes, or have someone draw such a figure on cardboard, coloring it red. With a safety razor blade cut it into many pieces. A group will get a lot of enjoyment out of assisting with this jig-saw puzzle. This could be made into a race by providing two such puzzles and have one group compete against the other in assembling it.

Christmas Music Tag

THE GAME starts with two groups of equal number. The object is for each group to win recruits by tagging members of the other group. A person is only safe when he is singing a Christmas song or Christmas carol.

Cranberry Yard Dash

If the guests have been divided into two groups, one or more players may be selected from each group to represent that group in a cranberry yard dash. This may be made a relay race by having all participate, one at a time. Lay two yardsticks on a table and give each player a cranberry and a toothpick. When the signal is given, each player must lay his cranberry on one end of the yardstick and roll it to the other end, propelling it with the toothpick. If the cranberry rolls off the yardstick (which it probably will), the player must roll it back on the yardstick with the toothpick. The person who first completes the dash is the winner, or the group whose last player finishes first is the winner.

Wishbone Cranberry Roll

On a large cardboard draw several turkey wishbones. Number each of these, one with 50, another 25, others 10 and 5. Each player is given twelve cranberries, or they may use the same cranberries and pass them along when each player has finished throwing. Individuals or teams may play the game by rolling the cranberries onto the cardboard one at a time in an effort to make them land in one of the numbered wishbones. Each player or team keeps score and a token prize is given the individual or team with the highest score. A small bag of candy would be a good prize.

Circle Scramble

For a period of lively activity which will serve to break the December ice, play Circle Scramble. The leader calls out, "Form in circles of ten." There will be much pulling, counting, and eliminating before the correct count is made. Then the leader calls, "Get in circles of six." When this has been accomplished, the leader reduces the number to five. After each count, the group that formed the circle in the quickest time is the winner. The leader may reduce the number to four or even three. The game might end by the leader calling, "Girls find a partner and form into couples," or "Boys find a partner for refreshments."

Section 10

leisure time activities

Directed Leisure Time Activities

THE AVERAGE person finds himself with a great deal of leisure time on his hands. The machine age has shortened the working time. The average tradesman today works eight hours a day for five days a week. In 1890 the average workman worked ten hours a day and six days a week. The working time is thereby reduced at least thirty-three and a third per cent. There is talk of still further reducing the working time to thirty hours a week.

On the basis of the average working day for the tradesman and for the average professional man as well, about forty hours a week are given to the task. The "long arm of the job" consumes only twenty-three and eight-tenths per cent of the 168 hours in each week. If we subtract another 56 hours for sleep, this leaves 72 hours that the average person has for leisure.

The business interests are noting this and they are inventing every form of commercialized leisure. The people of the United States spend more for commercialized leisure than for anything else except for food. There are many millions admissions to the movies every day. Television claims millions of viewers every day and night. No one could estimate the number of admissions to sporting events. Professional baseball, little league baseball, college football, professional football, high school, college and professional basketball, are increasing in popularity and attract millions. More people are playing golf and tennis; more persons are purchasing boats and spending leisure hours on lakes or rivers. It is not unusual to fill the largest available parks or stadiums for professional sports. But there are several types of commercialized recreation that are not conducive to character development. Young people should be guided to shun these cheap forms of recreation for the more wholesome type.

Wise leaders in all character building organizations have come to realize that the wise use of leisure time is essential to character development. If those character building organizations do not provide and encourage a type of social and recreational life which is on a high plane for its young people, they are likely to find their recreation in cheap places of amusement which are harmful. Commercialized recreation is constantly tempting young people to turn away from a wholesome recreational life. It has been wisely said that the proper use of leisure time is the greatest problem of our generation. "The proper use of leisure time has created every civilization which has ever existed; the improper use has killed each one in turn."

What should be the object of our leisure time activities? Their purpose should not be merely to kill time. This is not to say that to engage in recreation on a high plane is not enjoyable. The purpose of a directed leisure time activity should be to encourage friendliness, develop personality, make good sportsmen, and develop a taste for the cultural things of life. The proper kind of recreation and social life will develop the right attitude toward life. Character should be developed during leisure time. The object of a directed recreational program is to vitalize leisure time and make its use profitable as well as enjoyable.

In the following pages some ways are suggested in which to spend leisure time which will be interesting and helpful.

Hobbies

In that very interesting book, *The Care and Feeding of Hobby Horses,* E. E. Calkin says that a hobby makes you interesting to other people. "When you find out that a man you have just met climbs mountains, or makes ship models, or knows the name and songs of every bird in the neighborhood, or prints little books on his own attic printing press, or has a collection of painted fans, or pewter tankards, or old fire backs, doesn't that make him more interesting to you? Don't you like to hear about his exploits or see the things he makes or collects?"

Mr. Calkin further says that occupation for leisure time falls into four classes. (1) Doing things, (2) Making things, (3) Acquiring things, and (4) Learning things.

Among the suggested things to do he lists—calisthenics, hiking, picnicking, spelling bees, swimming, walking, wrestling. Parties, aquatic events, and games would come under this head. There are thousands of games that any group will enjoy playing if someone will take the trouble to teach them and show the group how to play.

There are many games on the market today that will provide a lot of fun to a small group for an evening or for the children in the home. Parker Brothers at Salem, Massachusetts, manufactures many such games. Among these is Monopoly. This is a game that is full of interest for either children or adults. Rook is a good game and is played with Rook Cards which may also be purchased from Parker Brothers or at almost any bookstore or five- and ten-cent store. Camelot is another such game manufactured by Parker brothers. It is somewhat like chess but not so complicated. Four may play at one time and it is a very interesting game for two. There are many other games such as Flinch, Pit, and Authors, that old and young will enjoy playing.

In this list we find the handicrafts. There are many things that we may make. The creative games that we have suggested in a preceding section serve as examples. Other suggestions are artificial flies for angling, basket weaving, bead work, bookbinding, china painting, glass blowing, leather craft, puppet shows, modeling in clay, photography, pottery making, silhouettes, taxidermy, woodwork. This is only a small list. What do you make? It will be very interesting to have members of any group tell what they are able to make.

The following are some things that we might collect or acquire. Antiques, autographs, beads, books, cigar bands, canes, coins, dolls, elephants, fans, Indian arrowheads, maps, paper money, phonograph records, stamps, samples, ship models, sheet music, sea shells, Bibles, and a thousand other things. What do you collect? Have members of your social group tell of any collection of anything they may have.

There are so many things that we may learn in our leisure time. Archaeology, astronomy, botany, biology, geography, geology, philosophy, psychology, languages, natural sciences, social science. Books on any of these subjects may be found at almost any good library, and such a library may be found in almost any city.

In the following pages some interesting hobbies are suggested.

Life Masks and Plaques

(By Chester G. Nelson, Florida City, Fla.)

A Life Mask is made from the living face of a subject, and when well done is a perfect reproduction of the face in every detail. It is made by putting a soft mixture of a quick-setting plaster of Paris upon the oiled surface of the face.

The detailed process is thus carried out. (1) The subject lies down upon his back; the entire face, or such portion of it as he wishes copied, is slightly oiled by using cold cream, Wesson oil, olive oil, or white Vaseline, preferably cold cream. (2) A pasteboard box is cut to fit closely around the face, leaving a small margin to hold plaster in place. Place this about the face, taking in a portion of the hair which has been well oiled, and combed close to the head, and also a part of the neck. (3) Mix about four quarts of plaster of Paris mixture thus: Pour about two quarts of water into a vessel and then add the plaster of Paris to the water, stirring it slightly, adding the plaster until a thick batter is made. (Note: The person of whom the mask is to be made should be ready, face oiled and lying comfortably before the mixing is started.) (4) With the pasteboard shield in place, now pour the plaster of Paris over the closed eyes and then over the mouth and face, spreading it evenly so that no bubbles or wrinkles are formed near the face. Lay it carefully over the upper lip and end of the nose, leaving small holes through which the subject may breath while the plaster sets. (Breathing tubes in the nostrils distend the nose so it is not natural, and by care the plaster may be laid about the lip and nose so breathing may continue normally.) (5) The subject just breathes slowly through the nose, being careful not to swallow or laugh, or otherwise to move the face or jaws and crack the plaster while it is setting. A good brand of plaster will set sufficiently to be removed without cracking within a few minutes. Lift the case from the hair and forehead first, and push slightly toward the chin, lifting it from the face. (6) Allow the mold to set for a few minutes until firm enough to handle safely, then correct any flaws on the inside of the mold by filling in bubbles and places not molded to the face. (7) Oil the inside of the cast, which is the intaglio, or negative, using either of the above named oils, allowing the plaster to absorb some of the oil; then it is ready to be poured. Do not excessively oil the intaglio, nor pour too soon; let it cool first. (8) Mix about the same amount of plaster as before, leaving it slightly thinner than the first mixing was. Pour this into the intaglio, and by either rocking or with the finger, see that the plaster forms no bubbles or flaws. When the cast is filled, let it set until thoroughly set. Do not rush. When ready, carefully break the intaglio away, leaving the cameo or life mask. This may then be touched up as is necessary, though the least touching up, the more lifelike it will be.

We advise the use of Molding Plaster for this work. It would be advisable to seek the advice of a building materials dealer for the choice or brand to use. Ask for white, quick-setting molding plaster. While Plaster of Paris will work, the molding plaster is more refined and will set quicker.

The casting of plaques, the handprint, the foot, leaf molds, fish, birds, or even small animals is possible. This is done by putting a small amount of plaster in a box large enough to contain the object to be cast; the object, well oiled, is then laid or set down into the plaster, just half covering it. When the plaster is set, lift the object out. Oil the mold and the top surface of the casting, replace the object, and pour the plaster entirely over the object. When set, separate the first and second casting carefully, remove the object, and after touching up, cut a hole so the thin plaster may be poured in when the two casts are tied together. Oil both well, but not excessively, tie them together, and mix thin plaster and fill, shaking the plaster about as it is being poured. When the object is removed from the case, carefully cut the appendage from the cast and dress it down.

A little imagination and experimentation on your part will enable you to make good casts of many different objects. The addition of salt will make a casting set much harder than without the addition of salt, though if it is to be painted, it will affect the paint. Not a great deal of salt is necessary, about a teaspoon or slightly more to the quart of dry plaster being sufficient.

Where the time element is not important, perhaps a cheaper form of cement or plaster could be used. The quick-setting plaster may be used for the intaglio and a cheaper form used for the cameo. Use your imagination and experiment as you will. This article is not intended to be the "last word" in the making of life masks and plaques. It is suggestive only.

Dramatics

ORGANIZE a dramatic club and get a lot of benefit and pleasure from this type of recreation. Almost any church publishing house sends out materials to be used in dramatics of a worth-while kind. Plays may be put on from time to time. Dramatics will enlist the talent and interest of almost every one in the group.

Music

MUSIC as a form of recreation has many interesting and profitable possibilities—collecting records, attending concerts, learning to play some instrument. It may include singing solos, taking part in duets, quartettes or even choruses or orchestras. Drum and bugle corps create a lot of interest. Band music and harmonica bands will interest some.

Writing in *The Reader's Digest* on the subject "Play It Yourself," Doron K. Antrim says: "The instruments you can pick up and play right off are so numerous that anybody who wants to play can play. Why not start with instruments so simple that they can be played on sight? Get the thrill of it and then go on." The article goes on to say that you can learn to play the ukulele by learning a half dozen of the more important chords in an evening, and then you are ready to cash in on the enjoyment of it. The ukulele is ideal for accompaniment to singing and one can learn the accompaniment to some well-known tunes in five minutes. And it is, according to Antrim, an easy stepping stone from the ukulele to the guitar. Another instrument that is easy to learn is the harmonica. One eleven-year-old boy learned to play the harmonica so well in a week that the next week he taught a group of his school mates—at five cents a lesson.

All ages, on all occasions, will enjoy listening to records, both popular and classical. The world's best music is now available on stereo and hi-fi records, and these offer an excellent opportunity for "music appreciation" evenings or for relaxed enjoyment.

Reading

ONE of the most profitable ways of spending leisure time is in reading. The important thing is to read the proper kind of literature. This does not mean that one should read classical literature all the time, but that parents and teachers should be consulted as well as trained librarians so that the best may always be read. Children should be taught to read. If they have not formed such a habit in childhood, they should be led to form this habit when older.

Book Lover's Convention

A "BOOK LOVERS' " convention held from time to time will stimulate reading and an interest in good literature. A part of the program could be a review of some current book in which all would be interested. At such a convention, the leader might read a story, preferably one appropriate to the season. For example, at a meeting near Christmas he might read "The Other Wise Man," by Henry Van Dyke; *A Christmas Carol,* by Charles Dickens; or selections from *Mary,* by Sholem Asch.

Debates

A GOOD WAY for a group to spend a profitable evening is to have a debate. There is no finer way to develop poise and the ability to think on one's feet. There should be two or three speakers on the affirmative side, and an equal number on the negative side. The participants speak alternately, beginning with the first speaker on the affirmative side, who should give a short rebuttal after all others have spoken.

At least three judges who will decide which side won should be selected in advance. These judges should each write on a slip of paper either "affirmative" or "negative." The side receiving at least two out of three votes is declared the winner.

The following are some suggested subjects for debate:

1. Resolved: That children should be taught to believe in Santa Claus.
2. Resolved: That labor-saving machinery is an advantage to the laborer.
3. Resolved: That labor should have a six-hour day.
4. Resolved: That poverty is a greater hindrance than wealth to Christian living.
5. Resolved: That public utilities should be owned by the cities.
6. Resolved: That the reading of fiction is a waste of time.
7. Resolved: That public libraries and museums should be open on Sunday.
8. Resolved: That the principle of parole should be extended.
9. Resolved: That a president of the United States, during his second term, not being eligible for re-election, is thereby rendered ineffective.
10. Resolved: That capital punishment should be abolished.
11. Resolved: That the United States should sell the Panama Canal to the Republic of Panama.

Story Teller's Convention

ANNOUNCE a story teller's convention for one evening and invite the group to assemble and enjoy the program of the convention. If a conference or group is meeting in a college or hotel ask the members to assemble in the lounge or lobby. If the weather is cool and a fireplace is available, seat the group informally around the fireplace and ask the story tellers to stand in front of or to the side of the fireplace. An outdoor setting, such as the side of a hill, a garden, or campfire would be equally effective.

Open the program with the singing of well-known songs. The Master Story Teller should then introduce the program, announce the first story, and seat himself in the circle. He should only rise again when it is absolutely necessary to insure the continuity of the program. Of course, the story tellers should all be secured ahead of time, and should be persons who are adapted to entertaining in this way. Spontaneous stories from the group would be entirely in place, as informality is the keynote to the Story Teller's Convention. Some of the following suggestions may help in working out a well balanced program: humorous stories, stories of heroes or heroines (these might be stories of characters known to certain members of the group), poems, myths, missionary stories, travel or adventure stories, and character building stories. The climax of the evening should come with a story with a spiritual aspect.

Following the last story, the group should be asked to spend a few moments in meditation and silent prayer. The Master Story Teller should lead in a closing song, such as "Follow the Gleam," the four "Good Nights," "Taps," or any song which the group is accustomed to use as a benediction.

Stunt Night

For an evening of good entertainment and fellowship a stunt night is suggested. Such a program may also be used as a money making entertainment by charging admission. Many times social directors at Young People's Conferences put on a stunt night as one of the evening entertainments for the whole group. Groups from different cities are asked to produce a stunt. These stunts usually include a mock faculty meeting, musical numbers, and stunts taken from stunt books. Churches in many cities are now using stunt nights and the various organizations in the church, such as the youth groups, church-school classes, and so on, are asked to produce a stunt. A Stunt Book suggestion is: *Cokesbury Stunt Book Revised,* Depew, Abingdon Press.

Handicraft

There are many forms of handicraft which are full of interest. Among these may be mentioned silver work, especially the making of bracelets, which is easily learned. Leather work is another handicraft that is fascinating. Many useful things may be made of wood in a workshop, such as book ends, and magazine racks. Needle work, knitting and crocheting are always full of interest for women.

Service Projects as Leisure Time Activities

MANY churches, through their publishing houses, provide literature for guidance of young people who would like to spend a summer vacation in some service project. Sometimes this includes service in vacation Bible schools by teams that travel from church to church for one week's service. Often service projects are found in children's or intermediate camps. Young people are invited to render service in benevolent homes for the aged or children. Many opportunities for service are to be found in home mission institutions, migrant camps, in European rehabilitation programs, or in nearby foreign mission fields.

Many community welfare organizations offer a wide variety of service projects for interested youth as well as older persons. Hospitals need semi-skilled volunteers for many types of work. Those who have a knowledge of crafts may be asked to teach in hospital wards, rehabilitation centers, and on playgrounds.

Soap Carving

SOAP CARVING will be interesting to any group that will try it. When you want to use this idea for a party, it will only be necessary to have a bust or a plaque for the group to carve and to provide prizes for the one who exhibits the greatest amount of skill.

alphabetical index